# Test Item Listing
## *for* Test Generator CD–ROM
### *with* TestBuilder Software *for* Macintosh® and Windows®

# *Call to* FREEDOM

**HOLT, RINEHART AND WINSTON**
Harcourt Brace & Company
Austin • New York • Orlando • Atlanta • San Francisco • Boston • Dallas • Toronto • London

Cover: Christie's Images

Copyright © by Holt, Rinehart and Winston

Printed in the United States of America

ISBN 0-03-054542-0

3  4  5  6  7  8  9   095   02   01   00

# ★ C O N T E N T S ★

### About the *Call to Freedom Test Generator*

The *Call to Freedom Test Generator* contains 75 test items for each chapter of the *Call to Freedom* textbook. For your easy reference, this *Test Item Listing* contains a complete printout of the test items that are stored on the *Test Generator CD–ROM*. It also contains information that is specific to the use of the program with those questions.

The *User's Guide*, which is included in the test generator package, contains directions for installing the program and for using the program.

### Chapter Files

Test items are stored in files called "chapters." There is a "chapter" file for each chapter of *Call to Freedom*.

### Question Types

Each test item is classified by its question type. The test generator lets you use question types when selecting questions for a test. The question types contained in the *Call to Freedom Test Generator* are

| | | | |
|---|---|---|---|
| Matching | Graphic Image | True and False | Enhanced |
| Multiple Choice | Short Answer | Essay | |

### Editing Test Questions and Writing Test Questions

The test generator program allows you to edit the questions that are supplied on the disc and to write your own questions. Your *User's Guide* describes these features of the program. Because the CD–ROM is a read-only disc, in order to edit test items or add test items to the chapter files, you must first copy the chapter files to your computer's hard disc drive or to diskettes.

### Objectives and Difficulty

The test generator program allows questions to be classified by learning objective and level of difficulty. The test items in the *Call to Freedom Test Generator* are not classified by objective or difficulty level, but you may use those fields for questions that you write. Your *User's Guide* describes these features of the program.

### Technical Support

The **HRW Test Generator User's Guide** should answer any questions you have about the program. However, if you need assistance, call the Holt, Rinehart and Winston Technical Support Center at 1-800-323-9239. You also can access a knowledge base of solutions to common problems and answers to common questions by calling the Technical Support Center's Fax on Demand Service at 1-800-352-1680.

In addition, you can contact the Technical Support Center through the World Wide Web at http://www.hrwtechsupport.com or by e-mail at tsc@hrwtechsupport.com.

## Chapter 1 The World Before the Opening of the Atlantic

**MATCHING**

**In the space provided, write the term or the name of the person that best fits the description. Choose your answers from the list below. Not all answers will be used.**

Renaissance
culture
colony
kivas
Crusades

environments
societies
Paleo-Indians
Zheng He
artifacts

Islam
Kublai Khan
feudalism
archaeology
Iroquois League

1) _____ commanded the Ming fleet that brought wealth and knowledge of other cultures to China

2) _____ objects made by humans

3) _____ language, government, and family relationships of a society

4) _____ rebirth of interest in ancient Greece or Rome

5) _____ climates and landscapes that surround living things

6) _____ system of government in which people pledged loyalty to a lord in exchange for protection

7) _____ study of the unwritten past

8) _____ the first Americans

9) _____ religion that spread from the Arabian peninsula across the Mediterranean Sea

10) _____ groups that share common values and traditions

**TRUE/FALSE**

**Write T if a statement is true or F if it is false. If a statement is false, explain why.**

11) _____ The Crusades were fought between 1096 and 1221 for possession of the Holy Land.

_____

12) _____ Mississippian people held religious activities in circular ceremonial rooms called potlatches.

_____

13) _____ The first Paleo-Indian migration into Alaska occurred sometime between 50,000 B.C. and 10,000 B.C.

_____

14) _____ During potlatches, hosts gave away most of their goods in order to gain respect.

_____

15) _____ Manors were large estates owned by groups of peasants.

_____

16) _____ People in matrilineal societies traced their ancestry through their fathers.

_____

17) _____ Hunter-gatherers are people who hunt animals and gather wild plants to provide for their needs.

_____

18) _____ The Silk Road stretched across the Mediterranean Sea from North Africa to Sicily.

_____

19) _____ Mesoamerica includes present-day New Mexico and portions of Central America.

_____

20) _____ The Middle Ages began when the Roman Empire collapsed.

_____

## MULTIPLE CHOICE
**For each of the following, circle the letter of the best choice.**

21) The first European explorers known to have reached the shores of North America were

    a. English knights led by King John.
    b. French explorers led by William the Conqueror.
    c. Scandinavian Vikings led by Erik the Red.
    d. Scandinavian Vikings led by Leif Erikkson.


22) The most important crop grown by Paleo-Indians in Mesoamerica was

    a. maize.                     c. beans.
    b. sweet potatoes.         d. sunflowers.


23) For transportation, the Inuit and Aleut used dogsleds and one-person canoes called

    a. wigwams.                c. kayaks.
    b. totems.                 d. igloos.


24) Acorns were the

    a. primary food plant for California culture groups.
    b. most important resource of the Chehalis, Nootka, and Skokomish culture groups.
    c. only edible plant available in the Great Basin.
    d. life-giving force of Pueblo existence.


25) The Iroquois League, made up of the Seneca, Oneida, Mohawk, Cayuga, and Onondaga tribes,

    a. controlled trade among the seminomadic bands north of the Great Lakes.
    b. were the only Native American culture group controlled economically by women.
    c. lived in small circular huts called longhouses.
    d. descended directly from the Mogollon and Anasazi culture groups.


26) China was invaded in the 1200s by

    a. Christians motivated by Pope Urban II.
    b. Islamic warriors who had already conquered the Persian Empire.
    c. Muslims led by Muhammad across the Adriatic Sea to China's southern coast.
    d. Mongols, nomadic warriors from Central Asia.


27) Through a process called domestication, people learned to

    a. gather wild plants to meet food and clothing needs.
    b. hunt wild animals to meet specific human needs.
    c. grow and breed wild plants and animals to meet specific human needs.
    d. tame wild animals to meet farming and transportation needs.

28) Timbuktu became a center of Islamic culture and learning because

a. Mali's kings embraced Islam.
b. Islamic traders introduced Ghana to Islam.
c. Bantu and Arab influences declined in North Africa as Islamic influences increased.
d. the Songhay Empire's Christian leaders were defeated by Muslims from Mali.

29) Rectangular dwellings made from logs and bark and that house 8 to 10 families were known as

a. wigwams.
b. longhouses.

c. glyphs.
d. kivas.

30) The Aztec created a large empire and trading network by conquering most of

a. present-day Canada.
b. central Mexico.

c. the southwestern regions of North America.
d. Mesoamerica and Cuzco.

31) Mammoths, saber-toothed tigers, bison, and giant wolves roamed North America

a. during the same period that the Toltec ruled South America.
b. until around 1400 A.D.
c. between 50,000 and 10,000 B.C.
d. while European Christians launched the Crusades, and the Ming Dynasty ruled China.

32) Farming that created food surpluses and allowed large groups of people to settle permanently in one place led to

a. the development of complex societies among many Native American groups.
b. the rising importance of maize in Mesoamerica and South America.
c. domestication among Paleo-Indian groups by 10,000 B.C.
d. advanced Mesoamerican civilizations that influenced Paleo-Indian cultures.

33) Semi-nomadic groups including Athapascan and Algonquian speaking peoples of North America

a. developed large populations that survived by hunting, trading, and fishing for salmon.
b. left their homes to follow the seasonal migrations of the caribou.
c. lived on the dry, treeless plain of the Columbia Plateau.
d. descended from the Pueblo culture group that did not practice agriculture.

34) Two of the main Native American groups in the Northeast were the

a. Pequot and the Narragansett, who lived in longhouses.
b. Caddo and the Tonkawa, who lived in dome-shaped dwellings of 30 to 50 feet in diameter.
c. Iroquois and the Algonquian, who lived in longhouses and wigwams.
d. Zuni and the Hopi, who lived in wigwams and kivas.

Call to Freedom

35) Long-distance trading networks were developed in West Africa by

a. European traders who exchanged goods with Bantu-speaking peoples.
b. Ethiopians who traded ivory in port cities along the Nile River.
c. Kushite rulers who dominated the region in the 700s B.C.
c. Berbers, North African nomads who used camels to carry goods across the desert.

36) Native Americans in the Northwest used the many evergreen trees to

a. carve images of totems—ancestor or animal spirits—on tall poles.
b. build longhouses that housed 8 to 10 families each.
c. build totems—circular huts—and large multifamily lodges.
d. build kivas—circular ceremonial rooms—for religious ceremonies.

37) Migration refers to the movement of

a. animals from one region to another.
b. people from one region to another.
c. animals and people from one region to another.
d. people from one culture group to another.

38) Some of the Pueblo culture groups of the Southwest may have descended directly from the

a. Inuit and the Aleut.
b. Mogollon and the Anasazi.
c. ancient Mississippi mound builders.
d. Northwest culture groups that demonstrated their wealth by holding potlatches.

39) During the Middle Ages, large estates were called

a. colonies.
b. longhouses.
c. vassals.
d. manors.

40) The Mississippian people

a. controlled an area from present day Columbia to central Chile.
b. built mounds in the Ohio and Mississippi River valleys.
c. declined around A.D. 200 when farming societies developed.
d. built Monks Mound, near present-day Cahokia, Illinois.

41) Paleo-Indians who first migrated into North America were

a. semi-nomadic traders.
b. hunter-gatherers.
c. farming societies.
d. invaders who conquered people to gain human sacrifices.

42) Pueblos, above-ground dwellings made mostly of cut stone or adobe, were invented by the

a. Hohokam.
b. Mogollon.
c. Anasazi.
d. Inca.

43) During the mid- and late-Middle Ages,

   a. feudalism developed as local rulers sought a defense against the Black Death.
   b. Muslim rulers built splendid cathedrals throughout western Europe.
   c. trade and communication networks improved as city populations decreased.
   d. nobles lost power as monarchs expanded their control over vast areas.


44) Southwestern peoples who developed agriculture had to

   a. depend on yearly buffalo hunts to supplement their crops.
   b. irrigate their land to grow crops.
   c. move from place to place to find adequate grassland.
   d. distribute food crops under the guidance of the Iroquois League.


45) Tenants, serfs, and slaves were

   a. peasants who farmed land that belonged to a lord.
   b. vassals who gave their services to nobles in exchange for land.
   c. field laborers who owned a portion of the manor.
   d. domestic laborers who slept in the manor house and educated the lord's children.


46) The Inuit adapted to their environment by sometimes using

   a. dried buffalo dung to fuel their fires.
   b. abundant evergreen trees to build large dugout canoes.
   c. blocks of ice to build domed shelters called igloos for housing in the winter.
   d. logs and bark to build rectangular dwellings called longhouses.


47) The Middle Ages extended from the collapse of the Roman Empire to the beginning of the

   a. Crusades.                              c. Kublai Khan's reign in China.
   b. Germanic invasion of Europe.          d. Renaissance.


48) Native Americans in the Great Basin region were

   a. mound builders.
   b. agricultural peoples who irrigated their land.
   c. hunter-gatherers who highly valued rabbits as a source of food and clothing.
   d. raiders who may have descended from the Zuni and the Hopi.


49) From 1346–1351, one third of Europe's population died as a result of

   a. war and famine.                       c. a Mongol invasion led by Kublai Khan.
   b. famine and the Black Death.           d. fierce raids led by Erik the Red.


50) Symbols and images that represent ideas are

   a. artifacts.                            c. translations.
   b. charters.                             d. glyphs.

Call to Freedom

51) The Renaissance was a rebirth of European interest in the arts and teachings of

a. Kublai Khan.
b. Muhammad.
c. ancient Greece and Rome.
d. the Songhay Empire.

52) A mild climate and a rich supply of game animals, sea life, and wild edible plants

a. allowed the people of the Mississippi culture to build mounds rather than develop an agrarian society.
b. allowed Pacific coast peoples to develop large populations without depending on agriculture.
c. provided the Chippewa, Penobscot, and Menomini with food during the entire year.
d. encouraged Aztec and Inca people to live in Tenochtitlán.

53) The mixture of Bantu and Arab influences in East Africa developed into a

a. culture in which people practiced Islam and spoke Swahili.
b. Christian culture that adopted Egyptian writing and architecture.
c. dynasty founded by Mansa Musa.
d. Muslim dynasty within the Songhay Empire.

54) Merchants who created joint-stock companies

a. shared their profits with the Medici family that loaned money to monarchs and nobles.
b. borrowed money from Venetian banks that did not charge interest.
c. increased their individual risk of starting a new business.
d. jointly invested and shared in the profits and losses.

55) The first Americans to domesticate plants to meet specific human needs were

a. Mesoamericans who began to grow corn.
b. Paleo-Indians who were primarily hunter-gatherers.
c. Asians who migrated into North America around 1,000 B.C.
d. the Aztec and the Inca who built complex civilizations.

56) Capital is money

a. borrowed from a bank.
b. invested in a joint-stock company.
c. or property that is used to earn more money.
d. earned as interest on loans.

57) The Christians who embarked on the Crusades were urged to do so by

a. King John.
b. Leif Erikkson.
c. William of Normandy.
d. Pope Urban II.

58) Algonquian people sometimes lived in small circular huts called

a. dugouts.
b. wigwams.
c. pit houses.
d. pueblos.

Call to Freedom

59) William of Normandy used the Domesday Book to

a. regulate trade with merchants in Italian coastal cities.
b. address the nobility's land rights and help protect the rights of free individuals.
c. establish taxes, distribute land fairly, and determine how many knights and foot soldiers each lord owed in military service.
d. record the burial sites of some 75 million people who died from bubonic plague.

60) Changes in technology, trade, and political power marked the

a. end of Europe's Middle Ages.
b. Mongol conquest of the Ming Dynasty.
c. decline of the Songhay Empire.
d. rise of feudalism under William of Normandy.

**ENHANCED QUESTIONS**
**For each of the following, circle the letter of the best choice. Next, expand on the subject by answering the second question in the space provided.**

61) The Iroquois were one of the most powerful peoples in North America

a. after they conquered and enslaved non-Iroquois peoples in the Northeast.
b. under the guidance of the Iroquois League council.
c. as a result of irrigation systems developed and controlled by village councils.
d. with a complex religion focusing on death and the afterlife.

What role did women play in Iroquois culture?

_____

_____

62) Muhammad, a merchant who lived on the Arabian Peninsula, founded a religion called

a. Islam.
b. Qur'an.
c. Christianity.
d. Bantu.

Where did this religion spread?

_____

_____

8

Call to Freedom

63) Paleo-Indians first entered North America

    a. around 1,000 B.C.        c. by crossing from Asia to Alaska.
    b. before the last Ice Age.     d. by boat through numerous lakes and swamps.

    What role did Beringia play in migration?

_____

_____

64) The Commercial Revolution was a period of economic development that dramatically changed the way

    a. many merchants conducted business.
    b. taxes were collected.
    c. European merchants imported goods.
    d. silk and spices were brought from China to Europe.

    Describe these changes and their impact on cities.

_____

_____

65) One of the first documents to help protect the rights of free individuals was the

    a. *Courtier*.         c. Qur'an.
    b. Domesday Book.    d. Magna Carta.

    How did this document change the power of kings?

_____

_____

Call to Freedom

9

## GRAPHIC IMAGE QUESTIONS
**Examine the image, and then answer the following questions.**

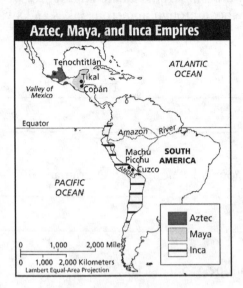

66) What were the main cities in the Maya Empire?

_____

67) What was the northernmost empire on this map?

_____

68) Which empire controlled Cuzco and Machu Picchu?

_____

## SHORT ANSWER
**Write a brief answer for each of the following.**

69) How did Paleo-Indians adapt to the environmental changes brought about by the end of the Ice Age?

_____

_____

_____

Call to Freedom

70) Why were the Vikings able to sail long distances in their explorations?

_____

_____

_____

71) What advances did southwestern civilizations make in response to their environment?

_____

_____

_____

72) Explain how Zheng He shaped Chinese culture and trade during the reign of the Ming dynasty.

_____

_____

_____

73) What factors led to the rise of feudalism in the early Middle Ages?

_____

_____

_____

**ESSAY**
**On a separate sheet of paper, write an essay on one of the following.**

74) Describe the Native Americans of the Pacific Northwest Coast and the Northeast.

75) How did the Commercial Revolution expand business?

# ANSWER KEY

1) Zheng He

2) artifacts

3) culture

4) Renaissance

5) environments

6) feudalism

7) archaeology

8) Paleo-Indians

9) Islam

10) societies

11) T

12) F
Mississippian religious activities were held in temples built on the top of pyramid mounds.

13) T

14) T

15) F
Manors were owned by lords and nobles, and farmed by peasants.

16) F
People in matrilineal societies traced their ancestry through their mothers.

17) T

12

# ANSWER KEY

18) F
The Silk Road, an overland trade route, stretched from the Black Sea to China.

19) F
Mesoamerica includes present-day Mexico and portions of Central America.

20) T

21) d

22) a

23) c

24) a

25) b

26) d

27) c

28) a

29) b

30) b

31) c

32) a

33) b

34) c

35) d

36) a

37) b

38) b

39) d

40) b

41) b

42) c

43) d

44) b

45) a

46) c

47) d

48) c

49) b

50) d

51) c

52) b

53) a

Call to Freedom

ANSWER KEY

54) d

55) a

56) c

57) d

58) b

59) c

60) a

61) b
Women owned the material possessions and had the responsibility for most aspects of community life. Women selected the male members of the Iroquois League council, could overrule decisions made by the council, and could remove some of its members in some instances.

62) a
the Arabian Peninsula, Jerusalem and the Holy Land, Syria, Persian Empire, Egypt, North Africa, Sicily, Spain, and Portugal

63) c
During the last Ice Age, ocean water froze into vast sheets of ice known as glaciers. As water levels dropped, a land bridge called Beringia was exposed. Many scholars believe that the first people in the Americas crossed Beringia from Asia.

64) a
Merchants and craftspeople became more aggressive about raising or lowering prices to make a profit. Landlords encouraged farmers to specialize in crops or other goods that could be sold for a higher profit in distant markets. Cities became centers for commerce and many cities grew wealthy, and became prosperous trade centers dealing in rare goods brought from faraway lands.

65) d
In the charter, John promised to consult the nobility before raising new taxes. The charter established that even monarchs must observe the law.

66) Tikal, Copán

67) Aztec Empire

68) Inca Empire

69) They continued to hunt mammals and birds, and ate more berries, nuts, roots, and seeds. They also made grinding stones and baskets to process and store the plants they gathered.

70) The Vikings' ships were safer and quicker than other European ships and carried them farther. Their unique ships curved upward on each end rode the rough waves of the North Atlantic. These ships carried them to Iceland, Greenland, and North America.

71) The Mogollon and Hohokam adapted to a dry environment by developing irrigation systems to water their crops. They also built pit houses into the ground for protection from temperature extremes. The Anasazi invented and built pueblos on the high mesas and later they built their homes in cliffsides for protection.

72) Zheng He commanded the Ming treasure fleet on seven voyages for nearly 30 years. His voyages to India, Arabia, and Africa brought the wealth and knowledge of other cultures to China.

73) After the Roman Empire collapsed, trade and communication networks broke down, city populations declined, and much of Europe experienced political disorder. Feudalism, a system of government in which people pledged loyalty to a lord in exchange for protection, gradually arose.

Call to Freedom

74) Some of the Native American tribal groups in the Northwest Pacific coast region included the Chehalis, Nootka, Salishan, Skokomish, Tillamook, and Tlinglit. The region stretched 2,000 miles along the coast from present-day southern Alaska to northern California. Native Americans there enjoyed a mild climate and lived by fishing, gathering, hunting, and trading. Their most important resource was salmon, although they also hunted sea otters and whales from large dugout canoes. They used evergreen trees to build houses and provide wood for building totem poles. Native Americans in the Northwest prospered because they had so many nearby resources and generally did not farm. They demonstrated their wealth and earned respect by holding potlatches, events at which hosts gave away most of their possessions.

Northeastern tribal groups lived in an area stretching from the Atlantic Ocean to the Mississippi River Valley and southeast from the Great Lakes to present-day Virginia. Two of the large main groups were the Algonquian and the Iroquois. Some Algonquian tribal groups included the Chippewa, Memomini, and Penobscot who lived north of the Great Lakes. They lived by hunting and gathering edible plants. Other Algonquian peoples included the Narragansett, Pequot, and Wampanoag who lived further south. They farmed as well as hunted, fished, and gathered plants. They lived in permanent villages and built a variety of housing structures, such as large multifamily lodges and small wigwams, or circular huts. To the east lived the Iroquois who relied primarily on agriculture but also hunted, fished, and traded with other tribes. The Iroquois League was a political confederation which included the Cayuga, Oneida, Onondaga, and Seneca tribes and made these groups very strong. The League was responsible for waging war and making peace with non-Iroquois peoples. Women exercised a great deal of power in the Iroquois society. They selected the male members of the League council. They could also overrule council decisions and in some instances remove its members. Women were also responsible for raising children and planting and harvesting, while men hunted and traded. The Iroquois lived in longhouses, rectangular dwellings made from logs and bark. Longhouses ranged from 50 to 100 feet long and housed 8 to 10 families.

75) During the Commercial Revolution, trade became more important. Merchants and craftspeople became more aggressive in selling their goods and services. In order to earn more money to buy these goods, nobles encouraged the peasants on their manors to grow profitable crops such as grapes for wine. Workers were also able to buy more goods because their wages were higher due to a shortage of labor after the Black Death. As trade increased, some cities grew as centers for trade. Some like Florence and Venice in Italy became famous for manufacturing—Florence for wool dyeing and Venice for glass blowing. As merchant families in the cities made more money, they looked for ways to invest their capital to make a profit. Some became bankers and began loaning money for interest. Others invested their money in joint-stock companies so that they could undertake larger ventures and limit their losses. As a result of all these developments, cities and trade continued to grow.

# Chapter 2 New Empires in the Americas

## MATCHING

In the space provided, write the term or the name of the person that best fits the description. Choose your answers from the list below. Not all answers will be used.

| | | |
|---|---|---|
| charter | caravel | conquistadores |
| plantations | presidios | borderlands |
| strait | sea dogs | monopoly |
| circumnavigate | Columbian Exchange | astrolabe |
| pueblos | Northwest Passage | Line of Demarcation |

1) _____ to sail completely around

2) _____ document granting permission to establish a colony

3) _____ towns in New Spain

4) _____ route around or through North America that would allow ships to sail from the Atlantic to the Pacific

5) _____ small but sturdy ship built to be fast and maneuverable

6) _____ English sailors who helped England oppose Spain without officially declaring war

7) _____ allowed navigators to determine their ship's position by charting the position of the stars

8) _____ narrow sea passage

9) _____ exclusive control

10) _____ large farms that specialized in one kind of crop, such as sugar

## TRUE/FALSE

Write T if a statement is true or F if it is false. If a statement is false, explain why.

11) _____ On October 12, 1492, Columbus landed on the shores of the present-day United States.

_____

12) _____ In 1513 Balboa discovered an ocean that he named the Pacific Ocean.

_____

13) _____ Magellan's sailors were the first people to circumnavigate the earth.

_____

14) _____ Of the 1 million people who lived on Hispaniola in 1492 before Columbus came, all but about 500 hundred died of European diseases within the next 60 years.

_____

15) _____ Missions were settlements established by priests to convert local Indians to Christianity.

_____

16) _____ Conquistadores were Portuguese sailors who brought the spirit of the *Reconquista* to the American continents.

_____

17) _____ In the 1500s, Spain controlled as much as 75 percent of the spice trade between Europe and Asia.

_____

18) _____ After Magellan discovered a western route to Asia, Spain increased its trade with Africa and Africa.

_____

19) _____ The Council of the Indies resolved Spanish and Portuguese disputes over ownership of gold and unusual plants and animals brought to Europe from the Indies.

_____

20) _____ Prince Henry the Navigator paid for expeditions to the coast of Africa in the hopes of finding a sea route to Asia.

_____

**MULTIPLE CHOICE**
**For each of the following, circle the letter of the best choice.**

21) Portugal sought a sea route to Asia in the 1400s because

    a. Spain controlled all the riches in present-day Mexico and South America.
    b. Coronado had returned to Portugal with gold discovered in the Seven Cities of Cíbola.
    c. Venice monopolized Asian trade on the Silk Road and the Mediterranean sea.
    d. the Treaty of Tordesillas gave Portugal rights to all of Asia.

22) A common European name for the lands of Asia was

    a. the "New World."            c. the Indies.
    b. San Salvador.             d. Hispaniola.

23) Columbus's 1492 voyage from the Canary Islands across the unknown waters of the Atlantic

    a. ended 33 days after he set sail.
    b. resulted in the mutiny of his Spanish crew.
    c. took him beyond the Portuguese side of the Line of Demarcation.
    d. took him around the Cape of Good Hope and into the Indian Ocean.

24) Spanish military settlements and bases in New Spain were called

    a. pueblos.              c. *encomiendas.*
    b. presidios.             d. borderlands.

25) England's most successful sea dog was

    a. Sir Francis Drake.        c. John Cabot.
    b. Sir Walter Raleigh.      d. Henry Hudson.

26) During the centuries-long *Reconquista*, Spain fought to conquer

    a. between 3 and 4 million American Indians who lived in the borderlands.
    b. the Aztec Empire.
    c. English monarchs who established the Anglican Church and defended the Protestants.
    d. North African Moors who had invaded Spain hundreds of years before.

27) Spain's all-water route to Asia that Columbus sought in 1492 was discovered

    a. by John Cabot in 1498.
    b. by Italian explorer Amerigo Vespucci in 1501.
    c. 30 years later when Magellan's crew circumnavigated the earth.
    d. only after Spain and Portugal agreed to move the Line of Demarcation 700 miles further east of the Azores.

28) A center for the study of navigation, mapmaking, shipbuilding, and sailing was established by

a. King Ferdinand and Queen Isabella of Spain.    c. King Henry VIII of England.
b. Prince Henry of Portugal.    d. Queen Elizabeth I of England.

29) The European race for a sea route to Asia was won by

a. Portugal.    c. England.
b. Spain.    d. Italy.

30) Trading for Africans who had been enslaved through war or raiding was begun by the

a. Spanish.    c. English.
b. Portuguese.    d. Dutch.

31) The first English person to sail around the world was

a. Sir Humphrey Gilbert.    c. John Cabot.
b. Sir Walter Raleigh.    d. Sir Francis Drake.

32) The Strait of Magellan is

a. the narrow sea passage discovered in South America by Magellan.
b. located in the present-day Philippines.
c. Magellan's route to a great sea that he named the Southern Ocean.
d. the gateway to Africa, India, and the Americas.

33) The conquistadores led military expeditions into the interior of the Americas

a. to found presidios.
b. searching for riches and fame.
c. hoping to build permanent settlements where they could govern themselves.
d. escaping King Manuel's brutal reign.

34) Bartolomé de Las Casas

a. established the fort of St. Augustine in eastern Florida.
b. brought enslaved Africans to work on his many plantations in New Spain.
c. worked against the *encomienda* system that mistreated Indians.
d. established a mission in El Paso in 1659.

35) After Vasco Da Gama rounded the Cape of Good Hope and reached southwest India, the Portuguese

a. discovered that European trade with India was monopolized by Spain.
b. realized that Muslim traders could not communicate with Portuguese interpreters.
c. discovered a new culture that had never traded with Silk Road merchants.
d. established trading forts in India, Africa, and China.

Call to Freedom

36) With the help of Malintzin, an American Indian woman who served as a guide and interpreter,

    a. Cortés gathered an army of American Indian allies and marched on Tenochtitlán.
    b. Balboa discovered a great sparkling blue sea that he named the "Southern Ocean."
    c. Magellan's crew survived an Indian attack in the present-day Philippines.
    d. Columbus found gold nuggets and exotic treasures on the island he called Hispaniola.

37) Cabot, Cartier, Champlain, and Hudson were explorers who

    a. sailed under the English flag in search of the golden Seven Cities of Cíbola.
    b. searched for a Northwest Passage through or around North America.
    c. founded forts—such as Detroit, St. Louis and New Orleans—on the Great Lakes and along the Mississippi River.
    d. based their claims to the northern coast of North America on Sir Walter Raleigh's explorations.

38) Columbus's theory that he could reach Asia by sailing west was considered daring because

    a. Bartolomeu Dias had already proven that an eastern land route was more profitable.
    b. caravels were not capable of maneuvering through the Straight of Magellan.
    c. scholars believed that the 10,000-mile voyage necessary to reach Asia would be impossible.
    d. such a journey would require Columbus to circumnavigate the earth.

39) One of the last borderland areas settled by the Spanish was

    a. Florida.               c. Texas.
    b. California.         d. New Mexico.

40) At trading posts on the African coast, the Portuguese traded cloth, armor, and guns for

    a. silk and spices.         c. gold, silk, and ivory.
    b. ivory, gold, and spices.    d. gold, ivory, and slaves.

41) The Southern Ocean was renamed the Pacific during the voyage of

    a. Magellan.           c. Columbus.
    b. da Gama.          d. Dias.

42) The Portuguese and most other Europeans believed that it was acceptable to enslave people who were not

    a. Europeans.         c. domesticated.
    b. Christians.        d. willing to engage in trade and commerce.

Call to Freedom

43) Columbus called the Taino "Indians" because

a. he wanted to convince Ferdinand and Isabella that he had discovered North America.
b. they convinced him that they had descended from Asian culture groups.
c. they resembled natives of India that he had observed on previous voyages.
d. he believed that he had landed in the Indies.

44) French claims to much of Canada began with

a. Henry Hudson's 1610 voyage.
b. the withdrawal of the Dutch from the region.
c. the explorations of Cartier and Champlain.
d. the pope's approval of the Line of Demarcation.

45) The Cape of Good Hope was named by the

a. Portuguese.                    c. Spanish.
b. English.                       d. French.

46) With the help of Indian allies, Pizarro

a. explored Florida's west coast in 1527.
b. west across the Mississippi River into Arkansas.
c. conquered the Inca Empire and gained huge amounts of gold and silver.
d. took Moctezuma prisoner and invaded his empire.

47) The Dutch were attracted to North America by the

a. Dutch West India Company's ability to attract large numbers of settlers.
b. possibility of trading with American Indians for valuable furs.
c. hope of finding a Northwest Passage.
d. opportunity to spread Christianity in all parts of the continent.

48) Balboa's discovery of the Southern Ocean in 1513

a. proved that Columbus was incorrect to assume he could sail west to reach Asia.
b. inspired Magellan to sail east to reach Asia.
c. inspired da Gama to sail around the Cape of Good Hope to reach Asia.
d. convinced Magellan to trust Columbus's instinct to sail west to reach Asia.

49) Founded around 1609–10, one of the most important settlements in the borderlands was

a. El Paso.                       c. San Francisco.
b. Santa Fe.                      d. St. Augustine.

50) Permanent North American settlements were established in present-day Nova Scotia, New Brunswick, and parts of Maine by the

a. French.
b. Dutch.
c. Spanish.
d. English.

51) The conquistador whose expedition traveled north from Mexico to the Grand Canyon, and as far east as Kansas, was

a. de Soto.
b. Narváez.
c. Coronado.
d. Pizarro.

52) The Protestant Reformation began soon after

a. Martin Luther nailed the 95 theses to the door of Castle Church in Wittenberg, Germany.
b. King Henry VIII founded the Church of England.
c. Henry VIII proclaimed himself the head of the Anglican Church.
d. Pope Alexander VI drew the Line of Demarcation that resulted in civil war throughout Europe.

53) The Mississippi River Valley was claimed for

a. France by Jacques Cartier who named the area New France.
b. England by Sir Walter Raleigh who named the entire area Virginia.
c. the Dutch by Peter Minuit who called it New Netherland.
d. King Louis XIV of France by La Salle who named it Louisiana.

54) The conquistador who led an expedition of 600 to Florida, North Carolina, and Arkansas in 1539 was

a. Coronado.
b. de Soto.
c. de Vaca.
d. Pizarro.

55) Parts of present-day Connecticut, Delaware, New Jersey, and New York were known in 1624 as New

a. France.
b. Amsterdam.
c. Netherland.
d. England.

56) A Spanish soldier named de Vaca and a Moor named Estevanico

a. established a mission at San Diego in 1769.
b. organized a small army in an invasion of the Inca Empire in 1531.
c. lived with American Indian tribes in Texas for eight years.
d. searched Florida for water reported to make old men young again.

Call to Freedom

57) An English expedition that landed in present-day Virginia and North Carolina was funded by

a. John White.
b. John Cabot.
c. Sir Francis Drake.
d. Sir Walter Raleigh.

58) Columbus failed to acquire Portuguese funding for a westward expedition

a. because King John II preferred Dias's eastern route around Africa.
b. due to the monopoly Venice held over western trade routes.
c. after Portugal signed the Treaty of Tordesillas.
d. because King John II refused to entrust Portuguese ships to an Italian sailor.

59) Ponce de León was one of many conquistadores who hoped to find wealthy empires in

a. Mexico.
b. Florida.
c. California.
d. New Mexico.

60) One of the earliest European visual records of North American wildlife was the work of talented artist and botanist

a. Peter Minuit.
b. Isaac Jogues.
c. John White.
d. Virginia Dare.

## ENHANCED QUESTIONS

**For each of the following, circle the letter of the best choice. Next expand on the subject by answering the second question in the space provided.**

61) The Line of Demarcation gave all lands west of the line to

a. the Netherlands, and lands east of it to England.
b. England, and lands east of it France.
c. Portugal, and lands east of it to Spain.
d. Spain, and lands east of it to Portugal.

How did the Treaty of Tordesillas affect these two nations?

_____

_____

62) Columbus's conviction that he could reach Asia by sailing west across the Atlantic Ocean

a. differed from the convictions of Portuguese sailors who believed the best way was by sailing east.
b. was opposed by Prince Henry the Navigator who competed with Columbus for funding.
c. echoed opinions he learned in Italy where he spent his boyhood.
d. was reinforced by sea voyages he made to Genoa during his youth.

Why did King Ferdinand and Queen Isabella hesitate until 1492 to fund Columbus's voyage?

_____

_____

63) To reward settlers for moving to new lands in the Americas, Spain established

a. presidios to protect remote frontier areas.
b. the *encomienda* system.
c. trading posts where settlers could grow wealthy trading with local Indians.
d. the Council of the Indies to grant enormous amounts of land to settlers.

How did this plan affect local Indians?

_____

_____

64) The Great Lakes and St. Lawrence River region proved valuable to France because of

a. Champlain's earlier treaties with local Indians.
b. existing forts—such as Detroit, St. Louis and New Orleans—abandoned by Spain in the late 1500s.
c. the fur trade.
d. abundant wildlife and rich soil suitable for farming.

Why was this important, and how did it affect France's relationship with American Indians?

_____

_____

Call to Freedom

65) Protestants were reformers who protested

    a. Charles V's organization of the Anglican Church.
    b. corruption in the Church of England.
    c. Martin Luther's 95 theses.
    d. some practices of the Catholic Church.

Describe the Protestants' religious movement and its impact on Europe.

_____

_____

## GRAPHIC IMAGE QUESTIONS
**Examine the image, and then answer the following questions.**

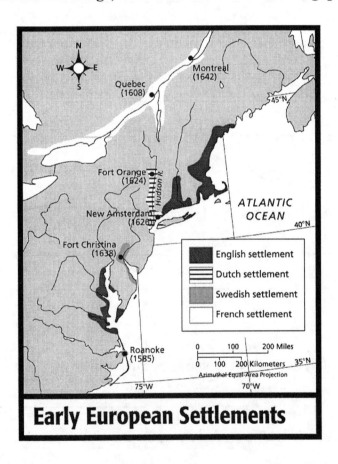

**Early European Settlements**

66) Which settlement was the furthest south? Which settlement was the furthest north?

_____

67) Why do you think the settlements were so close to the Atlantic Ocean?

_____

68) What is the oldest settlement shown on the map?

_____

**SHORT ANSWER**
**Write a brief answer for each of the following.**

69) What were the borderlands? Why were the Spanish slow to settle there?

_____

_____

_____

70) Why did King Philip II assemble the Spanish Armada? Explain the significance of the armada's defeat.

_____

_____

_____

71) Why did wealth from the Americas help lead to Spain's decline?

_____

_____

_____

72) How did the new continents across the Atlantic Ocean come to be called America?

_____

_____

_____

Call to Freedom

73) Name the explorers who did not always sail under the flag of their native land. Under what nation's flag did these explorers sail?

_____

_____

_____

**ESSAY**
**On a separate sheet of paper, write an essay on one of the following.**

74) Describe the system of government and the social structure of Spain's American Empire.

75) Explain the significance of the Columbian Exchange.

# ANSWER KEY

1) circumnavigate

2) charter

3) pueblos

4) Northwest Passage

5) caravel

6) sea dogs

7) astrolabe

8) strait

9) monopoly

10) plantations

11) F
Although Columbus named the island San Salvador, exactly where he landed is a mystery.

12) F
Balboa named the waters the Southern Ocean.

13) T

14) T

15) T

16) F
Conquistadores were Spanish soldiers who brought the spirit of the *Reconquista* to the American continents.

Call to Freedom

# ANSWER KEY

17) F

Portugal controlled this trade.

18) T

19) F

Based in Spain, the Council of the Indies was responsible for writing laws, appointing officials, and overseeing all government in Spanish America.

20) T

21) c

22) c

23) a

24) b

25) a

26) d

27) c

28) b

29) a

30) b

31) d

32) a

33) b

34) c

ANSWER KEY

35) d

36) a

37) b

38) c

39) b

40) d

41) a

42) b

43) d

44) c

45) a

46) b

47) b

48) d

49) b

50) a

51) c

52) a

Call to Freedom

ANSWER KEY

53) d

54) b

55) c

56) c

57) d

58) a

59) b

60) c

61) d
In the Treaty of Tordesillas, Spain and Portugal agreed to move the Line of Demarcation farther west, which gave Portugal rights to all of Africa as well as Brazil in South America.

62) a
They were busy with the *Reconquista*. However, in January 1492 the last Moorish kingdom in Spain surrendered, ending the *Reconquista*. With this centuries-old struggle behind them, Ferdinand and Isabella then agreed to fund Columbus's voyage. They ordered him to bring back items of value, and to claim all new lands that he explored for Spain.

63) b
This system gave many settlers, known as *encomenderos*, the right to tax or demand labor from local Indians. Although settlers were not permitted to enslave Indians, in practice they often forced them to work in harsh conditions. As a result, many Indians died of disease and exhaustion.

64) c
Europeans used animal furs, particularly beaver pelts, to make expensive hats. The French traded tools, jewelry, and cloth with Indians in exchange for furs. Because of their close trading relationships, the French generally respected American Indians' rights more than did many other Europeans.

65) d

The Protestant Reformation began in some German towns in the 1520s and soon spread to the Netherlands, Switzerland, England, and France. Throughout Europe fighting broke out between Catholics and Protestants, often leading to civil war and widespread destruction in some nations.

66) Roanoke; Montreal

67) provided access to shipping and trade

68) Roanoke, founded in 1585

69) The borderlands included northern Mexico, Florida, and parts of present-day Arizona, California, New Mexico, and Texas. During the first 100 years of Spain's American empire, most settlers went to the areas where they could gain the greatest wealth. Few Europeans lived in the borderlands where settlement took place slowly over several centuries.

70) During the late 1500s Philip II of Spain tried to put down the Protestant Reformation. His chief opponent and defender of the Protestants was England's Queen Elizabeth I. In 1588 King Philip assembled an invasion fleet, the Spanish Armada, to attack England. However, English ships attacked and destroyed the armada ships. The armada's defeat symbolized Spain's declining power.

71) The increased amounts of gold and silver coming into Spain created inflation and pushed Spanish prices very high, causing many Spaniards to purchase goods from abroad. Buying so much from abroad discouraged the Spanish from producing their own goods. Eventually, as the Americas produced less gold, the Spanish found that they could neither buy nor produce the food and products needed to maintain their great power.

72) A German map maker was so impressed with the writings of explorer Amerigo Vespucci that he published a book with a large map showing new continents across the ocean and labeled them "America" in honor of Vespucci. The book and map became popular, and Europeans began using the names North and South America.

73) Columbus, an Italian sailor, was funded by Portugal. Another Italian, John Cabot, sailed under the English flag. Vespucci, an Italian explorer, sailed with a Spanish expedition. Magellan, a Portuguese sea captain, was funded by Spain. Hudson, an English captain, sailed on different expeditions under the Dutch and the English flags.

Call to Freedom

ANSWER KEY

74) Spain ruled its American empire through a system of royal officials. At the top was the council of the Indies, based in Spain. Beneath the council were the viceroy of Peru and the viceroy of New Spain. Both viceroys appointed many local officials. Spanish law divided the population of Spain's American Empire into social categories based on birthplace and race. About 80 percent of the population were American Indians; the rest were whites, Africans, and people of mixed racial background. *Peninsulares*, Spaniards born in Spain, held the most important political offices in Spanish America. Next in status were the *criollos*, Spanish people born in the Americas, and the mestizos, who were born to Spanish and Indian parents. American Indians had their own rights and restrictions, while enslaved Africans had few legal protections and endured terrible living and working conditions. These social divisions were less rigid in the borderlands, allowing talented people to reach a higher social status.

75) The Columbian Exchange—the transfer of plants, animals, and diseases between the "Old World" of Europe, Asia, and Africa and the "New World" of the Americas—benefited Europeans who valued American plants such as corn, potatoes, and tomatoes. European settlers and explorers also brought plants and animals from Africa, Asia, and Europe to the American continents. Horses and cattle soon ran wild in the Americas. European farmers brought grains such as wheat and barley, which became very important. Along with new plants and animals, the explorers also unintentionally brought diseases such as smallpox, measles, and typhus. American Indians had never encountered these illnesses before and had no natural immunity, or resistance, to them. No one knows how many Indians of North and South America died from foreign disease, but the loss of life was staggering. For example, Spanish diseases quickened the fall of the Aztec Empire as hundreds of thousands of Indians died from smallpox alone.

## Chapter 3 The English Colonies

**MATCHING**

**In the space provided, write the term or the name of the person that best fits the description. Choose your answers from the list below. Not all answers will be used.**

| | | |
|---|---|---|
| sect | covenant | Pilgrims |
| dissenters | Separatists | William Bradford |
| proprietors | John Winthrop | House of Burgesses |
| George Calvert | immigrants | Roger Williams |
| Puritans | John Smith | Toleration Act of 1649 |

1) _____ sacred agreement

2) _____ people who have left the country of their birth to live in another country

3) _____ owners of a colony

4) _____ wanted to separate from the Church of England entirely rather than reform it

5) _____ Virginia's elected assembly

6) _____ governor of the Massachusetts Bay Colony

7) _____ religious group

8) _____ people who disagree with official religious or political opinions

9) _____ made restricting the religious rights of Christians a crime

10) _____ wanted to reform, or purify, the Church of England

**TRUE/FALSE**

**Write T if a statement is true or F if it is false. If a statement is false, explain why.**

11) _____ Plymouth Colony was founded by Pilgrims, and Massachusetts Bay Colony by Puritans.

_____

12) _____ The Powhatan Confederacy was a powerful alliance of Algonquian Indians under the leadership of Wahunsonacock.

_____

13) _____ By 1730 Virginia had the highest slave population in the colonies.

_____

14) _____ The Society of Friends, or the Quakers, made up one of the largest groups in New Jersey.

_____

15) _____ The Pilgrims were a Puritan sect that wanted to reform the Church of England.

_____

16) _____ The colony of Georgia was founded for English citizens who had been jailed for debt.

_____

17) _____ The first Africans in Virginia arrived on board a Dutch ship in 1619 and were immediately sold into slavery.

_____

18) _____ Puritans believed that the Massachusetts Bay Colony would become a "City upon a Hill," an ideal Christian community that other people would admire.

_____

19) _____ In 1605 the region called Virginia extended from present-day Maine to Florida.

_____

20) _____ During the Great Migration, at least 80,000 English men, women, and children left England for America.

_____

**MULTIPLE CHOICE**
**For each of the following, circle the letter of the best choice.**

21) Until the 1670s, the growth and success of the Virginia colony was obstructed most by

    a. disease and high death rates.
    b. disputes with the Powhatan Confederacy.
    c. poor colonial leadership.
    d. a scarcity of women and families in the colony.

22) Because Pilgrims were persecuted by English authorities, they

    a. offered religious freedom to all Christians who settled in their Massachusetts colony.
    b. fought with Oliver Cromwell against the forces of King Charles II.
    c. immigrated from England to America in 1620.
    d. left England and moved to the Netherlands in 1607.

23) After they arrived in America, most Pilgrims became

    a. hunters and fishermen.        c. farmers.
    b. fur traders.              d. craftspeople.

24) The colony of Carolina was founded in 1663 by

    a. proprietors who supported Charles II during the English Civil War.
    b. proprietors who supported Cromwell during the English Civil War.
    c. French Huguenots and plantation owners from the British West Indies.
    d. the London Company that sold large grants of land to eight proprietors.

25) The most common farm products sold and traded in New England were

    a. tobacco and rice.        c. dairy products and wheat.
    b. hogs and corn.          d. corn and tobacco.

26) The London Company hoped that the Virginia colony would offer new opportunities for

    a. dissenters who faced religious persecution in England.
    b. English immigrants who left their homeland during the Great Migration.
    c. adventurers who could discover gold without having to establish a settlement.
    d. the growing numbers of homeless, landless, and unemployed people in England.

27) England's Great Migration occurred

    a. after Cromwell's army defeated the forces of King Charles II in 1646.
    b. when economic and political circumstances became unbearable for dissenters.
    c. because Separatists were not welcome in England or in other European nations.
    d. after the London Company was granted a charter to settle Massachusetts.

Call to Freedom

28) Conflicts between the Powhatan and Virginia colonists increased

a. when John Rolfe married Pocahontas, daughter of the leader of the Powhatan Confederacy.
b. after John Smith gained control of the colony in 1608.
c. because many colonists wanted to grow tobacco on Indian lands.
d. after Opechancanough died in 1618.

29) South Carolina began to rely on slave labor because

a. the colony's eight proprietors were slaveholders.
b. English settlers from the Caribbean brought enslaved Africans with them to raise rice.
c. the colony's proprietors encouraged the cultivation of large grants of land.
d. colonists were unable to grow enough food for themselves without many hands to help.

30) William Bradford and Captain Miles Standish led and defended the

a. Plymouth colony.
b. Virginia colony.
c. Massachusetts Bay colony.
d. Carolina colony.

31) The Virginia colony began to thrive economically after

a. John Smith introduced a new variety of tobacco for export to England.
b. the Powhatan taught the colonists how to grow corn and tobacco.
c. John Rolfe introduced West Indian tobacco in 1612.
d. women began arriving in the colony in 1619.

32) Most Puritans stopped emigrating to America around 1642 because

a. firsthand accounts of starvation, illness, and hostile Indians dampened their enthusiasm.
b. King Charles II refused to grant charters to Puritan dissenters.
c. the economic depression lifted in England.
d. they fought and won more rights for themselves during the English Civil War.

33) In 1729 most of the settlers in the new colony of North Carolina were

a. trappers who traded for furs with local Indians.
b. French Huguenots who established the colony's first towns and churches.
c. Quakers who founded the town of Bath.
d. poor farmers who had moved south from Virginia.

34) Generous land grants, religious tolerance, and a thriving fur trade brought Jews, French Huguenots, Puritans, Africans, and others to the town of

a. New Amsterdam, located on Manhattan Island.
b. Boston, the chief city and capital of the Massachusetts Bay colony.
c. Philadelphia, capital of the Pennsylvania colony.
d. Charles Town, later called Charleston.

35) What became known as the first Thanksgiving was celebrated by

   a. Quakers and Algonquian Indians in Massachusetts.
   b. Pilgrims and Wampanoag Indians in Massachusetts.
   c. Puritans and Narragansett Indians in Massachusetts.
   d. Puritans and Pawtuxet Indians in Massachusetts.


36) The first colonists who arrived in Jamestown

   a. established peaceful relations with Pawtuxet Indians in the region.
   b. learned from Squanto how to grown corn and tobacco.
   c. searched for gold.
   d. built sturdy shelters and planted seeds brought from England.


37) Maryland and Virginia were similar in that

   a. most settlers in both colonies were men who raised tobacco for profit.
   b. both were proprietary colonies that later became royal colonies.
   c. most settlers in both colonies were Catholics who opposed England's separation from the Roman Catholic Church.
   d. settlers in both colonies bought their land from American Indians.


38) Puritans and merchants who planned a Puritan colony in North America

   a. were granted a charter to settle in Massachusetts in 1620.
   b. applied for permission to settle in Virginia in 1620.
   c. formed the Massachusetts Bay Company and named John Winthrop as governor of the colony.
   d. put William Bradford and Captain Miles Standish in charge of the Puritan families who left England on the *Mayflower*.


39) The Virginia colony experienced a brief period of peace with the Powhatan

   a. after Governor Berkeley made peace with Opechancanough in 1644.
   b. during John Rolfe's four-year marriage to Pocahontas, Wahunsonacock's daughter.
   c. after Governor Francis Wyatt initiated a treaty with Wahunsonacock in 1618.
   d. after Sir Thomas Gates enforced strict regulations that prevented colonists from encroaching on Indian lands.


40) Pilgrims gained farming and fishing skills from

   a. Samoset.                           c. Pocahontas.
   b. Squanto.                           d. Massasoit, chief of the Wampanoag.

Call to Freedom

41) Captain John Smith's main contribution to the Virginia colony was his

a. knowledge of its waterways.
b. ability to get along with Indian leaders.
c. military skills that prevented complete destruction of the colony in 1622.
d. strong leadership.

42) Only white male church members could vote in

a. Virginia.    b. Maryland.    c. Plymouth.    d. Massachusetts Bay.

43) In 1702 England created a single royal colony that united

a. Massachusetts and New Hampshire.    c. East New Jersey and West New Jersey.
b. New Netherland and New Amsterdam.    d. Pennsylvania and Delaware.

44) The colony that developed a General Court with a two-house legislature was

a. Pennsylvania.    c. Virginia.
b. Massachusetts Bay.    d. Georgia.

45) Methodist minister John Wesley came to America with colonists who founded

a. Providence.    b. Philadelphia.    c. Savannah.    d. Portsmouth. Bay.

46) The first Jamestown colonists arrived in

a. 1607.    b. 1619.    c. 1620.    d. 1630.

47) One of the first public education laws in Europe or the Americas was passed in

a. Virginia in 1633.    c. Connecticut in 1639.
b. Massachusetts in 1647.    d. Rhode Island in 1636.

48) After the Dutch lost control of New Netherland in 1664, England's Duke of York

a. replaced General Peter Stuyvesant as governor of the colony.
b. was given all the land between the Hudson and Delaware Rivers.
c. granted New Netherland to Sir George Carteret and Lord John Berkeley.
d. renamed the colony New York.

49) In 1639, the Reverend Thomas Hooker established the

a. General Court of Rhode Island.
b. colony of Connecticut.
c. Fundamental Orders, a code of government which gave more people the right to vote.
d. Salem Court that tried more than 100 colonists for witchcraft.

50) Women were more likely to have property rights and business licenses if they lived in

a. Plymouth.
b. Massachusetts Bay.
c. Connecticut.
d. Rhode Island.

51) The Quakers were a

a. Separatist sect founded by Puritans in England.
b. Protestant sect founded by George Fox in England.
c. Puritan sect founded by William Penn in America.
d. Puritan sect founded by the Revered John Robinson in England.

52) The colony of New Hampshire was settled by

a. Pilgrims from Plymouth.
b. Puritan colonists from Massachusetts Bay.
c. Dutch settlers from New Netherland.
d. Quakers from Pennsylvania.

53) The city that became a model used by city planners in other colonies was

a. Savannah, designed by James Oglethorpe.
b. New Amsterdam, designed by Peter Stuyvesant.
c. Philadelphia, designed by William Penn.
d. Boston, designed by John Winthrop.

54) Community and religious conflicts peaked in New England with the

a. trial of Anne Hutchinson in 1637.
b. banishment of Roger Williams from Massachusetts in 1633.
c. separation of Thomas Hooker's congregation from the Puritan Church of New England.
d. Salem witch trials in 1692.

55) In 1634 the second Lord Baltimore established a new colony in America for

a. Catholics.
b. dissenters.
c. Separatists.
d. English citizens who had been jailed for debt.

56) After the starving time, Virginia grew stronger under the leadership of

a. Captain John Smith.
b. John Rolfe.
c. a new governor, Sir Thomas Gates.
d. Deputy Governor Sir Thomas Dale.

57) The centerpiece of local New England politics was the

a. General Court.
b. town meeting.
c. Puritan Church.
d. community school.

Call to Freedom

58) After death rates dropped in Virginia, many farmers

   a. brought over indentured servants to work on the developing tobacco plantations.
   b. purchased land from local Indians in order to cultivate more varieties of tobacco.
   c. planted more acres of corn than tobacco, in order to feed themselves and their servants.
   d. preferred enslaved African laborers to indentured servants who had to be set free at the end of their contracts.

59) Catholics were persecuted in England because of their

   a. political and religious affiliations with the Netherlands.
   b. loyalty to George Cromwell during the English Civil War.
   c. connections with foreign powers and their opposition to England's separation from the Roman Catholic Church.
   d. support of Separatists who cut off all ties with the Church of England.

60) Pilgrims immigrated from the Netherlands to America to escape the limitations of unskilled labor and to

   a. provide an English culture and heritage for their children.
   b. practice their religion freely.
   c. reform the Church of England in America.
   d. build an ideal Christian community that would serve as an example for other Separatists.

## ENHANCED QUESTIONS
**For each of the following, circle the letter of the best choice. Next, expand on the subject by answering the second question in the space provided.**

61) Jamestown was attacked and burned by former indentured servants, slaves, and freed slaves who were followers of

   a. Nathaniel Bacon.                    c. Opechancanough.
   b. William Berkeley.                   d. Wahunsonacock.

   What provoked this attack? How were slaves and Indians affected as a result?

   _____

   _____

Call to Freedom
43

62) Roger Williams was banished from Massachusetts because he believed in the

a. Fundamental Orders that disagreed with the General Court of Massachusetts.
b. separation of Church and Government, and the duty of the colony to pay Indians for their land.
c. concept of "immediate revelation" from God, rather than from the Puritan pulpit.
d. idea that God's teachings were in the Bible, not in later revelations.

How did Williams practice his beliefs after he was banished?

_____

_____

63) The Toleration Act of 1649 was created for the colony of

a. Pennsylvania by William Penn.
b. Georgia by James Oglethorpe.
c. Maryland by the second Lord Baltimore.
d. Portsmouth by Anne Hutchinson.

What was the significance of this law?

_____

_____

64) The South Carolina colony thrived after African laborers taught the colonists how to raise

a. corn.                                      c. wheat.
b. tobacco.                                   d. rice.

Why and how did this crop affect the population of South Carolina?

_____

_____

65) Colonists who agreed to work from four to seven years for those who paid their ship fare to America were

a. headrights.                               c. immigrants.
b. indentured servants.                      d. proprietors.

What percentage of early Virginians came as indentured servants?

_____

_____

## GRAPHIC IMAGE QUESTIONS
**Examine the image, and then answer the following questions.**

### Founding the Colonies

| | COLONY | DATE OF SETTLEMENT | REASON FOR FOUNDING |
|---|---|---|---|
| **NEW ENGLAND COLONIES** | Massachusetts: *Plymouth* | 1620 | Religious freedom |
| | *Massachusetts Bay* | 1630 | Religious freedom |
| | New Hampshire | 1623 | Farming |
| | Connecticut | c. 1633 | Trade; farming; religious freedom |
| | Rhode Island | 1636 | Religious freedom |
| **MIDDLE COLONIES** | New York | c. 1624 | Trade (originally settled by the Dutch; became an English colony in 1664) |
| | Delaware | 1638 | Trade (originally settled by the Swedish; became part of the English colonies in 1664; was part of the Pennsylvania colony from 1682 until 1776) |
| | New Jersey | 1660 | Religious freedom; farming (originally settled by the Dutch; became an English colony in 1664) |
| | Pennsylvania | 1643 | Religious freedom (originally settled by the Swedish; land granted to William Penn in 1681; first Quaker colony established in 1682) |
| **SOUTHERN COLONIES** | Virginia: *Jamestown* | 1607 | To establish a permanent colony; search for riches |
| | Maryland | 1634 | Religious freedom; farming |
| | Carolinas | 1669 | Trade; farming |
| | Georgia | 1733 | Relief for poor people; buffer against Spanish Florida |

66) Which colonies were founded in part for trade purposes?

_____

_____

67) What was the last colony founded?

_____

68) Which colonies were established for religious freedom?

_____

_____

## SHORT ANSWER
**Write a brief answer for each of the following.**

69) Describe the legal contract that made Plymouth a self-governing colony.

_____

_____

_____

70) Why did Puritan leaders banish Anne Hutchinson from Massachusetts?

_____

_____

_____

71) What did Quakers believe? How did William Penn put his Quaker faith into action in Pennsylvania?

_____

_____

_____

72) Why did James Oglethorpe outlaw slavery and limit the size of land grants in Georgia? Why and how did his rules change after 1753?

_____

_____

_____

73) How did the headright system work? How did this system affect land distribution in Virginia?

_____

_____

_____

Call to Freedom

## ESSAY
**On a separate sheet of paper, write an essay on one of the following.**

74) Describe how the impact of climate, American Indians, and settlers' goals for their colonies led to the creation of two unique cultures in Virginia and New England.

75) Explain how Catholics and Puritans goals of gaining religious freedom in America affected the lives of future settlers in Maryland and Massachusetts Bay.

ANSWER KEY

1) covenant

2) immigrants

3) proprietors

4) Separatists

5) House of Burgesses

6) John Winthrop

7) sect

8) dissenters

9) Toleration Act of 1649

10) Puritans

11) T

12) T

13) F
By 1730 South Carolina had the highest slave population in the colonies.

14) T

15) F
Pilgrims were a Separatist sect that wanted to separate from the Church of England.

16) T

17) F
Of the first Africans in Virginia in 1619, some were indentured servants and others had been enslaved.

Call to Freedom

18)  T

19)  F
Virginia extended from present-day Maine to South Carolina.

20)  F
About 40,000 English immigrants moved to other nations in Europe. Another 40,000 or so immigrated to English colonies in the Caribbean and New England.

21)  a

22)  d

23)  c

24)  a

25)  b

26)  d

27)  b

28)  c

29)  b

30)  a

31)  c

32)  d

33)  d

# ANSWER KEY

34) a

35) b

36) c

37) a

38) c

39) b

40) b

41) d

42) d

43) c

44) b

45) c

46) a

47) b

48) d

49) c

50) a

50

51) b

52) b

53) c

54) d

55) a

56) b

57) b

58) d

59) c

60) a

61) a
Bacon and his followers attacked some friendly Indians, hoping to gain their land. When Governor Berkeley tried to intervene, Bacon's group attacked and burned Jamestown. After Bacon's Rebellion, Virginia colonists found it more difficult to make peace with Indians. In addition, farmers began to use more slave labor because they feared another rebellion by former indentured servants.

62) b
He and some of his supporters purchased land from the Narragansset Indians and established a settlement called Providence, which later became the colony of Rhode Island. He supported religious tolerance for all members of the Providence community and tried to establish fair dealings with local Indians.

63) c
The act, which made restricting the religious rights of Christians a crime, was the first law of its kind passed in America. It was one of the first efforts in the colonies to provide some religious freedom and to protect the rights of minority groups.

64) d
Rice production required many workers. This need for labor, combined with the skill of African workers at growing rice, led to a steady increase in slavery as rice production expanded. By 1730 almost 20,000 enslaved Africans were living in the colony, compared to only 10,000 whites.

65) b
Nearly two thirds of indentured servants died before their term was over because of poor living conditions and disease. However, the third that survived their period of indenture gained their freedom and were able to claim their own farmland.

66) Connecticut, New York, Deleware, Carolinas

67) Georgia

68) Plymouth, Massachusetts Bay, Rhode Island, New Jersey, Pennsylvania, Maryland

69) On November 20, 1620, the 41 male passengers on the *Mayflower* signed a legal contract which they called the Mayflower Compact. In it they agreed to create "such just and equal laws . . . as shall be thought most meet and convenient for the general good of the colony." The Mayflower Compact defined the basic laws and social rules that would govern their colony.

70) Like some others, Anne Hutchinson openly disagreed with some Puritan beliefs. In Boston, where other dissenters met in her home, she angered authorities by publicly discussing religious ideas that some leaders thought radical. She thought that people's relationship with God did not require guidance from the clergy. Nor did she and her followers believe that the performance of good deeds on Earth was a sign of being one of God's chosen. Puritan women were supposed to follow only the teachings of men . After she was put on trial, she said she had learned her ideas through "an immediate revelation" from God. This private revelation particularly troubled the court, because Puritans believed God's teachings were in the Bible, not in later revelations. The court ordered her banished from Massachusetts.

71) Quakers believed in liberty and equality for all people—that all people are equally good, and that the sexes are equal before God. This belief in equality led them to practice religious tolerance for all peoples, and nonviolence. Their beliefs shocked other Christians who believed that they themselves were God's "chosen elect." Penn acted out his faith by establishing a colony that offered religious freedom to all Christians and a government that Penn hoped would "secure the people from the abuse of power." He favored good discipline and just government. His system offered colonists benefits such as government care for the poor. He treated local Indians with respect, and learned the language of the local Delaware tribe so he could speak with them more effectively. Under his leadership, Pennsylvania developed a peaceful and stable society.

ANSWER KEY

72) Oglethorpe was determined that Georgia would develop differently from the other southern colonies, which had large plantations ruled by a few wealthy individuals. He hoped that the colony would fill with poor farmers who had some skills. To accomplish this, he outlawed slavery and limited the size of land grants to 500 acres each. However, many settlers wanted to develop large plantations worked by slaves. When Oglethorpe's charter expired in 1753, the English government made Georgia a royal colony wherein many of Oglethorpe's restrictions would not apply. Coastal Georgia soon filled with vast rice plantations worked by thousands of slaves, while elsewhere in the colony poor farmers struggled to survive.

73) Under this system, each colonist who paid his or her own way to Virginia received 50 acres of land plus 50 more acres for every additional person they brought from England. The system allowed wealthy colonists to gain large plots of land by bringing servants or relatives to Virginia.

74) The first Virginia colonists were adventurers who wanted to make their fortune and return to England. No families came to Jamestown, and very few colonists had farming experience or useful skills. Jamestown was surrounded by swamps filled with disease-carrying mosquitoes, and the river water was too salty to drink. Surrounding lands belonged to the Powhatan Confederacy. These factors contributed to illness, death, warfare, and overall disastrous beginnings for the Virginia colony. The relationship between settlers and Indians was not peaceful, in part because settlers attacked Indians and their lands, and in part because a great many Indians lived in Virginia. Settlers' goals for personal fortune became more attainable after tobacco was introduced as a major cash crop. Tobacco production led to a plantation system made possible in part by the headright system, indentured servants, and the widespread use of slavery. Wealthy settlers acquired so much land that little was left for indentured servants. Families were few. During the early years of settlement, men outnumbered women seven to one. The first families provided for themselves, and taught their children at home, since there were no schools, and few churches. Life in early Virginia revolved around scattered farms rather than towns. With easy access to river transportation, settlers did not need towns for trade. Overall, Virginia developed a plantation economy. Society was composed of the wealthy and their slaves, poor farmers, and hostile Indians who were being pushed off their lands. On the other hand, New England's first settlers arrived in a region where few Indians lived. The few they did meet were helpful and friendly. Pilgrims and Puritans came to America to establish and practice their religion and culture, and they came prepared to build communities with churches, schools, and governments of their own making. They brought large supplies of tools and livestock. Puritans had the advantage of trading with the earlier Plymouth colony. Although New England winters were harsh, and claimed many lives during the first few years, the region's climate was healthy overall. Few colonists died from diseases, unlike Virginia. Life in New England was centered around family and public duties. For this reason New England communities were more stable and structured than those in Virginia. While colonists in Virginia tended to be wealthy or poor, most New England colonists were somewhere in between. Many were skilled workers or experienced farmers. Others became successful in fishing enterprises or fur trading. Most New England farms were run by families that raised food rather than crops such as tobacco. In general, families were common in the Pilgrim and Puritan settlements, unlike in Virginia. Most colonists either came to New England in family groups or quickly formed families once they arrived. Education was important to Pilgrims and Puritans. Massachusetts law required education for children. America's first college, Harvard, was founded in Massachusetts. By 1700 about 70 percent of men and 45 percent of women in New England could read and write. These figures were much higher than for colonists in Virginia, where fewer people were concerned about education. Pilgrim families also educated and trained their indentured servants, unlike Virginia colonists who provided only physical necessities for their servants and slaves. Thus by 1700 Virginia and New England each had a unique culture that had come about as a result of climate, their relationships with Indians, and their goals for their colonies.

Call to Freedom

75) English Catholics and English Puritans came to America for the same reason--to escape religious persecution. The colonies that each developed in America were very different, however. Catholics immigrated to Maryland. George Calvert, the first Lord Baltimore, had applied for the charter of a new colony in America for Catholics. His son, the second Lord Baltimore, established the colony. Although Maryland was established by and for Catholics, an increasing number of Protestants began moving there in the 1640s. Soon religious conflicts arose between Catholics and Protestants in the colony. To ease these tensions, Lord Baltimore initiated the Toleration Act of 1649 that protected the religious rights of all Christians--not only Catholic Christians. Maryland became known for its tolerance and for the religious freedom it granted to new settlers. Thus Maryland's leaders established an American colony that exemplified the reason for its very existence: religious freedom. On the other hand, Puritans came to Massachusetts Bay with the belief that they had made a covenant with God to build an ideal Christian community that would be specially blessed. Politics and religion were closely linked in their colony. Government leaders were also church leaders, and ministers possessed a great deal of authority in Puritan communities. Only white male church members could vote. Colonists achieved full membership in the church by becoming God's elect as they were called. Individuals had to pass a public examination to prove the strength of their faith. Around 1700 the colony began allowing property owners outside the elect to vote. When colonists such as Roger Williams and Anne Hutchinson disagreed with Puritan teachings, they discovered that Puritan leaders would not grant freedom of thought, or freedom of religion, to anyone who did not conform to Puritan standards. The General Court tried, convicted, and banished people who did not conform. Thus the Puritans practiced the same sort of religious persecution in America that they had detested in England. Community and religious conflicts peaked with the Salem witch trials which resulted in the execution of 19 people as witches. Whereas Maryland became known for tolerance and acceptance, Massachusetts Bay became known for intolerance and persecution.

## Chapter 4 Life in the English Colonies

**MATCHING**

**In the space provided, write the term or the name of the person that best fits the description. Choose your answers from the list below. Not all answers will be used.**

mercantilism          Privy Council          libel
Eliza Lucas Pinckney  Samuel Sewall          John Smibert
Parliament            balance of trade       Benjamin Franklin
cash crops            George Whitefield      staple crops
duties                John Peter Zenger

1) _____ one of the most popular ministers of the Great Awakening

2) _____ crops that are continuously in demand

3) _____ set policy for all 13 colonies

4) _____ creating and maintaining wealth by carefully controlling trade

5) _____ held the first art exhibit in America

6) _____ founded the first circulating library in the colonies

7) _____ false statement that damages a person's reputation

8) _____ import taxes

9) _____ antislavery activist who published *The Selling of Joseph*

10) _____ published criticism of the royal governor of New York

**TRUE/FALSE**

**Write T if a statement is true or F if it is false. If a statement is false, explain why.**

11) _____ Colonial smuggling increased as a result of English trade restrictions.

_____

12) _____ Young girls and boys learned skilled trades by serving as apprentices.

_____

13) _____ Imports are items that are sold to other countries.

_____

14) _____ The Privy Council allowed most colonial governments to run their own affairs.

_____

15) _____ The colonies' assemblies were modeled on the English Parliament, or legislature.

_____

16) _____ Samuel Sewall made the first recorded colonial protest against slavery.

_____

17) _____ The Scientific Revolution began in mathematics and astronomy and eventually affected all areas of natural science.

_____

18) _____ In 1686 the New England colonies united to form one government that they called the Dominion of New England.

_____

19) _____ To establish a favorable balance of trade, a government must increase its imports and decrease its exports.

_____

20) _____ The purpose of revivals was to revive an excitement for religion through emotional and inspiring sermons.

_____

## MULTIPLE CHOICE
**For each of the following, circle the letter of the best choice.**

21) As a result of revivals held during the 1730s and 1740s,

a. Charles Chauncy experienced a great awakening that transformed Boston's First Church.
b. George Whitefield's sermon, "Sinners in the Hands of an Angry God," was heard by thousands of worshipers.
c. Congregational pastor Jonathan Edwards was appointed president of Yale College.
d. people throughout the colonies experienced a great awakening in their religious beliefs.

22) The first college that was founded in the English colonies was

a. Yale.                                    c. Boston College.
b. Harvard.                                 d. the University of Pennsylvania.

23) Slave codes passed by colonial legislatures

a. regulated the number of slaves that could be imported into the colonies each year.
b. defined the relationship that existed between a slaveholder and his slaves.
c. controlled slaves by establishing rules of conduct for them.
d. protected slaves from mistreatment by their slaveholders.

24) The first assembly formed in the colonies was

a. a bicameral legislature established in Jamestown, Virginia in 1619.
b. the Virginia House of Burgesses, formed in 1621.
c. established by Puritans in the Massachusetts Bay Colony.
d. a bicameral legislature established at Plymouth in 1620.

25) Mathematical Principles of Natural Philosophy was published in the late 1600s by

a. Nicholas Copernicus, and explained that the planets revolve around the sun.
b. Galileo Galilei, whose theories explained the behavior of objects on Earth and in the sky.
c. Benjamin Franklin, one of the most significant thinkers of his time.
d. Sir Isaac Newton, and became the foundation for physics for the next 200 years.

26) Itinerant preachers were important to frontier settlers because

a. these ministers brought the message of the Great Awakening to the countryside.
b. there were few established churches on the frontier.
c. more "New Light" believers lived on the frontier than in populated areas.
d. more "Old Light" believers lived on the frontier than in populated areas.

27) Crops grown mainly to be sold for profit are

    a. cash crops.                          c. enumerated articles.
    b. staple crops.                        d. specialty crops.

28) The power to raise taxes, organize local governments, and control the military belonged to

    a. the Privy Council.                 c. colonial assemblies.
    b. Parliament.                       d. royal governors.

29) Science as it is known and practiced today is based on the methods and discoveries of

    a. Sir Isaac Newton.                c. Copernicus.
    b. Galileo.                         d. the Scientific Revolution.

30) In the middle and southern colonies, the Great Awakening inspired growth in church membership among

    a. Congregationalists.              c. Presbyterians.
    b. Episcopalians.                 d. Baptists and Methodists.

31) The main idea of the Enlightenment was that

    a. an evangelical belief in God would bring people salvation.
    b. reason can be used to improve people's quality of life.
    c. government should work to best serve the people.
    d. an educated citizenry would develop a stable nation.

32) The trade network that developed into a so-called triangular trade

    a. went from the colonies to the West Indies to Britain.
    b. was created by Great Britain after the 1707 Act of Union.
    c. went from Africa to the West Indies to Britain.
    d. depended on colonial smugglers who disregarded the Navigation Acts.

33) The first botanical garden in the American colonies was established by

    a. Benjamin Franklin at Philadelphia.
    b. botanist John Bartram at Philadelphia.
    c. the American Philosophical Society in 1769.
    d. botanists at Harvard College in 1710.

34) By the late 1700s, the largest colonial city was

    a. New York City.                 c. Newport.
    b. Boston.                       d. Philadelphia.

35) The Great Awakening appealed especially to

    a. women on the frontier.
    b. women, members of minority groups, and poor people.
    c. enslaved African Americans.
    d. indentured servants, free African Americans, and slaves.

36) Many laws in Massachusetts enforced the Puritans' efforts to

    a. please the Privy Council.
    b. establish a bicameral legislature.
    c. combine the church and state.
    d. borrow ideas from Virginia's House of Burgesses.

37) By 1700 slavery existed

    a. only in the southern colonies.
    b. in all the southern and middle colonies.
    c. only in royal colonies, rather than in company or proprietary colonies.
    d. in all the colonies.

38) The primary cash crops in the southern colonies were

    a. cotton and tobacco.         c. tobacco, rice, and cotton.
    b. tobacco, rice, and indigo.    d. tobacco, rice, cotton, and indigo.

39) Town schools were established in New England because colonists there

    a. wanted to educate a ministry for future generations.
    b. believed in the importance of science and philosophy.
    c. wanted to encourage Enlightenment ideals in their children.
    d. wanted to educate future teachers for Harvard and Yale.

40) Most children in the middle and the southern colonies

    a. used the New England Primer to learn to read.
    b. were taught by parents or private tutors.
    c. attended town schools that were paid for by the community.
    d. were taught by ministers of Anglican churches.

41) Parliament has a bicameral legislature, which is

    a. a law-making body ruled jointly by the people and the monarch.
    b. an assembly consisting of two Burgesses for every jurisdiction.
    c. a law-making body made up of two houses, or groups.
    d. an assembly made up of a Council of State and a Council for the People.

42) The most important colonial center for the study of science was

    a. Philadelphia.                 c. New Haven.
    b. Boston.                     d. Williamsburg.

43) Staple crops such as wheat, barley and oats

    a. were grown primarily on large plantations in Delaware.
    b. required a great deal of difficult work and a large labor force.
    c. created a favorable balance of trade with the southern colonies and New England.
    d. were produced in the middle colonies.

44) The Great Awakening encouraged colonial communication between colonies when

    a. people from the southern and the middle colonies traveled to revivals in New England.
    b. people throughout the colonies attended Whitefield's revivals in Georgia and Virginia.
    c. ministers from different colonies began communicating with one another.
    d. African Americans and white colonists attended revivals together.

45) Phillis Wheatley and Anne Bradstreet

    a. celebrated Christian religion in their poetry.
    b. were influenced more by the Great Awakening than by Enlightenment ideas.
    c. wrote poems that taught children about the Bible and religious values.
    d. wrote religious poems that were published in The Tenth Muse in London.

46) The ministers of the Great Awakening focused less on the love of God and more on the

    a. love of Christ for only those people who attended evangelical revivals.
    b. condemnation of humanity by an unforgiving God.
    c. wrath of God and the hopeless condition of sinners.
    d. the sinful state of humanity and everyone's equal chance to be saved.

47) Parliament asked the rulers of the Netherlands to lead England as joint monarchs

    a. Mary was the daughter of James II.
    b. William of Orange was the Protestant ruler of the Netherlands.
    c. James II wanted to change England back to a Catholic nation.
    d. James II wanted to disband Parliament and rule England alone.

48) The discovery that lightning is a form of electricity came when

    a. Galileo was observing the night sky.
    b. Newton focused his newly built telescope on Jupiter.
    c. Benjamin Banneker accurately predicted an eclipse.
    d. Benjamin Franklin flew a kite during a thunderstorm.

49) Rich fishing waters and abundant timber

    a. created a demand for shipbuilding in the early 1700s.
    b. made fishing and shipbuilding two leading industries in New England.
    c. motivated southerners to produce whale oil and pitch.
    d. attracted many carpenters, rope makers, and shipbuilders to the middle colonies.

50) Most of the nine colleges founded by colonists were

    a. located in New England.
    b. located in the middle colonies and New England.
    c. open only to men and women who trained for the ministry.
    d. open only to men who studied religion, the sciences, or law.

51) The middle colonies' need for a growing labor force was largely filled by

    a. skilled laborers.             c. indentured servants.
    b. slaves and free African Americans.    d. apprentices.

52) The colonial clockmaker who surveyed boundaries for more than half the colonies was

    a. Benjamin Franklin of Philadelphia.
    b. David Rittenhouse of Philadelphia.
    c. Benjamin Banneker, a free African American who lived in Maryland.
    d. Robert Beverley, who also wrote the History of the Present State of Virginia.

53) When practicing mercantilism, countries

    a. imported only to their colonies.
    b. exported only to their colonies.
    c. imported and exported to their colonies rather than foreign nations.
    d. exported to foreign nations rather than to their colonies.

54) The most successful newspaper in the colonies was

    a. Benjamin Franklin's *Pennsylvania Gazette*.
    b. *Poor Richard's Almanack*.
    c. started by the American Philosophical Society in 1732.
    d. printed by Robert Beverley in Williamsburg from 1721 to 1740.

55) The diverse northern economy demanded the labor of many

    a. skilled craftsmen who had trained as apprentices.
    b. slaves imported from the West Indies.
    c. indentured servants, many of whom were women.
    d. apprentices and indentured servants who worked for lower wages than artisans.

Call to Freedom

56) Most colonial artists such as Robert Feke were portrait painters because

    a. art exhibits consisted primarily of portraits of European kings and queens.
    b. that was the only art most colonists were interested in buying.
    c. regional landscapes were not popular outside the area they portrayed.
    d. portraits were the most popular art form in Europe.

57) One of the leading figures in the Scientific Revolution was

    a. Jean-Jacques Rousseau.      c. Voltaire.
    b. John Locke.      d. Galileo.

58) Enumerated articles, as specified in the Navigation Acts, were items

    a. England needed but could not produce.
    b. the colonists could not export to England.
    c. the colonists must transport on English ships.
    d. exported to England where duties were collected.

59) New England colonies developed a tradition of holding

    a. secret town meetings without permission from the Royal Governor.
    b. town meetings during county court sessions.
    c. weekly town meetings.
    d. annual town meetings.

60) The American Philosophical Society was the first colonial organization

    a. with the purpose of studying the planetary system.
    b. that taught classes in science as well as religion.
    c. with a mission to study science in the colonies.
    d. that brought Enlightenment thinkers together with leaders of the Great Awakening.

**ENHANCED QUESTIONS**
**For each of the following, circle the letter of the best choice. Next, expand on the subject by answering the second question in the space provided.**

61) As a result of the Great Awakening, the congregations of some established churches in the colonies divided into

    a. believers and non-believers.      c. traditionalists and evangelicals.
    b. men's and women's congregations.      d. Christians and non-Christians.

How did Gilbert Tennent's leadership impact this division in his church?

_____

_____

Call to Freedom

62) One of the most lasting and valuable achievements of the Scientific Revolution was the development of

    a. the scientific method.            c. botanical gardens.
    b. a new almanac.                 d. the printing press.

What was involved in the development of this achievement?

_____

_____

63) Between 1650 and 1696 Parliament passed a series of Navigation Acts to control

    a. the triangular trade between Britain, the West Indies, and the colonies.
    b. trade in the colonies and increase England's profits.
    c. colonial smuggling of sugar, tobacco, and cotton.
    d. trade in the colonies and colonial exports to foreign markets.

How did the Navigation Acts demonstrate mercantilism?

_____

_____

64) The Glorious Revolution described the

    a. Great Awakening in Europe.
    b. revival of interest in religion and spirituality in the United States.
    c. union of England and Scotland in 1707.
    d. overthrow of King James II.

How did the Glorious Revolution affect the English monarchy and the future of England's colonies?

_____

_____

65) A harsh climate, rocky soil, and unnavigable rivers best describes the environment of

    a. the South.               c. New England.
    b. the Middle Colonies.      d. the North.

How did this environment affect the development of slavery in this region?

_____

_____

**Examine the image, and then answer the following questions.**

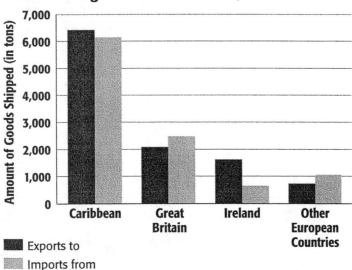

**Trade Through New York Harbor, 1754**

Source: *Historical Statistics of the United States*

66) About how many tons of goods were exported to Ireland in 1754?

_____

67) About how many tons of goods were imported from Great Britain in 1754?

_____

68) From which region or nation did New York receive the greatest amount of imports in 1754?

_____

**SHORT ANSWER**
**Write a brief answer for each of the following.**

69) What roles did women play in colonial arts and the colonial economy?

_____

_____

_____

70) Define and describe the Middle Passage.

_____

_____

_____

71) How did the colonies benefit under the mercantilism system?

_____

_____

_____

72) Why and how did Philadelphia and New York City benefit from the production of staple crops in the middle colonies?

_____

_____

_____

73) Why did enslaved Africans make up the main labor force in the southern colonies?

_____

_____

_____

**ESSAY**
**On a separate sheet of paper, write an essay on one of the following.**

74) Explain why New England—where few slaveholders lived—was involved in a triangular trade that sold and transported millions of enslaved Africans.

75) How did the Enlightenment influence ideas about how governments should function?

Call to Freedom

ANSWER KEY

1) George Whitefield

2) staple crops

3) Privy Council

4) mercantilism

5) John Smibert

6) Benjamin Franklin

7) libel

8) duties

9) Samuel Sewall

10) John Peter Zenger

11) T

12) F
Only boys served as apprentices.

13) F
Imports are goods purchased from other countries, while exports are goods sold to other countries.

14) T

15) T

16) F
Quakers in Germantown, Pennsylvania made the first recorded colonial protest against slavery.

17) T

18) F
James II formed the Dominion of New England.

19) F
Decreasing imports and increasing exports establishes a favorable balance of trade.

20) T

21) d

22) b

23) c

24) a

25) d

26) b

27) a

28) c

29) d

30) d

31) b

32) a

33) b

Call to Freedom

ANSWER KEY

34) d

35) b

36) c

37) d

38) b

39) a

40) b

41) c

42) a

43) d

44) c

45) a

46) d

47) c

48) d

49) b

50) b

51)  c

52)  b

53)  c

54)  a

55)  a

56)  b

57)  d

58)  a

59)  d

60)  c

61)  c
Presbyterian minister Tennent, a leader of the New Lights, published a pamphlet that attacked the traditionalists. As a result, the Presbyterian Church split into two groups. "Old Sides" opposed the Great Awakening and "New Sides" followed Tennent's teachings.

62)  a
The scientific method involved carefully examining natural events and then forming theories from experiments and observations.

63)  b
These acts demonstrated mercantilism because they required the colonists to do most of their trading with England.

64)  d
The ideas of the Glorious Revolution were expressed in the English Bill of Rights, which helped to increase Parliament's powers. The English Bill of Rights and a stronger Parliament greatly interested American colonists who increasingly valued their own right to elect representatives to decide local issues.

Call to Freedom

65) c

Few New England farms produced cash crops, and they therefore needed fewer farm laborers. As a result, slavery did not become as important in New England as it did in other regions.

66) 1,500 tons

67) 2,500 tons

68) the Caribbean

69) Women such as Anne Bradstreet and Phillis Wheatley were published poets. Women ran farms and businesses, such as clothing and grocery stores, bakeries, and drugstores, and worked as nurses, doctors, and midwives. Eliza Lucas Pinckney managed indigo plantations in the South. Female indentured servants and slaves worked both in and outside the home, contributing to the colonial economy.

70) The slave trade involved the transport of around 13 million Africans across the Atlantic Ocean to be sold as slaves in North America and the West Indies. This terrifying, and often deadly, voyage was called the Middle Passage and lasted from three weeks to three months or longer. During the voyage people were packed between the decks of the ships. Thousands died from disease or suicide or from being thrown overboard when ill.

71) The colonies had a protected or guaranteed market for their goods. High taxes on imports from outside the colonies made it difficult for foreigners to sell their products in England. The American colonies sold raw materials and some finished products to England, and bought finished English products such as hardware, machinery, and household items.

72) Merchants in Philadelphia and New York City benefited by exporting wheat from New York, and wheat and flour from Pennsylvania and New York.

73) Southern cash crops required a great deal of difficult work and a large labor force. By the 1700s Africans, who were enslaved for life, became the main labor force, replacing indentured servants who could leave after their contracted period of service ended.

74) Many New England colonists participated in the slave trade because New England's economy included ship building and the production of rum. In one variation on the triangular trade that went from the colonies to the West Indies to Britain, New England traders exchanged rum for slaves on the West African coast, transported the slaves to the West Indies where they exchanged the slaves for molasses which they then made into more rum in New England. Some of the slave ships were built in New England and were owned by New England merchants. Newport, Rhode Island was a major port of entry for slave ships.

Call to Freedom

75) Enlightenment thinkers applied reason and logic to study human nature and improve society. As a result, philosophers developed new theories about how government should work to best serve people. Some philosophers, particularly John Locke, began to assert that there was a social contract between rulers and the governed. Such thinkers believed that people had rights to equality and liberty. John Locke argued that people made a social contract with their rulers, voluntarily obeying their rulers only if the state fulfilled its responsibility to protect people's life, liberty, and property.

Call to Freedom

## Chapter 5 Conflicts in the Colonies

**MATCHING**
**In the space provided, write the term or the name of the person that best fits the description. Choose your answers from the list below. Not all answers will be used.**

| | | |
|---|---|---|
| repeal | casualties | writs of assistance |
| boycott | Stamp Act | Albany Plan of Union |
| pioneers | Sugar Act | Sons of Liberty |
| militia | backcountry | propaganda |
| Tea Act | casualties | Townshend Acts |

1) _____ people who are killed, wounded, captured, or missing in a war

2) _____ the first people to settle in an area

3) _____ refusal to buy certain goods

4) _____ stories and images designed to support a particular point of view

5) _____ the first law passed by Parliament specifically to raise money in the colonies

6) _____ civilians serving as soldiers

7) _____ special search warrants that allowed tax collectors to search for smuggled goods

8) _____ to abolish

9) _____ provided revenue to pay military expenses and the salaries of colonial governors

10) _____ frontier region between the Virginia and Carolina coastal settlements and the Appalachian Mountains

## TRUE/FALSE
**Write T if a statement is true or F if it is false. If a statement is false, explain why.**

11) _____ The war that colonists called the French and Indian War was called King George's War by Europeans.

_____

12) _____ The Sons of Liberty were secret societies who often used violence to frighten tax collectors.

_____

13) _____ The Sugar Act increased taxes on foreign cloth, coffee, and wines imported by colonists.

_____

14) _____ After repealing the Townshend Acts, Parliament kept the tea tax to show that it still claimed the right to tax the colonists.

_____

15) _____ Military alliances between British settlers and American Indians were often based on treaties that guaranteed both sides' borders.

_____

16) _____ The Boston Tea Party destroyed 90,000 pounds of the British East India Company's tea.

_____

17) _____ The conflict that the English called King Philip's War was also known as Queen Anne's War.

_____

18) _____ The colonists who participated in the Boston Tea Party were disguised as British soldiers.

_____

19) _____ Suspected smugglers tried in Vice-Admiralty courts were assumed innocent until proven guilty.

_____

20) _____ Fort Detroit was the political and trading center of the Great Lakes region.

_____

**MULTIPLE CHOICE**
**For each of the following, circle the letter of the best choice.**

21) Under the Albany Plan of Union the colonies were to be united under

a. the British Parliament.
b. the Iroquois.

c. a colonial king.
d. a president general and a grand council.

22) The French wanted the Ohio River valley and the area around the Great Lakes in order to

a. establish a fur trade in North America.
b. protect their already profitable fur trade.

c. establish colonies in North America.
d. destroy British colonies in North America.

23) Parliament passed the Tea Act after the

a. British East India Company proposed selling its tea directly to the colonies.
b. British East India Company's tea was destroyed in Boston Harbor.
c. colonists ended their tea boycott and began buying British tea.
d. colonists refused to pay taxes on smuggled tea.

24) The Currency Act was meant to prevent colonists from

a. paying for imported goods with colonial currency.
b. paying for smuggled tea with colonial currency.
c. borrowing British currency to pay colonial debts.
d. paying taxes or debts with colonial currency.

25) As a result of King Philip's War, the Wampanoag Indians

a. formed a stronger alliance with British colonists in the Ohio River valley.
b. formed a military alliance with the French in the Great Lakes region.
c. formed an alliance for protection against the encroaching colonists with nearby Indians.
d. suffered 3,000 casualties as compared to 600 colonial casualties.

Call to Freedom
75

26) In 1768 the Royal Governor of Massachusetts disbanded the legislature and called British troops to Boston

    a. as a result of the Boston Massacre.
    b. to restore order after the seizure of John Hancock's ship.
    c. to enforce the Tea Act.
    d. in retaliation for the Boston Tea Party.


27) The first law of Parliament that directly taxed the colonies, not just trade goods, was the

    a. Stamp Act.                     c. Tea Act.
    b. Currency Act.              d. Quartering Act.


28) The British assumption that the Treaty of Paris granted Britain the Indian lands in France's North American territory resulted in a conflict known as

    a. the French and Indian War.       c. Pontiac's Rebellion.
    b. King Philip's War.             d. Queen Anne's War.


29) During King Philip's War, the colonial militia was assisted by

    a. British troops supplied by George III.
    b. Metacomet.
    c. Chief Massasoit of the Wampanoag Indians.
    d. their Indian trading partners who agreed to fight against Metacomet.


30) After Parliament repealed the Stamp Act, they next issued the

    a. Declaratory Act.            c. Tea Act.
    b. Townshend Acts.         d. Coercive Acts.


31) More settlers began crossing the Appalachian Mountains in the late 1760s because

    a. the departure of the French opened the fur trade to British colonials.
    b. the British victory in the French and Indian War reduced their concerns about Indian raids.
    c. Indians no longer expected gifts of trade goods from settlers in exchange for safety.
    d. Britain now owned all Indian lands in regions formerly controlled by France.


32) During the late 1600s, Indian groups viewed French settlements as

    a. less threatening than the rapidly growing English colonies.
    b. less beneficial than existing trade partnerships with the English colonies.
    c. an alarming threat to resources such as forests, soil, and wild game.
    d. intrusions on Massachusetts lands that belonged to the Abenaki and the Mohawk.

33) In 1763, British citizens in England

   a. paid no taxes, whereas Britain colonists in America were overwhelmed with taxes.
   b. paid higher taxes than British colonists in America.
   c. were taxed at lower rates than British colonists in America.
   d. shared Britain's tax burden equally with British colonists in America.


34) As a result of the treaty signed after Queen Anne's War, Britain received

   a. Hudson Bay, present-day Newfoundland, and Nova Scotia from France.
   b. the Great Lakes area from France.
   c. the Ohio Valley and the Great Lakes area from France.
   d. present day Newfoundland, Acadia, and Hudson Bay from France.


35) The Boston Massacre gained its name and reputation as a result of the

   a. unwarranted murder of 17 innocent civilians by British troops.
   b. large number of civilian casualties gunned down by British troops.
   c. propaganda used by Samuel Adams and other Boston protesters.
   d. Boston militia's retaliation against the British after 54 Sons of Liberty were murdered.


36) The capture of Port Royal in Canada occurred during

   a. Queen Anne's War, which England fought against France.
   b. King William's War, which England fought against France.
   c. Queen Anne's War, which England fought against France and Spain.
   d. King George's War, which had a greatest impact on North America than did Queen Anne's War or King William's War.


37) England and France wanted to trade with American Indians in exchange for

   a. military alliances against the Spanish.
   b. military alliances against the Iroquois League.
   c. furs that they sold for large profits in the American colonies.
   d. furs that they sold for large profits in Europe.


38) The slogan "No taxation without representation" was based on the ideas of

   a. Samuel Adams and James Otis.
   b. Benjamin Franklin and George Washington.
   c. Patrick Henry and John Robinson.
   d. Crispus Attucks and Paul Revere.


39) Parliament's right to tax everyday items produced in the colonies was first enforced by the

   a. Sugar Act.                        c. Intolerable Acts.
   b. Stamp Act.                        d. Townshend Acts.

40) Colonial merchants and smugglers opposed the Tea Act out of fear that the

a. British East India Company would monopolize trade with its cheap tea, and put them out of business.
b. British East India Company would be allowed to sell tea in the backcountry as well as in the colonies.
c. trade alliances they had gained with Indians would be monopolized by the British East India Company.
d. British East India Company would boycott all tea imported to Boston Harbor.

41) King William's War ended in a treaty

a. that awarded northeastern Canada to Britain.
b. that changed the boundaries of four British colonies in North America.
c. between England, France, and Spain that altered the boundaries of colonial America.
d. between England and France that left boundaries of colonial America unchanged.

42) In 1753 the Royal government of Virginia sent George Washington as a messenger to the French because

a. Washington, although only 21 years old, was a seasoned frontiersman.
b. the French had built forts on land claimed by the British colony of Virginia.
c. Washington outranked General Edward Braddock as commander of the colonial militia.
d. Virginia planned to build forts on land held by the French.

43) Colonists responded to the Townshend Acts with

a. the new slogan "No taxation without representation."
b. pamphlets, editorials and plays that criticized the British government's actions.
c. another large-scale boycott of British goods.
d. propaganda that gave British officers in Boston names such as "Brigadier Hateall" and "Hum Humbug."

44) Committees of Correspondence were created by the

a. Massachusetts House of Representatives to unite protesters against the Sugar Act.
b. Sons of Liberty to unite protesters against the Tea Act.
c. Daughters of Liberty to organize boycotts of imported goods.
d. Boston town council to organize the propaganda efforts after the Boston Massacre.

45) As tensions between the French and British increased in the 1750s, British colonists recognized their need for

a. stronger trading ties and economy.
b. an alliance with the Iroquois League.
c. a strong united colonial leadership.
d. a larger colonial population than that of France.

Call to Freedom

46) Pioneers in the Ohio River valley in the 1750s found

   a. that fur traders had already depleted much of the wild game in the region.
   b. that many backcountry settlements already existed along major rivers.
   c. protection within the French fort built at the forks of Ohio.
   d. a fertile territory with large forests and bountiful game.


47) During what colonists called the French and Indian War,

   a. British General Edward Braddock fought against commander George Washington.
   b. Braddock and Washington fought against an alliance of French and Indian troops.
   c. Washington and the French fought against an alliance of British and Indian troops.
   d. Washington with the Algonquin Indians fought the French and Mohawk Indian alliance.


48) The Currency Act created economic problems in the colonies because

   a. colonists could no longer use British currency to pay taxes or British debts.
   b. colonial currency was no longer accepted by tea smugglers who sought British currency.
   c. colonial merchants refused to accept official British currency.
   d. official British currency was in short supply in America.


49) One of the first colonists to discuss the issue of unfair taxation was

   a. John Hancock.                    c. Patrick Henry.
   b. Mercy Otis Warren.               d. James Otis.


50) The Indian tribes who aligned against the British in the 1760s were led by

   a. Chief Metacomet of the Wampanoag.    c. the Delaware Prophet.
   b. Chief Pontiac of the Ottawa.         d. Prince Philip.


51) The Stamp Act was viewed as unjust by

   a. colonists in Massachusetts and New York.
   b. merchants throughout the colonies.
   c. colonists and London merchants.
   d. colonists, London merchants, and some members of Parliament.


52) The turning point of the French and Indian War came when

   a. Washington won Fort Necessity from the French.
   b. the French lost their Indian allies while the British gained some.
   c. Wolfe defeated de Montcalm on the Plains of Abraham.
   d. General Edward Braddock recaptured Fort Duquesne.

53) After the Proclamation of 1763,

    a. colonists in the upper Ohio River valley returned to seaboard colonies.
    b. colonial settlement expanded west of the Appalachians.
    c. Indians resettled on lands previously held by British colonists in the backcountry.
    d. most colonies gained more land than was granted in their original charters.


54) The Massachusetts legislature held a Stamp Act Congress after

    a. the Virginia House of Burgesses supported some of Patrick Henry's resolutions.
    b. the arrival of British troops in Boston.
    c. Benjamin Franklin's appeal to Parliament to repeal the Stamp Tax.
    d. propaganda circulated in the colonies by Committees of Correspondence.


55) Parliament repealed the Townshend Acts

    a. to further reduce colonial tension after the Boston Massacre.
    b. after a Boston jury convicted seven British soldiers of murdering five colonists.
    c. when Lord North heard about the Boston Tea Party.
    d. after appointing General Thomas Gage as governor of Massachusetts.


56) The first battle of what colonists called the French and Indian War was

    a. won by the British who captured Fort Duquesne.
    b. won by French forces who defeated Washington at Fort Necessity.
    c. fought near the present-day city of Pittsburgh, Pennsylvania.
    d. fought on top of rocky cliffs above the St. Lawrence River.


57) Pontiac's alliance weakened as a result of

    a. the Proclamation of 1763 which drove his allies further west.
    b. stronger trade networks between the Abenaki and the British.
    c. his unsuccessful attacks on the British at Fort Detroit and Fort Pitt.
    d. his inability to defeat the French at Fort Detroit.


58) As lawyers for the British soldiers charged with murder in 1770, Josiah Quincy and John Adams argued that the soldiers

    a. should be tried in a Vice-Admiralty court.
    b. acted in self-defense during a riot.
    c. were guilty of starting a riot.
    d. were guilty of destroying colonial lives and property.


59) The boycott of British goods was a method of protest that

    a. started after a speech by James Otis to the New York legislature.
    b. was started by the Daughters of Liberty.
    c. was first suggested by Patrick Henry and spread from Virginia to Massachusetts.
    d. started in Massachusetts and soon spread to New York.

Call to Freedom

60) Colonial wars in the late 1600s were the result of

a. France and England's fight to dominate European and colonial power.
b. wars for colonial domination fought between France, England, and Spain.
c. conflicts between the French and the Indians in colonial America.
d. conflicts between the Indians and British settlers west of the Appalachian Mountains.

## ENHANCED QUESTIONS
**For each of the following, circle the letter of the best choice. Next, expand on the subject by answering the second question in the space provided.**

61) The first attempt to unite the colonies in times of crisis was proposed in

a. the Treaty of Paris of 1763.
b. Samuel Adams' circular letter to the Massachusetts legislature.
c. the Albany Plan of Union.
d. propaganda circulated by the Sons of Liberty after the Boston Massacre.

Describe this proposal and explain why the colonial governments rejected it.

_____

_____

62) In 1765 the Massachusetts legislature invited delegates from the other colonies to

a. attend a Stamp Act Congress in New York.
b. send a letter protesting the Tea Act to Lord North.
c. send a letter protesting the Stamp Act to Prime Minister George Grenville.
d. attend a Stamp Act Congress in Philadelphia.

What was the result of this action?

_____

_____

63) To enforce the Townshend Acts in 1767, British customs agents

a. moved the trials of accused smugglers to Britain.
b. used writs of assistance that allowed tax collectors to search for smuggled goods.
c. seized ships suspected of smuggling, and jailed the ships' owners without trial.
d. selected the juries for the Vice-Admiralty courts that tried smugglers.

How did colonial legislatures respond to the Townshend Acts?

_____

_____

64) Colonists first began using the slogan "No taxation without representation" after the passage of

a. the Sugar Act.                        c. the Townshend Acts.
b. the Tea Act.                          d. the Stamp Act.

In what other ways did the colonists protest this act?

_____

_____


65) During what colonists called the Boston Massacre,

a. the Sons of Liberty shot a lone British sentry near the Custom House.
b. Crispus Attucks led a charge on the Custom House.
c. five civilians were killed by British soldiers.
d. British soldiers fired into a peaceful civilian crowd, resulting in five deaths.

How did the Boston Massacre eventually lead to the Boston Tea Party?

_____

_____

## GRAPHIC IMAGE QUESTIONS
**Examine the image, and then answer the following questions.**

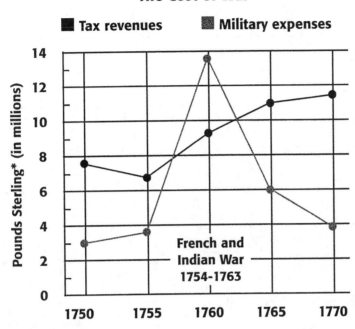

**The Cost of War**

 Tax revenues     ▨ Military expenses

French and
Indian War
1754-1763

* British Currency
Source: *Abstract of British Historical Statistics*

66) By how much did military spending exceed tax revenues in 1760?

_____

67) By how much did tax revenues exceed military spending in 1770?

_____

68) Which was greater in 1750: tax revenues or military spending?

_____

## SHORT ANSWER
**Write a brief answer for each of the following.**

69) How did the British occupation of the Ohio River valley differ from the French occupation of the area?

_____

_____

_____

70) How did the Treaty of Paris change the balance of power in North America?

_____

_____

_____

71) Explain how smuggling affected British colonial law.

_____

_____

_____

72) Describe how the Sons of Liberty and the Daughters of Liberty protested British colonial rule.

_____

_____

_____

73) How and why did the laws of the Intolerable Acts make an example of Massachusetts?

_____

_____

_____

**Call to Freedom**

**ESSAY**
**On a separate sheet of paper, write an essay on one of the following.**

74) Explain how the Proclamation of 1763 and colonial reactions to it showed that colonists and the British government had different ideas about what was best for the colonies.

75) Explain why Britain felt justified to tax its American colonies after 1763, and why the colonists felt justified to protest these taxes. Why do you think the Crown and the colonies could not compromise before the situation became "intolerable"?

# ANSWER KEY

1) casualties

2) pioneers

3) boycott

4) propaganda

5) Sugar Act

6) militia

7) writs of assistance

8) repeal

9) Townshend Acts

10) backcountry

11) F
Europeans called it the Seven Years' War, during which France and Britain fought throughout the world to maintain control of their colonial interests.

12) T

13) F
The Sugar Act set taxes on imported molasses and sugar.

14) T

15) F
Military alliances between British settlers and American Indians were often based on trade.

16) T

Call to Freedom

# ANSWER KEY

17) F
King Philip's War took its name from Metacomet who compared himself to King Charles II.

18) F
The colonists were disguised as Indians.

19) F
Suspected smugglers were assumed guilty until proven innocent.

20) T

21) d

22) b

23) a

24) d

25) d

26) b

27) a

28) c

29) d

30) c

31) b

32) a

33)  b

34)  d

35)  c

36)  c

37)  d

38)  a

39)  b

40)  a

41)  d

42)  b

43)  c

44)  a

45)  c

46)  a

47)  b

48)  d

49)  d

Call to Freedom

ANSWER KEY

50) b

51) d

52) c

53) b

54) a

55) a

56) b

57) c

58) b

59) d

60) a

61) c

The Albany Plan of Union called for the colonies to unite under a president general and a grand council, both of which would report to the Crown. The colonial governments rejected it because they did not want to give up their individual authority.

62) a

In October 1765, delegates from nine colonies met and issued a declaration that claimed the Stamp Act violated their rights and liberties. They then asked Parliament to repeal the act.

63) b

The Massachusetts legislature sent a letter to other colonial legislatures. This letter, written by Samuel Adams, argued that the Townshend Acts violated the legal rights of the colonists. Within a few months the legislatures of New Hampshire, New Jersey, Connecticut, and Virginia had decided to joint Massachusetts in opposition to the Townshend Acts.

64)  a

Colonists initially organized a boycott of the Sugar act. However, as more taxes were passed, the colonists also used violence to frighten tax collectors and the colonial legislatures were organized to protest to Parliament.

65)  a

The tensions that existed over the issue of taxation were made worse by the Boston Massacre. Britain hoped to relieve tension by repealing the Townshend Acts, but at the same time, it did not want to seem to be giving in to the colonists defiance. They passed the tax on tea to show that it still claimed the right to tax the colonies. However, the colonists continued to defy British authority by holding the Boston Tea Party to protest the Tea Act.

66)  by 4 to 4 1/2 million pounds

67)  by 7 million pounds

68)  tax revenues

69)  The French were primarily interested in the lucrative fur trade in America. Their small settlements did not threaten Indian lands and the French had used trade goods to earn the trust and cooperation of Indian leaders. British settlers, on the other hand, were most interested in farming the land. After the British occupied the region, settlers began arriving in greater numbers and occupying lands that Indians owned. Indians maintained that the English had conquered the French but not the Indians. Thus, the British occupation invited future conflicts between the British and the Indians, such as Pontiac's Rebellion.

70)  Britain gained Canada and all French lands east of the Mississippi River. Britain also received Florida from Spain, while Spain kept Louisiana as part of an earlier treaty. Thus Britain had a claim to all land east of the Mississippi River, and Spain was now its only major European competitor in North America.

71)  Illegal smuggling allowed colonists to avoid paying British duties on imports such as sugar, tea, and other trade goods. To put an end to these practices and raise revenue, after 1764 the British navy began stopping and searching ships for smuggled goods. Traders caught smuggling could have their cargo and ships seized by the courts. In addition, Parliament granted broader powers to the Vice-Admiralty courts which tried smugglers. As the problem continued, in 1767 Parliament established the writs of assistance under the Townshend Acts, which were designed to crack down on the smuggling that was common throughout the colonies. Thus as smuggling continued, Parliament passed new laws designed to control it.

72) The Sons of Liberty, secret societies, often used violence and threats of violence to frighten tax collectors. They attacked the houses of customs officials, demanding "no taxation without representation." In 1768 the Boston town council refused to curb the Sons of Liberty, fearing mob violence. In 1773 the Sons of Liberty demanded that three ships loaded with British tea leave Boston Harbor without dropping off their cargoes. The captains, afraid to anger the Sons of Liberty, lay at anchor in the harbor until their tea was vandalized and destroyed by colonists disguised as Indians. The Daughters of Liberty protested by playing a key role in the boycotts of British goods. They made cloth and other necessary goods at home. They held meetings to sew, support the boycotts, and discuss politics.

73) The Intolerable Acts, which the British called the Coercive acts, shut down Boston Harbor until Boston paid the cost of the tea destroyed at the Boston Tea Party, canceled Massachusetts's charter and gave the colony a legislature that met only when and where the governor chose, moved the trials of royal colonial officials to Britain, and required colonists to quarter the British soldiers who had arrived in Boston in 1768 to restore order. These acts were aimed at Massachusetts because it was the center of colonial protest.

74) After Pontiac's Rebellion, the British government wanted to avoid loss of life and increased expenses to maintain forts on the frontier. Therefore the Proclamation banned any further colonial settlement west of the Appalachian Mountains, creating a dividing line between colonial and Indian lands. Colonists who already lived in the upper Ohio River valley were ordered to leave. Many colonists hated the Proclamation because they believed that Britain should allow the colonies to expand rapidly in regions won from France. Feeling that they had the right to settle and trade in the Ohio River valley, the British colonists ignored the Proclamation. Britain used the Proclamation to protect its investment in North America. Colonists, on the other hand, protested that the Proclamation unfairly forced them to move off lands they had already settled or prevented them from occupying lands the British had won from France.

75) After supplying troops and supplies to help defend the colonies from the French and Indians, England believed the colonists should help pay for these expenses. Also, people in Britian were already overwhelmed with high taxes, while the colonists had much lower taxes. Since America was colonized at Britain's expense and chartered under British law, Parliament felt that its colonists were British subjects who must obey the law. However, these new taxes threatened the colonists financially. They protested that because they were not represented in Parliament, Parliament had no right to tax them. Perhaps the two could not compromise because they saw the purpose of the colonies differently and no longer shared the same history. Parliament believed that the colonies should serve Britain and that the Crown was the ultimate authority in England's colonies around the world. The colonists had been shaping their own history in America for 150 years and believed that they had the right to enjoy the profits from the hardships they had endured during settlement. The authority of the English Crown seemed less absolute at a distance, particularly to people who had been largely left alone. Thus, the two could not reach a compromise.

# Chapter 6 The American Revolution

## MATCHING
In the space provided, write the term or the name of the person that best fits the description. Choose your answers from the list below. Not all answers will be used.

| | | |
|---|---|---|
| Patriots | siege | Treaty of Paris of 1783 |
| Loyalists | mercenaries | Battle of Trenton |
| Continental Army | *Common Sense* | Declaration of Independence |
| Minutemen | Battle of Princeton | Lord Dunmore's Proclamation |
| Redcoats | Battle of Vincennes | |

1) _____ Massachusetts militia

2) _____ hired foreign soldiers

3) _____ December 26, 1776, battle between Hessians and Patriot forces

4) _____ resulted in victory for western Patriots led by George Rogers Clark

5) _____ colonists who chose to fight for independence

6) _____ colonists who sided with the British during the Revolution

7) _____ military blockade of a city or fort

8) _____ promised freedom to any slave who fought for the British

9) _____ established British recognition of the United States

10) _____ colonists' term for British soldiers

## TRUE/FALSE
Write T if a statement is true or F if it is false. If a statement is false, explain why.

11) _____ France was the first country to recognize the United States as an independent nation.

_____

12) _____ Thomas Paine was a self-educated British Quaker who wrote *Common Sense*.

_____

Call to Freedom

13) _____ Many women aided the American cause by fighting in the Continental Army.

_____

14) _____ John Paul Jones' ship, *Bonhomme Richard*, blockaded the British fleet at York town.

_____

15) _____ The United States was created on July 4, 1776, when the Continental Congress signed the Declaration of Independence.

_____

16) _____ Paul Revere and William Dawes warned Minutemen that "the British are coming" toward Concord.

_____

17) _____ Most volunteers in the Continental Army were experienced veterans of the French and Indian War.

_____

18) _____ The core of the Continental navy was a fleet of French ships commanded by John Paul Jones, a native of Scotland.

_____

19) _____ Although Cornwallis's troops outnumbered the Continental forces at Yorktown, Cornwallis surrendered upon hearing that France had suddenly allied with the Americans.

_____

20) _____ The American Revolution began when British troops opened fire on Minutemen at Lexington.

_____

**MULTIPLE CHOICE**

**For each of the following, circle the letter of the best choice.**

21) Although the original draft of the Declaration included a passage condemning the slave trade, the passage was removed because

    a. southern delegates objected to it.
    b. the Continental Army needed slaves to help fight the British.
    c. John Dickinson refused to sign the Declaration if the passage were included.
    d. George Washington and Thomas Jefferson objected to it.

22) The Patriots tried to persuade American Indians to

    a. join forces with the Continental Army.
    b. block trade between Spain and Britain along the Mississippi River.
    c. help George Rogers Clark defeat the British in the West.
    d. remain neutral in the war.

23) Confident after British victories in Canada and New York City, General Howe

    a. attacked Philadelphia on Christmas night in 1776.
    b. abandoned New York City on New Year's Day and marched on New Jersey.
    c. left New Jersey in the hands of Hessians and spent Christmas in New York City.
    d. moved his troops to Philadelphia while Hessians attacked the Patriots in New Jersey.

24) The primary author of the Declaration of Independence was

    a. Benjamin Franklin.            c. George Washington.
    b. Thomas Jefferson.           d. Richard Henry Lee.

25) In 1775 the Continental Army carried out a successful siege of Boston by

    a. strategically using Boston's hills for attacks and defense.
    b. staging a frontal assault against the British on Dorchester Heights.
    c. holding fast at Breed's Hill until the British surrendered.
    d. building forts on Bunker Hill, Breed's Hill, and Dorchester Heights.

26) The Spanish aided the Patriots

    a. by supplying molasses and corn meal to the troops at Camden.
    b. by organizing the Over Mountain Men, a band of Spaniards from Louisiana.
    c. on the Mississippi River and in the western frontier.
    d. in Quebec and Montreal, the major Spanish provinces in Canada.

27) Scots-Irish settlers on the western frontier were motivated to fight the British because

a. their ancestors were ill-treated by the English government in the early 1600s.
b. the British had burned Scots-Irish forts on Lake Erie and left the settlers vulnerable to Indian attacks.
c. the Proclamation of 1763 had prohibited the Scots-Irish from settling east of the Appalachians.
d. in 1775 General Howe's troops had destroyed their crops and killed their farm animals.

28) After General Howe crushed the Patriots at the Battle of Brandywine Creek,

a. he laid siege to Philadelphia before the Patriots could reorganize.
b. he joined Burgoyne in the British attack on the Patriots at Saratoga.
c. his troops were too sick and weary to chase the retreating Patriots to Princeton.
d. his hesitation to attack Philadelphia gave the Patriots a chance to reorganize.

29) Many American military leaders wanted to invade British Canada

a. before the Canadian navy set sail for Savannah and Charleston.
b. and make it the "14th colony."
c. in order to give it to France in exchange for supplies and financial support during the war.
d. and take back Fort Ticonderoga from the outlaw Ethan Allen.

30) Fort Ticonderoga was important because it

a. overlooked Boston from the south.
b. controlled access to Lake Champlain.
c. overlooked Boston from across its northern harbor.
d. controlled access to the Wabash River at Vincennes.

31) The colonists' greatest advantage over the British was

a. their familiarity with the land on which they fought.
b. the superior skills of George Washington as compared to the military skills of Howe, Cornwallis, and Burgoyne.
c. their belief in the cause for which they fought.
d. the drab color of their uniforms.

32) After the American victory at Saratoga, the British shifted their focus more toward the

a. American naval fleet.        c. southern colonies.
b. western frontier.            d. island of Manhattan.

33) The colonists' rebellion against Britain became a full-scale revolution when

a. the Continental Congress signed the Declaration of Independence.
b. George Washington organized the Continental Army.
c. Thomas Paine published *Common Sense*.
d. opening shots were fired on the Lexington village green.

Call to Freedom

34) The Second Continental Congress chose George Washington as commander of its Army because

a. he was the first qualified veteran to volunteer.
b. he had already proven his military abilities during the French and Indian War.
c. his wealth enabled him to outfit the Continental Army with uniforms and rations.
d. he was a well-respected veteran whose appointment would win support from Virginia and the other southern colonies.

35) "The Swamp Fox" was a name given to the guerrilla leader

a. Benedict Arnold.                          c. Ethan Allen.
b. Francis Marion.                           d. George Rogers Clark.

36) Six months after Patriot troops suffered a crushing defeat in Quebec, Washington's troops

a. retreated from New York in order to avoid complete destruction.
b. attacked the British forces at St. Johns, Canada, near Montreal.
c. retired to winter quarters at Valley Forge.
d. successfully drove back the British forces at Princeton.

37) To prevent the British from cutting New England off from the rest of the colonies in 1777, the Patriots

a. recaptured Fort Ticonderoga during a surprise attack at midnight.
b. enlisted help from the Iroquois who cut off Burgoyne's food supply.
c. sneaked up on the British under cover of a rainstorm and confiscated their cannon.
d. chopped down large trees across Burgoyne's path and hampered his march across New York.

38) George Rogers Clark wanted to take Kaskaskia because its location would give the Patriots control of the

a. Indian and British trading posts on the St. Lawrence River.
b. port cities of Savannah and Charleston.
c. Mississippi and Ohio Rivers, which would provide shipments of supplies from the Spaniards.
d. Great Lakes region with water access to Lake Champlain and British Canada.

39) George Rogers Clark believed that control of Kaskaskia would enable the Patriots to

a. starve out the British garrison at Detroit and to carry on trade with the Indians.
b. control the Tennessee River and establish trade with the Indians.
c. establish a fort on the Wabash River for trade with the Indians.
d. establish a fort in the Great Lakes region for trade with the Detroit Indians.

40) The colonists' ability to withstand a frontal assault from the British army was proved at the

a. village green in Lexington.                c. Battle of Trenton.
b. Battle of Bunker Hill.                     d. Battle of Brandywine Creek.

Call to Freedom

41) General Washington successfully used the tactic of surprise at the battles of

  a. Trenton and Princeton.          c. Princeton and Yorktown.
  b. Trenton and Saratoga.           d. Trenton and Yorktown.


42) On December 25, 1776, Washington and 2,400 Patriot soldiers surprised the enemy at Trenton by

  a. leaving the campfires burning while they sneaked out of camp.
  b. marching across New Jersey under a cover of darkness.
  c. splitting the forces to enable a frontal and rear assault.
  d. crossing the Delaware River at midnight.


43) The Second Continental Congress convened after

  a. Richard Penn delivered the Olive Branch Petition to King George III.
  b. King George refused to sign the Olive Branch Petition.
  c. the first shots were fired at Lexington and Concord.
  d. Thomas Jefferson drafted the Declaration of Independence.


44) Remaining in the colonies became more difficult for Loyalists after

  a. King George refused to sign the Olive Branch Petition.
  b. the Declaration of Independence was signed.
  c. General Cornwallis held Boston under siege.
  d. Boston organized a militia to fight the British.


45) On New Year's Eve 1775, the Patriots

  a. captured more than 900 Hessians at the cost of 5 American casualties.
  b. suffered a crushing defeat in Quebec, and lost almost half of their troops as casualties.
  c. lost their last fort on Manhattan Island, and feared complete defeat.
  d. finally captured Montreal under the leadership of General Richard Montgomery.


46) The Marquis de Lafayette, a wealth French aristocrat, fought for the Patriots

  a. for more than four years.
  b. when Washington requested his help at Yorktown.
  c. after he heard about the colonists' crushing defeat at Saratoga.
  d. from early 1781 until the British surrendered at Yorktown.


47) One of the most important Indian allies for the British was the

  a. Iroquois leader Joseph Brant.
  b. Georgian Indian leader Quamino Dolly.
  c. Cherokee band known as the Over Mountain Men.
  d. Mohawk leader Thayendanegea.


Call to Freedom

48)   The Patriot assault during the British siege of Boston resulted in

a. the loss of three cannons taken at Fort Ticonderoga.
b. France's recognition of the United States as an independent nation.
c. General Howe's retreat from Boston to Canada.
d. Spain's willingness to secretly aid the Patriots in their quest for Fort Detroit.


49)   In 1776 the American navy focused on

a. attacking the British fleet located near the Carolina coast.
b. attacking the British fleet on the high seas.
c. seizing British supplies from ships captured on the high seas.
d. seizing British supplies and weakening their naval forces in the West Indies.


50)   Mary Ludwig Hays earned the nickname "Molly Pitcher" by

a. loading cannons after her husband was killed in battle.
b. bringing water to Patriot troops.
c. serving as a spy while General Howe's troops were quartered in her Boston home.
d. guiding Washington's troops across the icy waters between Philadelphia and Trenton.


51)   Officers from the country of Poland aided the Patriot cause by

a. donating their army engineering and cavalry skills to the Continental Army.
b. donating more than $200,000 to support the Revolution.
c. secretly aiding the Patriots on the western frontier.
d. secretly supplying the American forces with weapons.


52)   King George III rejected the July 5, 1775 Olive Branch Petition because

a. the Declaration of Independence was signed before the petition was offered to the king.
b. he refused to make peace with outlaws and pirates such as Ethan Allen and John Paul Jones.
c. fighting in the colonies had intensified before the petition reached him in the fall.
d. spies told him that General Washington was organizing troops to fight the Crown.


53)   Some colonists objected to the Declaration of Independence because it failed to guarantee equal rights to

a. African Americans in New England.      c. immigrants and slaves.
b. Native Americans.                       d. women and slaves.


54)   When British Prime Minister Lord North received word of Cornwallis's surrender at Yorktown, he declared,

a. "I have not yet begun to fight!"        c. "It is all over!"
b. "It is a fine fox chase, my boys!"      d. "If they want a war, let it begin here!"

55) Thomas Paine reached a wider audience than most other pamphlet writers of his day because he

a. wrote in a style that only well-educated and influential people could understand.
b. wrote as a common man to common people.
c. was a gifted speaker as well as a convincing writer.
d. rejected Enlightenment thinking that was not popular in the colonies.

56) News of the fighting at Lexington and Concord

a. angered and shocked many colonists.
b. was celebrated by Tories as the British returned triumphantly to Boston.
c. inspired Thomas Jefferson to draft the Olive Branch Petition.
d. relieved the fears of Minutemen who heard that none of their fellow soldiers had been killed.

57) The British captured the port city of Savannah with the aid of

a. Eliza Lucas Pinckney, a Tory spy.
b. Quamino Dolly, a slave who showed them a secret trail.
c. Peter Salem and Salem Poor, Charleston slaves who led them across the Savannah River.
d. the Mohawk leader Joseph Brant, who guided them from Charleston to Savannah.

58) The national borders of the United States were laid out in

a. the Declaration of Independence.
b. Lord Dunmore's Proclamation.
c. the Treaty of Paris of 1783.
d. the Proclamation of 1763.

59) During the winter of 1777-78,

a. Washington's troops at Brandywine Creek suffered almost twice as many casualties as the British.
b. many of Washington's troops had to fight without shoes when they fought the Hessians at Princeton.
c. Washington accepted the help of thousands of slaves who were filing to fight for their freedom.
d. one fourth of Washington's troops died of disease and malnutrition at Valley Forge.

60) General Washington was most impressed by the Marquis de Lafayette's

a. combat experience.
b. willingness to donate money and supplies to America's Continental Army.
c. cavalry skills.
d. passion for the Patriot cause.

# ENHANCED QUESTIONS

**For each of the following, circle the letter of the best choice. Next, expand on the subject by answering the second question in the space provided.**

61) The writers of the Declaration of Independence drew inspiration from

   a. the Bible.
   b. the Enlightenment.
   c. French philosopher Jean-Jacques Rousseau.
   d. English philosopher Thomas Hobbes.

   How did this source of inspiration inspire a colonial revolution against Britain?

   _____

   _____

62) Soon after taking command of the Continental Army, Washington issued an order

   a. prohibiting women from serving as soldiers.
   b. allowing women to serve as cooks and laundresses but not as soldiers.
   c. allowing free African Americans to serve as soldiers.
   d. prohibiting African Americans, slave or free, from serving as soldiers.

   How did Lord Dunmore's Proclamation influence Washington's policy?

   _____

   _____

63) The Battle of Saratoga marked the

   a. greatest victory up to that point for the American forces.
   b. ability of the Patriots to withstand a frontal assault from the British army.
   c. Patriots' second chance to reorganize before Burgoyne could attack Philadelphia.
   d. defeat of the British plan to defend Canada.

   How did this battle help the Patriots gain the support of foreign nations?

   _____

   _____

64) The Patriots had to rebuild their southern army after a serious defeat at

a. Charleston.
b. Savannah.

c. Camden.
d. Brandywine Creek.

How did the southern army change their tactics after this defeat?

_____

_____

65) When the Declaration of Independence was signed in July 1776, slavery was legal in

a. all the colonies.
b. the southern colonies.
c. all the colonies except Massachusetts.
d. colonies south of Virginia.

How did the Revolution affect the status of slavery in the new American nation?

_____

_____

# GRAPHIC IMAGE QUESTIONS
**Examine the image, and then answer the following questions.**

### North America in 1783

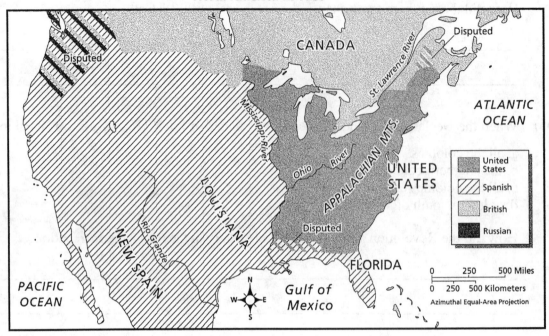

66) Which country claimed the area west of the United States?

_____

67) What geographic feature marked the boundary between the United States and its western neighbor?

_____

68) What country claimed the area north of the United States?

_____

## SHORT ANSWER
**Write a brief answer for each of the following.**

69) How did Thomas Paine's views reflect Enlightenment philosophy?

_____

_____

_____

70) What advantages and disadvantages did the Patriots have at the beginning of the war in relation to the British?

_____

_____

_____

71) How did the Continental Army benefit from Baron Friedrich von Stueben's presence at Valley Forge?

_____

_____

_____

72) Describe how George Rogers Clark's tactics, skills, and resources allowed him to attain victory with a minimum of violence.

_____

_____

_____

73) Name three compromises reached by the First Continental Congress in its debate on whether to respond to Britain with peace or with violence.

_____

_____

_____

**ESSAY**
**On a separate sheet of paper, write an essay on one of the following.**

74) Describe how the writings of Thomas Paine and Thomas Jefferson helped the Patriots win the Revolutionary War. Explain why you believe, or do not believe, that "the pen is mightier than the sword."

75) Explain how the use of non-traditional military tactics helped the Patriots defeat the British.

# ANSWER KEY

1) Minutemen

2) mercenaries

3) Battle of Trenton

4) Battle of Vincennes

5) Patriots

6) Loyalists

7) siege

8) Lord Dunmore's Proclamation

9) Treaty of Paris of 1783

10) Redcoats

11) T

12) T

13) F
Although a few women fought in the war, most women aided the American cause from behind the scenes.

14) F
The French fleet blockaded the British ships that attempted to reach Yorktown.

15) T

16) T

17) F
Few of the volunteers had combat experience.

Call to Freedom

104

ANSWER KEY

18) T

19) F
Cornwallis, outnumbered, surrendered without a fight because he feared a bloody defeat.

20) F
No one knows who fired the "shot heard round the world."

21) a

22) d

23) c

24) b

25) a

26) c

27) a

28) d

29) b

30) b

31) c

32) c

33) a

34) d

35)  b

36)  a

37)  d

38)  c

39)  a

40)  b

41)  a

42)  d

43)  c

44)  b

45)  b

46)  a

47)  d

48)  c

49)  d

50)  b

51)  a

Call to Freedom

# ANSWER KEY

52)  c

53)  d

54)  c

55)  b

56)  a

57)  b

58)  c

59)  d

60)  d

61)  b
Enlightenment philosophers thought that government was a social contract between people and their ruler. They thought that if the people determined that their ruler or form of government was corrupt, they had a natural right to overthrow it.

62)  d
After Lord Dunmore promised freedom to any slave who fought for the British, the Continental Army changed its policy and allowed free African Americans to enlist.

63)  a
After the Patriot victory at Saratoga, the French formally declared their support for the Americans. In May 1778 the Continental Congress approved a treaty of alliance with France.

64)  c
They switched to guerrilla warfare, engaging in swift, hit-and-run attacks designed to disable British communications and supply systems.

65) a

The Revolution began to stir debates about the existence of slavery within a society that valued liberty. Massachusetts abolished slavery in 1783. In the mid-1780s the rest of New England also acted to end slavery.

66) Spain

67) the Mississippi River

68) Britain (claim over Canada)

69) Paine wrote that the system of monarchy was unnatural and wrong, and that countries should be ruled by laws created by the people. Enlightenment philosophers also believed that societies should be run according to natural laws, and would improve over time if they respected the natural rights of individuals.

70) The colonists had no navy and no organized army, whereas Britain had a large military force of well-trained professionals plus the most powerful navy in the history of the world. However, the Patriots had the advantage of fighting on their own land, with available supplies, for a cause in which they strongly believed, whereas British soldiers had little personal stake in the war.

71) The Prussian army officer trained the American troops, focusing on basic military drills, until the disorganized Continental Army was a finely tuned fighting force.

72) Clark was a skilled frontiersman who knew his terrain, and he enlisted skilled mountain men to help him. His tactics included surprise attacks on the British, who surrendered without a shot, and peace talks with Indian leaders to enlist their support. Although the Battle of Vincennes was violent and bloody, the majority of Clark's victories were attained peacefully through effective communication and planning, his knowledge of geography, and the hardiness of his frontiersmen.

73) In compromising over the debate about making peace or making war, the delegates agreed to continue to boycott British goods, to prepare militias in case violence did break out, and to draft a Declaration of Resolves to present to King George III. The Declaration of Resolves declared the colonists' rights to life, liberty, and property.

74) Paine's words in *Common Sense* inspired many common people to think about their position as British colonists and as human beings deserving of liberty and fair government. His pamphlet became a turning point in changing many colonists' attitude toward Britain. As primary author of the Declaration of Independence, Jefferson declared that as free and independent people, the colonists were justified in fighting for their rights. These ideals fueled the Revolution and inspired men to fight the British. Students may say that the pen is as mighty as the sword, or they may entirely agree or disagree that the pen is mightier than the sword.

75) The Patriots did not wear eye-catching, colorful uniforms such as the Redcoats wore. They often marched at night, under cover of darkness, or in inclement weather when the enemy did not anticipate an attack. Surprise attacks went against the British tradition of marching openly into battle. In the north, the Patriots felled trees to halt the British advance. In the south, Francis Marion was so successful at guerrilla warfare that he and his men were always able to avoid capture while disabling British communications and supply systems. Clark marched his men through frontier rivers in order to surprise the enemy at night. Washington led his forces across the dark, icy Delaware river. Students may say that the Americans' tactics more closely resembled the tactics of Native Americans than the traditional tactics used by the British.

## Chapter 7 Forming a Government

**MATCHING**

In the space provided, write the term or the name of the person that best fits the description. Choose your answers from the list below. Not all answers will be used.

creditors              checks and balances         ratification
debtors                tariffs                     suffrage
republic               constitution                depression
amendments             Great Compromise            Constitutional Convention
federalism             Bill of Rights              Articles of Confederation

1) _____ official changes, corrections, or additions

2) _____ taxes on imports or exports

3) _____ voting rights

4) _____ first 10 amendments to the Constitution

5) _____ steep drop in economic activity

6) _____ formal approval

7) _____ people who lend money

8) _____ system to prevent any branch of government from becoming too powerful

9) _____ set of basic principles and laws that determine the powers and duties of the government

10) _____ people who owe money

**TRUE/FALSE**

Write T if a statement is true or F if it is false. If a statement is false, explain why.

11) _____ All the states had to ratify the Articles of Confederation before the new government could take effect.

_____

12) _____ In 1784 French officials closed the lower Mississippi River to U.S. shipping.

_____

13) _____ The U.S. Constitution is the oldest functioning written constitution in the world.

_____

14) _____ Delegates to the Constitutional Convention elected James Madison president of the convention.

_____

15) _____ The words slave and slavery were omitted from the Constitution.

_____

16) _____ The constitutions of each state contained a bill of rights.

_____

17) _____ After weeks of debates and discussions, all 42 delegates agreed to sign the Constitution before presenting it to Congress.

_____

18) _____ The Fundamental Orders of Connecticut was the first written constitution in America.

_____

19) _____ Many Antifederalists were wealthy planters, farmers, merchants, and lawyers.

_____

20) _____ Most of the land in the Northwest Territory was sold to individual farmers for $1 per acre.

_____

## MULTIPLE CHOICE
**For each of the following, circle the letter of the best choice.**

21) Supporters of the Constitution called themselves

    a. Federalists.

    b. Antifederalists.

    c. delegates.

    d. ratifiers.

22) Fundamental rights, such as religious liberty and equality before the law, are

    a. constitutional rights.

    b. states' rights.

    c. individual rights.

    d. natural rights.

23) A trade imbalance occurred when the amount of America's

    a. exports to Britain exceeded its amount of imports from Britain.

    b. imports from Britain exceeded its amount of exports to Britain.

    c. exports and imports failed to equal the amount of Spain's imports and exports.

    d. imports from Spain did not equal the amount of Spain's exports from Louisiana.

24) The Three-Fifths Compromise resolved the problem of how slaves would be counted

    a. as a part of each state's population when allotting representatives to the lower house.

    b. in deciding each state's taxes.

    c. when allotting each state's representatives to the Senate.

    d. in states where freed African Americans were allowed to vote.

25) The Articles of Confederation

    a. went into effect when nine states ratified the document.

    b. were ratified by every state except Rhode Island.

    c. created a central government with limited powers and gave more power to each state.

    d. created a strong central government with two congressional delegates from each state.

26) The Federalist Papers

    a. reassured people that the rights of individual states would not overpower the federal government.

    b. were a series of essays that defended the Constitution.

    c. contained plays, stories, and essays that defended the Constitution.

    d. opposed the Constitution by defending the natural rights of individuals.

27) The Three-Fifths Compromise was designed to resolve regional differences created by the

    a. state constitutions.

    b. New Jersey Plan.

    c. Virginia Plan.

    d. Great Compromise.

28) Magna Carta and the English Bill of Rights both

a. reflected the political philosophies of John Locke.
b. gave Parliament supreme power.
c. limited the powers of monarchs.
d. gave people's representatives in Parliament the strongest voice in government.

29) Antifederalists such as Patrick Henry feared that

a. checks and balances could not prevent the federal government from abusing its power.
b. the Constitution's checks and balances would give the states too much power.
c. more checks and balances were needed to guarantee that the federal government had enough power.
d. checks and balances alone would not solve America's economic problems.

30) Framers of state constitutions were careful not to

a. restrict the governor's authority over the people.
b. give the governor too much power over the people.
c. deny their governor the ability to veto bills passed by the state legislature.
d. make their courts free from the governor's control.

31) The distribution of governmental power between a central authority and the states or provinces that make up the nation is an idea known as

a. confederation.
b. democracy.
c. federalism.
d. checks and balances.

32) Interstate commerce is trade conducted between

a. two or more states.
b. three or more states.
c. two or more states, provinces, or territories.
d. states within the same geographical region of a country.

33) In order for the Constitution to go into effect,

a. all the states had to ratify it.
b. the majority of representatives from all the states had to ratify it.
c. New Jersey and Virginia had to ratify it.
d. nine of the states had to ratify it.

34) A type of government in which the head of state is elected and in which the people hold the political power is defined as a

a. constitution.
b. democracy.
c. republic.
d. confederation.

35) Under the Constitution, each state is committed to

    a. its own laws as guaranteed by the Great Compromise.
    b. the authority of the federal government's laws over state laws.
    c. the laws of the United States except when federal law conflicts with state law.
    d. the federal government's authority to establish schools and supervise religious bodies.

36) After the Constitution was ratified, some Federalists believed that a federal bill of rights was unnecessary because

    a. the United States was not a monarchy.
    b. portions of the English Bill of Rights had already been included in the Constitution.
    c. the system of checks and balances would prevent Congress from abusing its power.
    d. people were already promised these rights under state constitutions.

37) In response to the trade imbalance with Britain in 1784, the United States

    a. pursued Asian markets and opened trade with China.
    b. blocked British imports into the United States.
    c. forced American farmers to transport their products in British ships if they wanted to sell their goods in Britain.
    d. established tariffs on goods imported from Britain and Canada.

38) Many urban poor laborers, craftspeople, and traders

    a. opposed the Constitution.
    b. supported the Constitution.
    c. feared that the Constitution created special privileges for the wealthy.
    d. feared that the Executive would have too much influence over the Legislature.

39) Under the Articles of Confederation, the colonies were governed by a

    a. national Congress with representatives from each state legislature.
    b. Continental Congress.
    c. Committee of Thirteen with one member from each colony.
    d. Confederation Congress with representatives from each colony.

40) Delegates from the smaller states strongly objected to the Virginia Plan because

    a. a unicameral legislature would allow each state only one vote.
    b. Virginia's large slave population would grant Virginia more votes than any other state.
    c. small states would have very few representatives in Congress while large states would have many.
    d. the New Jersey Plan awarded small states more votes than large states.

Call to Freedom

41) The debate over ratification was especially difficult in Virginia because

a. some of the most well-respected Antifederalists lived in Virginia.
b. George Washington proclaimed that under the Constitution the president would soon become a monarch.
c. Thomas Jefferson's correspondence from France urged fellow Virginians not to ratify.
d. George Mason and Patrick Henry had refused to sign the Constitution.

42) The Mayflower Compact and the Fundamental Orders of Connecticut were

a. the only American examples of self-government in existence in 1781.
b. self-governing documents written by Americans before the Revolution.
c. inspired by the confederated government of the Iroquois League.
d. examples of representative government designed by Britain for its colonies.

43) Northern delegates to the Constitutional Convention agreed to let the slave trade continue for another 20 years if

a. the individual states would agree to free all enslaved people by 1810.
b. New Jersey would agree not to grant suffrage to women.
c. northern port cities could continue to import cotton and sugar produced by slave labor.
d. southern delegates would drop the demand that laws in Congress be passed with a two-thirds majority vote.

44) Treaty negotiations with Spain ended in 1786 because

a. Don Diego de Garoqui set terms that John Jay felt the United States could not accept.
b. John Jay's proposed commercial treaty was unacceptable to Spain.
c. difficulties getting the Congress to accept the treaty.
d. the Land Ordinance of 1785 gave France all authority over the Mississippi River.

45) American models for representative government and an effective legislature included

a. The Spirit of Laws and the Virginia Statute for Religious Freedom.
b. the New England town meeting and the Virginia House of Burgesses.
c. the Fundamental Orders of Connecticut and the Articles of Confederation.
d. the Declaration of Independence and the Treaty of Paris of 1783.

46) In 1784 the British forced American merchants to pay tariffs on

a. trade goods imported from the British West Indies.
b. trade goods exported or imported through Canadian ports.
c. British goods sold in America.
d. American goods sold in Britain.

47) Of delegates to the Constitutional Convention, one of the strongest supporters of preserving the powers of the states within a strong union was

a. James Madison, who drafted the Virginia Plan.
b. Benjamin Franklin, who supported the New Jersey Plan.
c. George Mason, who wrote Virginia's Declaration of Rights.
d. Gouverneur Morris, who supported the Three-Fifths Compromise.

48) The author of the Virginia Statute for Religious Freedom was

a. James Madison.
b. Thomas Jefferson.
c. George Mason.
d. Patrick Henry.

49) The ability of the Constitution to fit the needs of a changing nation is proven by its

a. first 10 amendments, or Bill of Rights.
b. unanimous ratification by all the states it governed.
c. guarantee that new states may join the Union whether or not they endorse slavery.
d. prohibition against slavery in any new state joining the Union after 1787.

50) When individual states issued too much paper money, the result was

a. increased interstate commerce.
b. decreased interstate commerce.
c. inflation.
d. foreclosures of banks and businesses.

51) A system that prevents any branch of government from becoming too powerful is defined as

a. federalism.
b. checks and balances.
c. compromise.
d. democracy.

52) The words and ideas of John Locke and Baron de Montesquieu

a. influenced the writers of the English Bill of Rights, the Articles of Confederation, and the Mayflower Compact.
b. are preserved in the Mayflower Compact.
c. constitute the first 10 amendments to the Constitution.
d. influenced leaders who wanted to create a representative democracy in America.

53) Many Southern delegates threatened that if the Constitution included an immediate ban on the slave trade, they would

a. withdraw from the Union.
b. assert their right to retain the slave trade within their own states.
c. create state constitutions that would protect the slave trade.
d. impose state tariffs on northern ports that imported southern crops.

Call to Freedom

54) By 1787 all state constitutions

   a. forbade state governments from establishing an official church.
   b. expanded suffrage to include free African Americans.
   c. restricted the governor's authority, and included a bill of rights.
   d. gave voting rights to free African Americans and white women.

55) By 1833, the Virginia Statute for Religious Freedom inspired other states to pass legislation that

   a. prevented any members of the clergy from serving as governor.
   b. limited religious liberty to prevent Catholics from gaining office.
   c. guaranteed other natural rights.
   d. prevented state governments from establishing an official church.

56) On authority granted by the Articles of Confederation, Congress

   a. asked the states to give money to help pay national war debts and operate the federal government.
   b. required each state to provide money to operate the federal government.
   c. established a national army to protect forts in the Northwest Territory.
   d. regulated interstate commerce and established treaties with France and Spain.

57) Some Federalists believed that the Constitution was itself a bill of rights because it

   a. was ratified by the people.
   b. ensured liberty for all citizens.
   c. established a republic in which the people hold the power.
   d. fit the needs of a changing nation.

58) The sole purpose of the 1787 Constitutional Convention was to

   a. put down Shays's Rebellion.
   b. create a constitution that would resolve conflicts between Federalists and Antifederalists.
   c. discuss revising the Articles of Confederation.
   d. discuss international relations, trade agreements, and interstate commerce.

59) After 1787, states had no control over

   a. local government, education, and the supervision of religious bodies.
   b. the chartering of corporations.
   c. the development and administration of civil and criminal law, and general oversight of the welfare of their citizens.
   d. negotiating treaties.

60) Federalists John Jay and Alexander Hamilton led the fight for ratification in

   a. Virginia.                          c. North Carolina.
   b. New York.                         d. Rhode Island.

Call to Freedom

# ENHANCED QUESTIONS
**For each of the following, circle the letter of the best choice. Next, expand on the subject by answering the second question in the space provided.**

61) Congress sold the nation's western lands to raise national revenue

    a. as a result of economic concerns voiced during Shays's Rebellion.
    b. and to promote interstate commerce.
    c. because Congress's ability to obtain money from the states was limited.
    d. after inflation led to a farmers' uprising in Massachusetts.

    How did Congress organize the sale of this land?

_____

_____


62) In Congress's first session, James Madison encouraged the legislators to

    a. add a Constitutional amendment banning slavery in the Northwest Territory.
    b. put together a bill of rights.
    c. adopt the amendments proposed by state ratifying conventions.
    d. adopt amendments written by the people rather than those written by state ratifying conventions.

    Why did some people believe this needed to be done?

_____

_____


63) To become a state under the Northwest Ordinance settlers in a portion of the Northwest Territory would have to

    a. establish trade relations with either Spain of Britain.
    b. form a land company.
    c. divide their area into townships of 36 square miles.
    d. number at least 60,000 free inhabitants and petition Congress.

    What other requirements did the Confederation Congress place over the Northwest Territory?

_____

_____

64) Although the Constitution officially went into effect after nine states ratified it, political leaders knew that it would not succeed without the support of

a. Virginia and New York.  
b. North Carolina and Rhode Island.

c. New York and Rhode Island.  
d. Virginia and North Carolina.

Why were these states important? What convinced them to ratify?

_____

_____

65) Under the Articles of Confederation, the central government could not

a. borrow money.  
b. force states to provide money and soldiers.

c. make treaties.  
d. resolve conflicts between states.

What problems did this limitation create?

_____

_____

# GRAPHIC IMAGE QUESTIONS
Examine the image, and then answer the following questions.

**Federalism**

| POWERS DELEGATED TO THE NATIONAL GOVERNMENT | POWERS SHARED BY NATIONAL AND STATE GOVERNMENTS | POWERS RESERVED TO THE STATES |
|---|---|---|
| • Declare war | • Maintain law and order | • Establish and maintain schools |
| • Maintain armed forces | • Levy taxes | • Establish local governments |
| • Regulate interstate and foreign trade | • Borrow money | • Set corporate laws |
| • Admit new states | • Charter banks | • Regulate business within the state |
| • Establish post offices | • Establish courts | • Make marriage laws |
| • Set standard weights and measures | • Provide for public welfare | • Provide for public safety |
| • Coin money | | • Assume other powers not delegated to the national government or not denied to the states |
| • Establish foreign policy | | |
| • Make all laws necessary and proper for carrying out delegated powers | | |

66) Which branch of government is responsible for levying taxes?

_____

67) Which branch of government is responsible for making marriage laws?

_____

68) Which branch of government is responsible for coining money?

_____

## SHORT ANSWER
**Write a brief answer for each of the following.**

69) Describe the relations between the United States and other nations under the Articles of Confederation.

_____

_____

_____

70) Who wrote the *Federalist Papers* and what did they argue?

_____

_____

_____

71) Describe how the Constitution organized and balanced the federal government.

_____

_____

_____

72) What issues were resolved by the Great Compromise? Describe the different plans that became part of the Great Compromise.

_____

_____

_____

73) Explain why you do or do not agree with Thomas Jefferson who said of Daniel Shays and his followers, "A little rebellion, now and then, is a good thing."

_____

_____

_____

**ESSAY**
**On a separate sheet of paper, write an essay on one of the following.**

74) Explain the basis for Antifederalists' fears that the government would "fall into the hands of the few and the great," and that the most power would forever be in the hands of wealthy, educated, professional men. How does the Constitution address these fears?

75) Explain why America was ridiculed as the "Dis-United States" in 1785, and how this comment helped bring about a stronger union by 1791.

Call to Freedom

ANSWER KEY

1) amendments

2) tariffs

3) suffrage

4) Bill of Rights

5) depression

6) ratification

7) creditors

8) checks and balances

9) constitution

10) debtors

11) T

12) F
Spanish officials closed the lower Mississippi River to U.S. shipping.

13) T

14) F
George Washington was elected president of the convention.

15) T

16) T

17) F
Elbridge Gerry, George Mason, and Edmund Randolph refused to sign the Constitution.

18)  T

19)  F
Many Antifederalists were small farmers and debtors, whereas many Federalists were wealthy planters, farmers, merchants, and lawyers.

20)  F
Land companies bought most of the land because it was sold only in such large sections.

21)  a

22)  d

23)  b

24)  a

25)  c

26)  b

27)  d

28)  c

29)  a

30)  b

31)  c

32)  a

33)  d

ANSWER KEY

34)  c

35)  b

36)  d

37)  a

38)  b

39)  d

40)  c

41)  a

42)  b

43)  d

44)  c

45)  b

46)  d

47)  a

48)  b

49)  a

50)  c

ANSWER KEY

51) b

52) d

53) a

54) c

55) d

56) a

57) b

58) c

59) d

60) b

61) c
The Land Ordinance of 1785 organized surveys and division of the lands. The surveys divided the lands into townships of six square miles, which were in turn divided into 36 lots of 640 acres each.

62) b
Many Antifederalists feared that the Constitution did not protect individual liberties and feared that the government would abuse its power at the expense of citizens and states. Many states only ratified the Constitution because they believed that the a bill of rights would be added.

63) d
Under the land Ordinance of 1785, each township had to set aside one lot of land for a public school and four lots for Revolutionary War veterans. The Northwest Ordinance contained a bill of rights that settlers had to respect and required citizens to provide public education. In addition, the Northwest Ordinance banned slavery in the Northwest Territory.

# ANSWER KEY

64) a

Virginia had the largest population in the nation, and New York was an important center for business and trade. Virginia Federalists, including James Madison convinced Virginia's delegates to ratify. Federalist New Yorkers, including John Jay and Alexander Hamilton, threatened that New York City would break away and join the new government if the state did not ratify. This threat convinced the New York delegates to ratify.

65) b

Because the government could not raise an army it could not protect its citizens or enforce treaties. For example, the United States had difficulties taking over British forts it had gained after the Treaty of Paris. In addition, because the government could not raise money it could not place tariffs on the cheap British goods that were driving American manufacturers out of business.

66) national and state governments

67) state governments

68) national government

69) Other nations recognized the weakness of the U.S. government and took advantage of it. First, Britain was slow to withdraw from their forts around the Great Lakes and the United States lacked the power to drive them out. In addition, Britain closed markets in the West Indies to the United States and passed high tariffs on goods entering Britain from the U.S. The weak central government was powerless to either negotiate better trade terms or pass tariffs that would drive up the price of British goods. Spanish officials closed the lower Mississippi to U.S. shipping. Again, the United States could do little to change the situation. These problems led to calls for a stronger central government that could negotiate with other nations.

70) Although the *Federalist Papers* were published anonymously, historians now know that Alexander Hamilton, James Madison, and John Jay each wrote some of the essays. They argued that people should not fear the power of the central government because the United States was so large and the interests of its citizens so diverse that no one group could ever gain too much power.

71) The federal government is organized under three branches. The legislative branch, or the Congress, is made up of the Senate and the House of Representatives. The executive branch includes the president and the government's administrative departments. The judicial branch is made up of all the national courts. The Constitution balanced these three branches by giving each branch some power over the others. For example, the legislative branch has the power to pass laws, but the president can check this by using his veto power.

72) Constitutional delegates were divided on representation, regional issues, and whether to have a strong national government. Large states favored the Virginia Plan that called for a strong national government and a bicameral legislature whose representatives were chosen in proportion to state populations. Small states favored the New Jersey Plan which called for states' sovereignty and a unicameral legislature with each state entitled to an equal number of votes. The Great Compromise proposed that every state, regardless of its size, receive two votes in the upper house of the legislature, and that in the lower house each state receive one representative for every 40,000 inhabitants.

73) Students should explain that Shays and his followers were Massachusetts farmers who were trapped in an economic depression. They revolted when state courts foreclosed on their property or ordered them to serve terms in debtors' prison or sell themselves into indentured servitude, meanwhile refusing to issue paper money for debt relief. Students may agree with Jefferson, who believed that citizens' ability to freely express their feelings toward their government was crucial to maintaining good government. They might mention that Shays's Rebellion pushed some political leaders to admit that the Articles of Confederation were not working. Shays's revolt thus paved the way for a Constitutional Convention and a stronger national government. Others may disagree with Jefferson, citing the wastefulness of the destruction and loss of life caused by Shays' Rebellion. They may feel that there were more positive and productive ways Shays could have made his point.

74) Many Antifederalists were debtors and small farmers such as Amos Singletary who thought that supporters of the Constitution "expect to get all the power into their own hands." His fears would have been fired by the types of men who meet to write the Constitution. Most were college educated, and well read in history, law, and political philosophy. Many of these leaders were wealthy landowners, planters, merchants, or lawyers and many of the Federalists who supported them were wealthy, professional men as well. The fact that these men created a centralized government and exceeded their initial authority, led Antifederalists to fear that the Constitution was undemocratic and created special privileges for a limited few. Federalists argued that individual rights would be protected by state constitutions and that no one group would be able to amass too much power because of the Constitution's system of checks and balances and the Constitution's guarantees of liberty to all citizens. Finally, many Federalists felt that the Bill of Rights would protect the rights of individuals. In addition, the Constitution could continue to be amended as needed.

75) Soon after the Articles of Confederation were ratified in 1781, the nation's leaders began to criticize the national government's limited authority. Under the Articles, Congress could not raise an army, establish tariffs, agree on treaties, regulate interstate commerce, or negotiate favorable trade agreements with foreign countries. State support of the national government was voluntary rather than mandatory. States could issue their own money, a situation that caused inflation and depression and, in Massachusetts, a farmers' revolt that Congress was powerless to stop. Many Americans began to recognize that their national government was weak and ineffective. The derogatory comment about the Dis-United States confirmed it. In 1786 disunity became more obvious when only five states sent delegates to a meeting about economic issues in Annapolis, Maryland. Congressional leaders agreed that changes to the central government were essential for the survival of the United States. The hard work and compromise of delegates to the Constitutional Convention resulted in a federal government safeguarded by a system of checks and balances. When the Bill of Rights was added in 1791, the United States possessed a living document that promised a strong union for generations to come.

# Chapter 8 Citizenship and the Constitution

**MATCHING**
**In the space provided, write the term or the name of the person that best fits the description. Choose your answers from the list below. Not all answers will be used.**

| | | |
|---|---|---|
| due process | libel | petition |
| executive orders | slander | double jeopardy |
| naturalization | propaganda | political action committees |
| draft | president pro tempore | Speaker of the House |
| apportionment | term limits | elastic clause |

1) _____ nonlegislative directives issued by the president that have the force of law

2) _____ organizations that collect money to distribute to political candidates who support the same issues as the contributors

3) _____ material that is slanted deliberately to support or harm a cause

4) _____ the intentional telling of lies that damage a person's reputation

5) _____ the fair application of the law

6) _____ distribution of representatives in the House of Representatives

7) _____ process that enables people from foreign countries to become U.S. citizens

8) _____ would restrict the number of times a member of Congress could be re-elected

9) _____ the intentional writing or printing of a lie that hurts another person

10) _____ the longest-serving senator of the majority party who leads the Senate if the vice president is absent

**TRUE/FALSE**
**Write T if a statement is true or F if it is false. If a statement is false, explain why.**

11) _____ The House of Representatives is the larger of the two houses of Congress.

12) _____ The Bill of Rights represent the essential protection of individual liberties for American citizens.

_____

13) _____ Each state has the right to deport an immigrant who breaks the state's laws or who is in the country illegally.

_____

14) _____ House apportionment is determined annually by both houses of Congress.

_____

15) _____ The only distinction between naturalized and native-born citizens is that naturalized citizens cannot be elected to Congress.

_____

16) _____ Antifederalists opposed the Constitution for fear that the government it created would be too powerful.

_____

17) _____ The First Amendment prohibited the U.S. government from establishing a state religion.

_____

18) _____ Patrick Henry put together the first set of amendments to the Constitution.

_____

19) _____ The President of the Senate, or the leader of the Senate, is the president *pro tempore*.

_____

20) _____ Any American citizen can present a petition, or formal request, to a government official.

_____

## MULTIPLE CHOICE
**For each of the following, circle the letter of the best choice.**

21) Federalists such as James Madison believed that the best safeguard of the people was

   a. a weak central government.        c. the Constitutional right to bear arms.
   b. a powerful president.             d. a system grounded in laws.

22) The Constitution gives the House of Representatives the authority to

   a. bring criminal charges against a president, and the Senate to try all impeachments.
   b. remove a president from office if he or she violates essential presidential duties.
   c. try all impeachments unless a president elects to resign rather than be impeached.
   d. impeach a president if the U.S. Supreme Court issues warrants for his or her arrest.

23) Writs of assistance

   a. protected the rights of American citizens against illegal searches and seizures.
   b. are a judge's order that gives authorization for the search of private property because the property seems likely to have evidence of a crime.
   c. allowed law officials to search colonists' property for illegal goods without first establishing a probable cause of illegal activity.
   d. allow the government to seize private property to further the public interest, but only if the government pays the owners a fair amount for the property.

24) The political party with the most members in each house of Congress is called the

   a. ruling party.                c. legislative branch.
   b. majority party.              d. judicial branch.

25) At the time the Constitution was written, most nations in the world had a

   a. Bill of Rights.                c. state press.
   b. state religion.              d. Court of Appeals.

26) Under the Constitutional requirement for apportionment, if a state gains some representatives in the House,

   a. it must hold a special election in order to maintain a representative democracy.
   b. those members must belong to the minority party in the Senate.
   c. those members must belong to the majority party in Congress.
   d. another state or states must lose some to maintain a total of 435 members.

27) People born in a foreign country are automatically U.S. citizens only if

   a. at least one of their parents is a U.S. citizen.
   b. both of their parents are U.S. citizens.
   c. both of their parents are naturalized U.S. citizens.
   d. neither of their parents have ever been deported from the United States.

28) In the past, what has the government done to raise the needed number of soldiers for service?

   a. It invoked the power of eminent domain.      c. It issued a draft.
   b. It issued an indictment.                      d. It applied due process.

29) The Tenth Amendment

   a. guarantees citizens freedom of religion, speech, the press, assembly, and petition.
   b. grants to the states the the people any powers that the Constitution does not specifically give to Congress or prohibit from the states.
   c. grants to all U.S. citizens the fundamental right of education.
   d. protects citizens from the unlawful deprivation of property without due process of law.

30) Any citizen can make a private financial contribution to a

   a. candidate directly or through political action committees.
   b. political action committee but not to a candidate directly.
   c. candidate in exchange for the candidate's support of the citizen's interests.
   d. candidate directly but not to a political action committee.

31) The Constitution describes the division of powers between the

   a. militia and private citizens.                 c. U.S. Supreme Court and the states.
   b. judicial branch and the U.S. Supreme Court.   d. states and the federal government.

32) Slander and libel

   a. represent freedom of speech and are protected by the First Amendment.
   b. are not protected by the First Amendment.
   c. have been called "the key to security and public information."
   d. are Writs of Assistance guaranteed to members of the press.

33) Foreign-born people who permanently move to another country are called

   a. naturalized citizens.                         c. immigrants.
   b. citizens of the commonwealth.                 d. potential draftees.

Call to Freedom
133

34) The government pays for many of its services with income derived from

a. taxes paid by public schools and other public institutions.
b. political action committees.
c. sales taxes, property taxes, and income taxes.
d. bail, or money that defendants pay to the court to guarantee that they will show up for trial.


35) As guaranteed by the Seventh Amendment, civil cases

a. usually involve disputes over money or property.
b. are always held before a judge alone—never before a jury.
c. usually involve a plea bargain.
d. must be settled before the U.S. Supreme Court.


36) The only president ever to have been impeached was

a. Andrew Johnson.              c. Lyndon Johnson.
b. Richard Nixon.               d. William Howard Taft.


37) Citizens who serve when called to jury duty

a. cannot experience double jeopardy by serving for jury duty again.
b. fulfill their fellow citizens' Sixth Amendment right to a trial by jury.
c. do so in accordance with the Second Amendment.
d. may "take the Fifth" if being forced to serve against their will.


38) The Fourth Amendment restricts authorities from searching a person's home without

a. a Writ of Assistance.        c. evidence to indict.
b. a naturalization process.    d. a search warrant.


39) A successful representative democracy requires

a. that the majority of citizens contribute to political candidates and PACs.
b. special interest groups to lobby politicians on issues that affect all citizens.
c. the involvement of all citizens in improving their communities.
d. illegal immigrants to begin the process of naturalization within five years of their arrival.


40) Life appointments to the federal court system are meant to ensure that

a. women as well as men may serve as federal judges.
b. judges make their decisions free from the influence of a particular party.
c. the lower courts carry out their requirements without the use of juries.
d. judges uphold lower courts' rulings without influence from PACs.

41) Powers retained by the state governments or by citizens are

a. legislative powers.
b. reserved powers.
c. concurrent powers.
d. delegated powers.

42) Before a person can be tried for a serious crime, a grand jury must decide if there is enough evidence to

a. convict, or find the person guilty of the crime.
b. exercise the right of eminent domain.
c. deport the accused if he or she is a naturalized citizen of the United States.
d. indict, or formally accuse, the person of the crime.

43) Regressive taxes, such as sales taxes,

a. apply equally to all Americans.
b. are designed to collect more money from those with higher incomes and wealth.
c. provide most of the funding for public schools.
d. require that Americans pay a percentage of their income to the federal government.

44) The president's cabinet is made up of the

a. governors of the 50 states and the president pro tempore.
b. heads of 16 standing Senate committees and 19 House committees.
c. heads of the 14 executive departments.
d. vice president and the chairman of the House Ways and Means Committee.

45) Most interest groups

a. are funded entirely by the states by means of apportionment.
b. represent the political views of the majority of Americans.
c. represent the views of a particular segment of society.
d. are designed to help get particular candidates elected to public office.

46) The president pro tempore

a. is usually the longest-serving senator of the majority party.
b. can cast a vote only if there is a tie.
c. becomes president of the United States if the sitting president dies in office.
d. is the elected leader of the House of Representatives.

47) According to the Fifth Amendment, no one can be deprived of property without due process of law unless that property

a. is confiscated by authorities with a search warrant.
b. belongs to a citizen who is accused of a crime.
c. is disputed in a civil case that involves a plea bargain.
d. was obtained through illegal activities.

48) If a person is indicted by a grand jury, the Sixth Amendment guarantees the person

   a. bail, unless the crime will be heard by the U.S. Supreme Court.
   b. a prompt, public trial by a jury.
   c. the right not to have to testify in his or her own trial.
   d. an opportunity to appeal the indictment to the U.S. Supreme Court.

49) Voters in the United States must be

   a. at least 18 years old.
   b. a registered member of a major political party.
   c. able to read, write, and speak English.
   d. willing to serve in the military if drafted.

50) The branch responsible for enforcing the laws approved by Congress is the

   a. judicial branch.                    c. executive branch.
   b. legislative branch.                 d. presidential branch.

51) The ability to tax, to borrow money, to enforce laws, and to provide for the health and welfare of the people are

   a. delegated powers of state governments.
   b. delegated powers of the federal government.
   c. reserved powers of the federal government.
   d. concurrent powers of the federal and state governments.

52) The required duties of American citizens include

   a. submitting to INS background checks and taking an oath of allegiance to the United States.
   b. obeying authority, paying taxes, serving in the military, and serving on juries.
   c. registering for the draft, participating in elections, and improving their communities.
   d. holding public office and residing in the United States.

53) Anyone found "not guilty" in a criminal trial cannot

   a. be indicted, or formally accused, of a civil crime.
   b. be punished without due process.
   c. participate in elections or run for public office.
   d. experience double jeopardy, or be tried again for the same crime.

54) Income and property taxes are designed to collect

   a. more money from those with higher incomes and wealth.
   b. money equally from all Americans.
   c. money for state and local governments.
   d. money for the federal government.

55) The Twenty-second Amendment, ratified in 1951,

   a. gives the House of Representatives the authority to impeach a president.
   b. allows a president to resign rather than be impeached.
   c. prevents any president from serving more than two terms.
   d. determines how much responsibility the vice president has.

56) Since 1939 the nation's higher courts have ruled that

   a. gun control laws do not violate the Second Amendment.
   b. members of the National Guard cannot be called to serve in wars.
   c. the Second Amendment does not refer to state militias.
   d. any state's right to form a militia cannot be restricted by the National Guard.

57) Elections form the basis of America's

   a. Bill of Rights.
   b. representative democracy.
   c. system of due process.
   d. right of eminent domain.

58) Congress holds regular sessions every year

   a. and special sessions if called by the president during a national emergency.
   b. beginning on July 4.
   c. and one special session to elect a Speaker of the House and president pro tempore.
   d. to appoint judges to the lower courts in the federal system.

59) In 1972 the Supreme Court ruled that the death penalty, as it was carried out by most states at the time,

   a. would remain solely a reserved power of the states.
   b. was unfair if ordered by juries in civil trials.
   c. could be applied only to noncitizens convicted of the most serious crimes.
   d. was cruel and unusual.

60) Ruth Bader Ginsburg and Sandra Day O'Connor

   a. are Federal Court justices.
   b. were vice presidential candidates in 1984.
   c. are U.S. Supreme Court justices.
   d. have both held the position of president pro tempore.

## ENHANCED QUESTIONS

**For each of the following, circle the letter of the best choice. Next, expand on the subject by answering the second question in the space provided.**

61) The power to coin money, to regulate interstate trade, and to declare war are some of the

    a. executive powers of the president.
    b. delegated powers of the federal government.
    c. reserved powers retained by the state governments during declared emergencies.
    d. concurrent powers held by the president and the federal government.

    What two purposes are served by these powers?

_____

_____

62) James Madison believed in

    a. adding a bill of rights to the Constitution to protect the rights of individuals.
    b. a strong national government that limited individual rights.
    c. a Constitutional bill of rights that would reserve some powers for the states.
    d. an elastic clause allowing Congress to expand the powers of the states over time.

    How did his position help convince Federalists and Anti-Federalists to ratify the Constitution?

_____

_____

63) In emergency cases the president may

    a. declare war.
    b. ratify treaties.
    c. issue an executive order that stretches the definition of laws enacted by Congress.
    d. issue executive orders that can be vetoed by a majority vote in Congress.

    How does this relate to the president's power to pardon?

_____

_____

64) Public interest groups

    a. are made up of political action committees with Congressional sponsors.
    b. are required by law to publish propaganda that supports their programs
    c. represent the views of a particular segment of society.
    d. lobby for issues that affect all Americans.

How have public interest groups influenced lawmakers' and citizens' views on drunk driving?

_____

_____

65) The process that allows people born in a foreign country to become U.S. citizens is

    a. deportation.           c. immigration.
    b. naturalization.        d. petition.

What steps must people take to complete this process?

_____

_____

## GRAPHIC IMAGE QUESTIONS
**Examine the image, and then answer the following questions.**

### Amending the U.S. Constitution

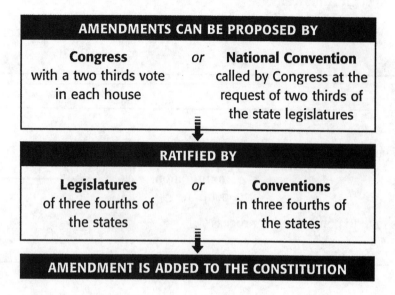

66) What role does Congress play in proposing amendments to the U.S. Constitution?

_____

_____

67) What proportion of states must ratify an amendment for it to go into effect?

_____

68) Which method of amending the Constitution seems most difficult?

_____

_____

## SHORT ANSWER
**Write a brief answer for each of the following.**

69) What role did Antifederalists play in the creation of a strong central government that protects the rights of all people?

_____

_____

_____

70) What five freedoms are spelled out in the First Amendment? What segment of society do these freedoms affect?

_____

_____

_____

71) What are the requirements for membership in the House and the Senate?

_____

_____

_____

72) Why did the framers of the Constitution feel the need to protect citizens against the quartering of soldiers?

_____

_____

_____

73) Why did the founders include the Second Amendment in the Bill of Rights?

_____

_____

_____

**ESSAY**
**On a separate sheet of paper, write an essay on one of the following.**

74) Explain how the Supreme Court's 1972 ruling on the death penalty upholds the division of powers approved by both Federalists and Antifederalists in 1787.

75) Explain why the executive and legislative branches must cooperate for the system of checks and balances to work.

Call to Freedom

# ANSWER KEY

1)  executive orders

2)  political action committees

3)  propaganda

4)  slander

5)  due process

6)  apportionment

7)  naturalization

8)  term limits

9)  libel

10) president pro tempore

11) T

12) T

13) F
    The U.S. government, not the states, has the right to deport.

14) F
    Apportionment is based on the U.S. Census, a population count taken every 10 years.

15) F
    Naturalized citizens cannot become president or vice president of the United States, and only naturalized citizens can lose their citizenship.

16) T

17) T

18) F

James Madison put together the Bill of Rights.

19) F

The president of the Senate is the vice president of the United States.

20) F

People who are not eligible to vote can influence the U.S. government in many ways. They can volunteer to work on election campaigns, contribute money through PACs, join interest groups, or speak directly with government officials.

21) d

22) a

23) c

24) b

25) b

26) d

27) a

28) c

29) b

30) a

31) d

32) b

33) c

**Call to Freedom**

34) c

35) a

36) a

37) b

38) d

39) c

40) b

41) b

42) d

43) a

44) c

45) c

46) a

47) d

48) b

49) a

50) c

51) d

# ANSWER KEY

52) b

53) d

54) a

55) c

56) a

57) b

58) a

59) d

60) c

61) b

These powers allow the national government to protect citizens and to assure a uniform economic system throughout the country.

62) a

Already an outspoken Federalist, Madison convinced the Antifederalists to support the Constitution by promising to add a bill of rights that protected the rights of individuals. His position helped him balance the needs of citizens and government.

63) c

Since laws passed by Congress must uphold the Constitution, the president may be stretching the definition of the law if he or she pardons a person convicted of a federal crime or facing criminal charges.

64) d

Mothers Against Drunk Driving (MADD) lobbies for tougher laws against drunk drivers. As a result, every state has strengthened its laws. MADD and Students Against Drunk Driving (SADD) work to educate people about the dangers of drunk driving.

Call to Freedom

ANSWER KEY

65) b
Legal immigrants who have lived in America for five years may petition for naturalization. The INS tests applicants' qualifications as law-abiding supporters of the Constitution. Applicants must prove that they can read, write, and speak English, and know about U.S. history and government. They must pass a background check, then go before a naturalization court where they take an oath of allegiance to the United States.

66) It can propose an amendment with a two thirds vote in each house or call a national convention at the request of two thirds of the state legislatures.

67) three fourths

68) Students will probably respond that the National Convention and state convention method seems most difficult.

69) Although Antifederalists feared and opposed a strong central government, their stance inspired the framers of the Constitution to create a division of powers between the nation and the states—a system of checks and balances that became the foundation of a strong national government—and a Bill of Rights. Without a strong central government, the Bill of Rights alone would not be able to protect individuals' rights or the rights of states.

70) Freedom of religion, speech, the press, assembly, and petition. These rights affect virtually all Americans.

71) Both must be residents of the state from which they are elected. House members must be at least 25 years old and U.S. citizens for seven years. Senators must be at least 30 years old and U.S. citizens for nine years.

72) Before the American Revolution, the British government pressured the colonies to provide food and shelter for British soliders.

73) The Revolution began when British troops tried to seize the weapons of the Massachusetts militia. Therefore, the founders believed it was important for states to continue to have militias for emergencies.

74) Federalists would be pleased that states cannot use the death penalty without following the guidelines set up by the Supreme Court. Antifederalists would be pleased that the Supreme Court cannot prevent any or all states from using the death penalty, but that individual states are free to make that choice.

75) The system can set the president against Congress, particularly when Congress is controlled by a party different than that of the president. Legislation favored by Congress can be vetoed by the president, and in turn Congress can override a veto, thus blocking legislation favored by either branch.

Call to Freedom

## Chapter 9 Launching the Nation

**MATCHING**
**In the space provided, write the term or the name of the person that best fits the description. Choose your answers from the list below. Not all answers will be used.**

protective tariff      Twelfth Amendment      Neutrality Proclamation
Judiciary Act           precedent              right of deposit
political parties       bonds                Democratic-Republican Party
Jay's Treaty          speculators          Virginia and Kentucky Resolutions
Pinckney's Treaty    Treaty of Greenville

1) _____ resolved differences between the United States and Spain

2) _____ groups that organize to help elect government officials and to influence government policies

3) _____ certificates that represent money owed to private citizens

4) _____ allowed American boats to transfer their goods at New Orleans without paying fees on their cargo

5) _____ gave the United States access to Indian lands and guaranteed safe travel for U.S. citizens crossing Indian territory

6) _____ created a federal court system with three levels

7) _____ investors who bought many bonds at low prices in the hope that the value would rise later

8) _____ declared that state governments could ignore any federal laws that they found to be unconstitutional

9) _____ resolved differences between the United States and Great Britain

10) _____ an action or decision that later serves as an example

**TRUE/FALSE**
**Write T if a statement is true or F if it is false. If a statement is false, explain why.**

11) _____ President Washington's troops put down the Whiskey Rebellion in 1794.

_____

12) _____ The electoral college was a group selected by state legislatures to represent the popular vote in determineing the winner of presidential elections.

_____

13) _____ Citizen Genet angered Americans when he persuaded French privateers to attack Great Britain.

_____

14) _____ General Anthony Wayne's forces defeated Indian confederation forces in the Battle of Fallen Timbers.

_____

15) _____ President Washington created four executive departments and selected their leaders.

_____

16) _____ Alexander Hamilton proposed a national bank to discourage states from chartering their own banks.

_____

17) _____ The Twelfth Amendment created a separate ballot for president and vice president.

_____

18) _____ The presidential election of 1810 began a new era in U.S. politics because the campaign included more than one candidate.

_____

19) _____ During the French Revolution, the people of France overthrew the French monarchy and replaced it with a republic.

_____

20) _____ Thomas Jefferson believed in a strong central government, while Alexander Hamilton wanted to protect the powers of the states.

_____

Call to Freedom

**MULTIPLE CHOICE**

**For each of the following, circle the letter of the best choice.**

21) As a result of strong differences between Jefferson and Hamilton,

    a. Washington retired from the presidency in 1796.
    b. John Adams did not appoint either man to his cabinet.
    c. Hamilton did not receive enough political support to run for president in 1810.
    d. Jefferson resigned as secretary of state in 1793.

22) The idea for the president's cabinet originated when

    a. Washington began meeting with executive department heads as a group.
    b. Adams became president.
    c. Chief Justice John Jay requested meetings with President Washington and the six judges on the Supreme Court.
    d. the Supreme Court required meetings with the attorney general and the president.

23) Shortly before the Battle of Fallen Timbers, Little Turtle

    a. formed a new confederation of American Indian tribes to fight the U.S. Army.
    b. lost the support of his British allies.
    c. demanded a new treaty from the U.S. government.
    d. was supplied with guns and ammunition from the French.

24) When political parties began to form during Washington's presidency, Washington

    a. asked John Adams to head the Democratic-Republican Party.
    b. asked Thomas Jefferson to head the Federalist Party.
    c. worried that parties posed a threat to national unity.
    d. believed that parties would encourage the "mass of the people" to become more involved in the election process.

25) Which leader supported strict construction, meaning that the federal government should do only what the Constitution specifically said it can do?

    a. Thomas Jefferson            c. James Madison
    b. Alexander Hamilton          d. Aaron Burr

26) The election of 1800

    a. was a triumph for proponents of manufacturing and commerce.
    b. weakened the Federalist Party and strengthened the Republicans.
    c. ruined the political careers of Aaron Burr and Thomas Pinckney.
    d. challenged Adams's authority over Congress and the Supreme Court.

27) George Washington was chosen as America's first president because of his

    a. political experience.
    b. military experience.
    c. support for strict construction of the Constitution.
    d. character, honesty, and patriotism.

28) The Alien and Sedition Acts were

    a. declared unconstitutional because they went beyond the powers granted to the federal government.
    b. opposed by Madison and Jefferson who wrote the Virginia Resolutions and the Kentucky Resolutions.
    c. repealed when the Virginia and Kentucky Resolutions passed in 1798–99.
    d. attacked by Federalists during the presidential election of 1800.

29) The army that suppressed the Whiskey Rebellion was led by

    a. General Anthony Wayne.
    b. Arthur St. Clair.
    c. Secretary of War Henry Knox.
    d. George Washington and Alexander Hamilton.

30) The Bank of the United States was

    a. founded and chartered by Alexander Hamilton in 1791.
    b. founded by President Washington who supported Hamilton's economic plan.
    c. chartered by Congress in 1791.
    d. established by President Washington for a period of 20 years.

31) "Millions for defense, but not one cent for tribute!" became the rallying cry of the American people during the

    a. XYZ affair.                c. Whiskey Rebellion.
    b. presidential campaign of 1810.     d. French Revolution.

32) During the French Revolution, the debate over U.S. foreign policy

    a. intensified when France asked the United States to declare war on Britain.
    b. divided both Congress and President Washington's cabinet.
    c. initiated a political feud between Thomas Jefferson and Edmund Randolph.
    d. resulted in a political alliance between President Washington and James Madison.

33) Washington accepted the presidency in 1789 because he

    a. felt that he owed his political experience to his country.
    b. had promised Lafayette that he would accept if asked to serve.
    c. hoped to move the capital from New York City to Virginia.
    d. felt it was his duty to serve his country, despite his lack of political experience.

34) Congressional approval of a peacetime army and a strengthened navy angered

a. Federalists.
b. Republicans.

c. settlers whose lands bordered Florida.
d. supporters of the Whiskey Rebellion.

35) The national debt is the amount of money owed by

a. speculators who invest in U.S. government bonds.
b. the individual states to the Bank of the United States.
c. the United States to various creditors, or lenders.
d. taxpayers to the U.S. Treasury Department.

36) America's 1800 treaty with France was the result of

a. the peace efforts of Charles Pinckney and John Jay.
b. a tie-breaking vote in the House of Representatives.
c. Alexander Hamilton's secret correspondence with cabinet members who favored the treaty.
d. President Adams's peace efforts.

37) During Washington's presidency, Spain disputed the border between the United States and

a. Florida.
b. Louisiana.

c. Texas.
d. the Northwest Territory.

38) The first vice president of the United States was

a. Thomas Jefferson.
b. James Madison.

c. John Adams.
d. Alexander Hamilton.

39) Who supported loose construction, meaning that the federal government could take actions that the Constitution did not specifically forbid?

a. Thomas Jefferson
b. Alexander Hamilton

c. the Republican Party
d. supporters of the Alien and Sedition Acts

40) The Whiskey Rebellion was a protest led by small farmers against

a. British merchants who traded whiskey to Indians on the frontier.
b. whiskey merchants in New York and Pennsylvania.
c. government officials who stopped the sale of whiskey in the Northwest Territory.
d. taxes on whiskey and other alcohol.

41) Thomas Jefferson became vice president in 1796 because he

a. was the second-place finisher in the presidential campaign.
b. campaigned vigorously in the south and along the western frontier.
c. defeated Charles Pinckney, the Federalist candidate.
d. defeated Aaron Burr, the Democratic-Republican candidate.

42) Indians in the Northwest who defeated U.S. troops were equipped with

    a. cannons supplied by the French.
    b. British guns and ammunition.
    c. weapons stolen from St. Clair's fort.
    d. only bows and arrows.

43) The question of whether the United States should support the French republic became more complex when

    a. revolutionaries beheaded King Louis XVI.
    b. Citizen Genet recruited American troops to fight against France.
    c. Great Britain declared war on France.
    d. France declared war on Great Britain.

44) Congress organized the government's judicial branch in 1789 because

    a. President Washington was not authorized to appoint judges to the Supreme Court.
    b. Washington's cabinet authorized Congress to establish a system of courts.
    c. the Constitution's requirements for the branch were not specific.
    d. Chief Justice John Jay's federal court plan was approved by Congress.

45) As the nation's first secretary of the treasury, Hamilton's biggest challenge was

    a. gaining the cooperation of Thomas Jefferson.
    b. paying off the national debt.
    c. repaying bondholders who had invested in the government.
    d. establishing a national mint to coin money.

46) Small farmers who protested a 1791 tax on U.S.-made goods claimed that

    a. they should be exempted from national taxes.
    b. the tax should also apply to farmers in the South.
    c. they would ally with the Miami confederation until Congress repealed the tax.
    d. the tax was unfair because they could not afford to pay it.

47) Hamilton's plan for debt assumption was controversial because he wanted

    a. the federal government to pay the states' war expenses.
    b. foreign allies to help assume America's war debts.
    c. to raise money by selling bonds to private citizens.
    d. speculators to assume the national debt by buying bonds at low prices and selling them at high prices.

48) Americans were outraged in 1793 when the British

    a. demanded repayment of debts owed to British merchants before the Revolution.
    b. helped an Indian confederation defeat U.S. forces in the Battle of Fallen Timbers.
    c. seized U.S. merchant ships and imprisoned or abandoned their crews.
    d. attempted to bribe a diplomatic team headed by John Jay.

49) After Republicans criticized Federalist support for war with France, Congress

    a. voted to strengthen the military.
    b. passed the Alien and Sedition Acts.
    c. forced two cabinet members to resign.
    d. strengthened the Navy by approving the creation of a small fleet.

50) The president was allowed to expel foreign citizens from the United States under the authority of the

    a. Sedition Act.                  c. Twelfth Amendment.
    b. Alien Act.                    d. Neutrality Proclamation.

51) Washington's stance on political unity was influenced by

    a. Hamilton's feud with Jefferson, Adams, and Burr.
    b. the power of the Democratic-Republican Party along the western frontier.
    c. the power of the Federalist Party in New England.
    d. Hamilton and Jefferson's feud, and the threat of the Whiskey Rebellion.

52) In 1796 and in 1800 Hamilton attempted to sabotage the presidential campaign of

    a. Thomas Jefferson.             c. John Adams.
    b. Aaron Burr.                  d. Thomas Pinckney.

53) What kind of experience did Washington's first secretary of state and secretary of war bring to their cabinet positions?

    a. One had governmental experience and the other was a gifted economic planner.
    b. One drafted the Kentucky Resolutions and the other had defeated Little Turtle in the Northwest.
    c. One supported the French republic, while the other supported the French monarchy.
    d. One served as ambassador to France and the other as a general in the Continental Army.

54) Most Americans favored Pinckney's treaty over Jay's Treaty because

    a. Jay's Treaty did not resolve trade issues in the Caribbean.
    b. Pinckney's Treaty opened the western frontier to further expansion.
    c. Pinckney's Treaty prevented another war with Britain.
    d. Jay's Treaty did not require the British to abandon their forts on the frontier.

55) When Hamilton proposed that the federal government repay the full promised value of all bonds, Jefferson

    a. strongly opposed the plan because he believed it cheated the poor and ignorant.
    b. agrued that speculators should share their profits with the original bondholders.
    c. agreed with the majority of Congress who supported Hamilton's plan.
    d. asked Hamilton to resign.

Call to Freedom

155

56) U.S. citizens were forbidden to "write, print, utter or publish" any false or hostile words against the government or its polices after Congress passed the

a. Alien Act.                                  c. Twelfth Amendment.
b. Sedition Act.                               d. Virginia and Kentucky Resolutions.

57) Hamilton wanted to pay off the national debt before the federal government

a. entered into treaties with France or Spain.
b. sent a diplomatic team to France in 1798.
c. lost the trust of foreign countries, state governments, and American citizens.
d. established a protective tariff on imported goods.

58) John Jay of New York and Edmund Randolph of Virginia were the nation's first

a. ambassadors to France.                      c. chief justice and attorney general.
b. ambassadors to Spain.                       d. secretary of state and postmaster general.

59) When France declared war on Great Britain, France asked the United States to

a. join France in declaring war on Britain.
b. declare war on Britain, Spain and the Netherlands.
c. honor its treaty with France by providing troops for Lafayette's French Republican Army.
d. help raise an army to drive the Spanish out of Louisiana.

60) After Congress heard about the XYZ affair, Federalists

a. called for war on France.
b. demanded that Citizen Genet return to France.
c. asked President Adams to raise a standing army to fight Spain.
d. disagreed with Republicans who wanted to declare war on France.

## ENHANCED QUESTIONS
**For each of the following, circle the letter of the best choice. Next, expand on the subject by answering the second question in the space provided.**

61) Washington's Neutrality Proclamation stated that the United States would remain neutral toward

a. Britain in its war with France and Spain.
b. France in its war with Britain and Spain.
c. Spain in its war with Britain and the Netherlands.
d. all nations at war in Europe.

What led Washington take this stand? How did Americans respond to it?

_____

_____

Call to Freedom

62) Republican Motherhood was

a. the idea that women played an important role in teaching their children to be good citizens.
b. a political movement led by Abigail Adams during her husband's presidency.
c. the idea that women should run for political office.
d. the idea that equal rights for American women were as important as equal rights for citizens of the new French republic.

How did the concept of Republican Motherhood spread in the United States?

_____

_____

63) Hamilton believed that debt assumption would

a. improve relations between Congress and state legislatures.
b. improve business in debtor states, and inspire greater support for the federal government.
c. produce enough revenue to pay off the national debt during Washington's presidency.
d. prove to Britain that the United States was a strong, united nation.

How did Hamilton get Congress to approve his debt assumption plan?

_____

_____

64) In 1784 Spain

a. refused to change the border between the United States and Louisiana.
b. closed the port of New Orleans to all U.S. trade.
c. encouraged its prime minister, Edmond Genet, to solicit U.S. privateers to fight France.
d. granted rights of deposit along the Mississippi.

Why did this situation alarm western settlers? How did Thomas Pinckney help resolve it?

_____

_____

65) After Indian tribes from the Ohio Valley formed a confederation, they

    a. demanded a new treaty from the U.S. government.
    b. stopped U.S. settlers from entering the Northwest Territory.
    c. prevented U.S. citizens from buying more Indian land.
    d. defeated Arthur St. Clair's forces in the Battle of Fallen Timbers.

    How did the U.S. government respond to this situation?

_____

_____

## GRAPHIC IMAGE QUESTIONS
**Examine the image, and then answer the following questions.**

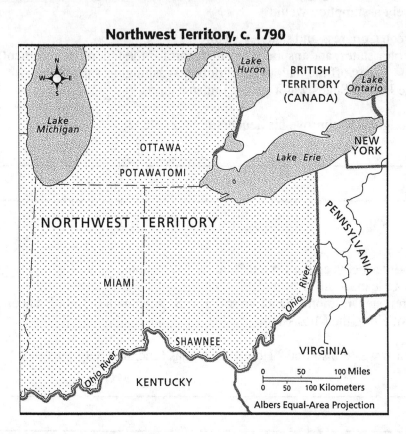

**Northwest Territory, c. 1790**

66) What geographic feature is used as the southern boundary for the Northwest Territory?

_____

67) What are two American Indian tribes that lived in the Northwest Territory in 1790?

_____

68) What three states bordered the eastern and southern edges of the Northwest Territory in 1790?

_____

**SHORT ANSWER**
**Write a brief answer for each of the following.**

69) How did Hamilton's proposal for a protective tariff reflect his goals for the country?

_____

_____

_____

70) Why did some Americans support the French Revolution while other Americans opposed it?

_____

_____

_____

71) What great threats to the republic did Washington name in his Farewell Address?

_____

_____

_____

72) What did Americans want from their government and its leaders in 1789?

_____

_____

_____

73) Compare the characteristics of the Federalist Party with those of the Democratic-Republican Party.

_____

_____

_____

## ESSAY
**On a separate sheet of paper, write an essay on one of the following.**

74) Explain how Jefferson and Hamilton's regional and political differences, and their mutual devotion to their country, ultimately shaped the outcome of the 1800 presidential election.

75) Describe the effect of the Treaty of Greenville, Jay's Treaty, and Pinckney's Treaty on the lives of American Indians and settlers who lived on the western frontier.

Call to Freedom

ANSWER KEY

1) Pinckney's Treaty

2) political parties

3) bonds

4) right of deposit

5) Treaty of Greenville

6) Judiciary Act

7) speculators

8) Virginia and Kentucky Resolutions

9) Jay's Treaty

10) precedent

11) F
Washington's troops ended the Whiskey Rebellion without a battle.

12) T

13) F
Genet persuaded U.S. privateers to support France by attacking Britain.

14) T

15) F
Congress created the executive departments, and Washington selected their leaders.

16) F
Hamilton encouraged the states to charter their own banks to prevent the national bank from having a monopoly.

17) T

18) F
The presidential campaign of 1796 included more than one candidate.

19) T

20) F
Hamilton believed in a strong central government, while Jefferson wanted to protect the powers of the states.

21) d

22) a

23) b

24) c

25) a

26) b

27) d

28) b

29) d

30) c

31) a

32) b

33) d

Call to Freedom

ANSWER KEY

34) b

35) c

36) d

37) a

38) c

39) b

40) d

41) a

42) b

43) d

44) c

45) b

46) d

47) a

48) c

49) b

50) b

51) d

52) c

53) d

54) b

55) a

56) b

57) c

58) c

59) d

60) a

61) d
The debate over U.S. foreign policy had divided Congress and the cabinet into pro-French and pro-British groups. Faced with these opposing viewpoints, Washington took a neutral position for which he was criticized by newspaper editors and the general public. James Madison believed that Washington had no right to issue the proclamation without Congress's approval.

62) a
Judith Sargent Murray wrote newspaper essays promoting education for young women. Some politicians, such as Dr. Benjamin Rush, also supported Republican Motherhood. Abigail Adams also hoped that women would be included in the democratic movement of the period.

63) b
Hamilton compromised with Jefferson and Madison who represented southern representatives who wanted to move the capital to a more southern location. Hamilton promised to persuade New Englanders to support moving the capital while Jefferson and Madison persuaded southern representatives to vote for debt assumption.

64) b
Without access to the mouth of the Mississippi River at New Orleans, western settlers were cut off from their most important link to the outside world. Pinckney persevered in Spain until that nation agreed to provide rights of deposit and reopen the port to shipping.

Call to Freedom

# ANSWER KEY

**65)** a

The U.S. government rejected the Indians' treaty offers, resulting in fighting that soon swept through the Northwest Territory.

**66)** Ohio River

**67)** Shawnee, Ottawa, or Potawatomi

**68)** Pennsylvania, Virginia, Kentucky

**69)** Hamilton wanted to promote the growth of manufacturing and commerce. The tariff on imported goods raised the prices of foreign products to make U.S. goods a better bargain for domestic consumers, thus creating greater demand for goods manufactured in America.

**70)** Supporters believed France was establishing a republic based on Enlightenment ideals, just as the United States had done. Non-supporters disliked the Revolution's violent riots and the increasing attacks on all forms of traditional authority.

**71)** Washington believed the greatest threats to the republic were public debt, dangerous foreign alliances, and political divisions at home.

**72)** Citizens wanted the government to protect their liberty, improve the economy, create fair tax laws and trade laws, and grant the right to settle new western lands.

**73)** The Federalist Party, which was most popular in New England, wanted to strengthen the power of the federal government and to promote industry and trade. The Democratic-Republican Party, which was most popular in the South and along the western frontier, wanted to preserve the power of the state governments and promote agriculture.

74) Hamilton, a wealthy New York financier, favored a strong central government led by influential, wealthy citizens. Jefferson, a wealthy Virginia farmer, believed farmers made the best citizens because they were self-reliant enough to be independent voters. Jefferson believed in protecting the powers of the states, and defended the right of the common people to rule the country. Hamilton favored an economy based on manufacturing and commerce while Jefferson favored agriculture. The two differed in their interpretation of the Constitution. Hamilton believed in creating laws "necessary and proper" for running the nation. Jefferson argued for strict construction of the document. In international affairs, Jefferson was pro-France while Hamilton was pro-British. As a result of these differences, the two political parties that emerged in 1796 were shaped by these two men. Hamilton influenced the Federalist Party that mirrored his belief in a powerful federal government and the promotion of industry and trade. Jefferson influenced the Democratic-Republican Party that was popular in the agricultural regions of the south and the west where people favored states' rights. However, during the 1796 election, Hamilton did not support the Federalist candidate for president, and he and Jefferson opposed Adams during his presidency. When Jefferson ran for president in 1800, Hamilton believed Jefferson was the better choice for president, and worked to elect him.

75) When the Ohio Valley Indian confederation's request for a treaty was denied in 1788, they were defeated in the fighting that followed. Confederation leaders who signed the 1795 Treaty of Greenville had already seen U.S. troops burn their villages and fields. The treaty gave the United States access to Indian lands and guaranteed safe travel for U.S. citizens crossing Indian territory. Thus, native Americans failed at the attempt to save their lands, while U.S. citizens benefited. As a result of Jay's Treaty in 1794, the British abandoned their forts on the western frontier, and continued to support American Indians on the frontier. Thus native Americans benefited more from Jay's Treaty than did U.S. citizens. In 1795, Pinckney's Treaty benefited all western settlers who depended on the port of New Orleans. Because this treaty opened the frontier to further expansion, it did not benefit native Americans who were already being pushed farther west as more settlers arrived.

Call to Freedom

# Chapter 10 The Expanding Nation

**MATCHING**
**In the space provided, write the term or the name of the person that best fits the description. Choose your answers from the list below. Not all answers will be used.**

Fort Detroit                Embargo Act              James Monroe
Tousssaint L'Ouverture      Battle of the Thames     Red River
impressment                 Battle of Lake Erie      embargo
Oliver Hazard Perry         John Marshall            Non-Intercourse Act
Zebulon Pike                Battle of Horseshoe Bend Meriwether Lewis

1) _____ Chief Justice whose ruling established the principle of judicial review

2) _____ the practice of forcing subjects to serve in the army or navy

3) _____ led a successful slave revolt that alarmed slaveholders throughout the Caribbean and the United States

4) _____ banned U.S. trade with Britain and France

5) _____ battle that broke British power in the Northwest and secured the Canadian border

6) _____ the banning of trade

7) _____ led an expedition to find the starting point of the Red River

8) _____ formed the western border of the Louisiana Territory

9) _____ captured by the combined forces of the Indians who were led by Tecumseh and the British

10) _____ ended the Creek War and led to a treaty that forced the Creek to give up millions of acres of their land

**TRUE/FALSE**
**Write T if a statement is true or F if it is false. If a statement is false, explain why.**

11) _____ The Treaty of Ghent resolved the problems of impressment and trade embargoes.

12) _____ The Louisiana Purchase doubled the size of the United States.

_____

13) _____ Of the kingdoms known as the Barbary States, only Tripoli required the United States to pay a yearly tribute.

_____

14) _____ In 1809 Congress repealed the Embargo Act and passed the Non-Intercourse Act.

_____

15) _____ When the defenders of Fort McHenry refused to surrender, the British stopped their two-day bombardment and retreated.

_____

16) _____ Thomas Jefferson was the first president to be inaugurated in the new capital city of Washington.

_____

17) _____ The brave leadership of Tecumseh was the Indians' main strength during the Battle of Tippecanoe.

_____

18) _____ The United States and Britain signed a peace treaty two weeks before the Battle of New Orleans was fought.

_____

19) _____ The Louisiana Territory stretched west from the Mississippi River to where the Columbia River emptied into the Pacific.

_____

20) _____ The victory of James Madison and his fellow Republicans represented the first major change in political power in the United States.

_____

Call to Freedom

**MULTIPLE CHOICE**
**For each of the following, circle the letter of the best choice.**

21) The first European explorers to reach the shores of North America were

a. English knights led by King John.
b. French explorers led by William the Conqueror.
c. Scandinavian Vikings led by Erik the Red.
d. Scandinavian Vikings led by Leif Eriksson.

22) The American ship that earned the name "Old Ironsides" was the USS

a. *Philadelphia.*    b. *Chesapeake.*    c. *Constitution.*    d. *Leopard.*

23) President Jefferson wanted to buy New Orleans

a. after James Monroe suggested the purchase as a means of diverting war with Britain.
b. rather than provoke a war with France.
c. rather than provoke a war with Spain.
d. after the Creek Indians became a threat in the South.

24) To improve the economy after he took office, Jefferson wanted to

a. eliminate the Bank of the United States.
b. improve living conditions in Washington and complete the U.S. Capitol.
c. increase domestic taxes.
d. decrease domestic taxes.

25) The most convincing U.S. victory during the War of 1812 was won during the

a. Battle of New Orleans.          c. Battle of the Thames.
b. Battle of Lake Erie.            d. Battle of Horseshoe Bend.

26) The Barbary States were located in

a. Algeria.                        c. North Africa.
b. Tripoli.                        d. southern France.

27) Members of the Lewis and Clark expedition were chosen by

a. President Jefferson.
b. Congress.
c. former army captain Meriwether Lewis.
d. Meriwether Lewis and Lieutenant William Clark.

28) During the Battle of lake Erie Captain Oliver Hazard Perry met the British with a flag that said

a. "Live free or die."      c. "United we stand."
b. "Don't give up the ship."      d. "Remember Detroit."

29) Before he was elected president, James Madison

a. helped Robert Livingston negotiate the Louisiana Purchase.
b. represented the United States at the Treaty of Ghent.
c. served as secretary of state in Jefferson's cabinet.
d. served on the Supreme Court with Chief Justice John Marshall.

30) Napoleon's plan to use Saint Domingue as a supply base was thwarted by troops led by

a. Toussaint L'Ouverture.      c. William Henry Harrison.
b. Andrew Jackson.      d. Oliver Hazard Perry.

31) The British were able to send more troops and ships to America after they

a. formed an alliance with Chief Red Eagle and Tecumseh.
b. passed search and seizure laws.
c. successfully stopped U.S. merchant ships that carried war supplies to France.
d. defeated Napoleon in 1814.

32) In the early 1800s many American merchants supplied both Britain and France with war supplies because

a. these merchants were lured by the opportunity to make high profits during the European war.
b. the Barbary States were still a threat to U.S. shipping in the Mediterranean.
c. the Neutrality Proclamation required U.S. merchants to trade with both warring nations.
d. the governments of Britain and France threatened to impress sailors on American ships that sailed into enemy ports.

33) When U.S. ambassador Robert Livingston prepared to negotiate with France in 1803, Jefferson sent

a. James Madison to assist Livingston.
b. James Monroe to assist Livingston.
c. Madison and Monroe to meet first with French minister Charles Talleyrand.
d. Monroe to France while Madison wrote the constitutional amendment that would bring Louisiana into the United States.

34) When America prepared to invade Canada in 1812, the U.S. Army was

a. under the command of the able and experienced Oliver Hazard Perry.
b. poorly equipped and unprepared for war.
c. commanded by Andrew Jackson who had already been victorious in the Creek war.
d. made up of state militia troops eager to fight the British in Canada.

Call to Freedom

35) During Jefferson's inaugural address, he told the Federalists that he would

a. allow their appointees to remain in office.
b. appoint as many Federalists as Republicans to his cabinet.
c. not let party conflicts interfere with running the government fairly.
d. oversee completion of the executive mansion and the Capitol.

36) Congress hoped that the Non-Intercourse Act of 1809 would

a. pressure Britain and France into changing their policies.
b. encourage U.S. merchants to trade with Britain and France.
c. prevent France from attacking U.S. merchants ships.
d. help end the European war between France and Britain.

37) Republicans gave the name "midnight judges" to Federal judges who

a. backed William Marbury in the court case Marbury v. Madison.
b. were appointed after midnight on March 3, 1801.
c. demanded that President Jefferson hand over their commissions before midnight on March 3, 1801.
d. received their appointments only hours before John Adams left office.

38) During the war of 1812 the U.S. Navy was aided by privateers who were

a. paid by the U.S. government for each ship they captured or sank.
b. authorized by the U.S. to seize British sailors whose ships entered U.S. waters.
c. licensed by the U.S. to attack British merchant ships.
d. licensed by the U.S. to patrol the American coast.

39) Jefferson's hesitation to purchase Louisiana because he did not think the Constitution granted the president that power,

a. exasperated Madison and other Federalists who urged Jefferson to act quickly.
b. reflected his strict construction viewpoint which he set aside in order to do what was best for the country.
c. proved to Republicans that Jefferson would not allow personal convictions to stand in the way of doing what was best for the country.
d. reflected advice that he received during correspondence with James Monroe in France.

40) Jefferson knew before his inauguration that Congress would support many of his plans for the country because

a. his authorship of the Declaration of Independence still garnered great respect.
b. he had already promised not to remove all Federalists from office.
c. his victory over Adams had proven that most Americans respected Jefferson's policies and wanted his plans to succeed.
d. the Republican Party had won control of both houses of Congress.

Call to Freedom
171

41) The Lewis and Clark expedition set out from St. Louis in May 1804 and

    a. reached the western boundaries of the Louisiana Purchase on November 7, 1805.
    b. canoed westward on unexplored rivers until they reached the Pacific in 1805.
    c. arrived by canoe back in St. Louis in late September 1806.
    d. returned to St. Louis by way of the Red River in 1807.

42) When Indian wars broke out on the frontier, William Henry Harrison was

    a. the governor of the Indiana Territory.
    b. a general in the Tennessee militia.
    c. a frontiersman who had already served under General Andrew Jackson.
    d. an explorer who had served as Jefferson's presidential assistant.

43) Jefferson and his cabinet changed many of the policies put in place by

    a. Republicans who had controlled Congress since the election of 1796.
    b. John Adams and Alexander Hamilton.
    c. John and Abigail Adams who had promoted Republican Motherhood.
    d. Federalist leaders Alexander Hamilton, Albert Gallatin, and James Madison.

44) The Supreme Court's decision in Marbury v. Madison concerned the powers given the Supreme Court in the

    a. Bill of Rights.
    b. Sixth Amendment.
    c. Constitution.
    d. Judiciary Act of 1789.

45) The strongest opponents of the War Hawks were

    a. Henry Clay and John C. Calhoun.
    b. Republicans in the West and the South.
    c. Federalists from New England.
    d. settlers who lived in the Great Lakes region.

46) Napoleon hoped that by occupying Louisiana the French would replace the

    a. British as the major European power on the Mississippi River.
    b. Spanish as the key European power in the American West.
    c. British and the Spanish as the key European powers in the United States.
    d. Americans who held economic control of the Caribbean and the American West.

47) The U.S. Army gained new hope in 1813 when the British withdrew after

    a. the Battle of Lake Erie.
    b. the attack on Fort McHenry.
    c. the Battle of the Thames.
    d. fighting Tecumseh's forces at Fort Detroit.

Call to Freedom

48) To allow the federal government to concentrate on repaying the national debt, Jefferson

   a. let the Bank of the United States function as it had under the Federalists.
   b. increased domestic taxes on whiskey and other alcohol.
   c. decreased military spending by reducing the size of the army and navy.
   d. agreed to keep most Federalists in their government positions.


49) The War Hawks were

   a. vessels captained by privateers who attacked British merchant ships.
   b. John C. Calhoun of South Carolina and Henry Clay of Kentucky.
   c. the U.S. Marines and mercenaries who marched through the desert to Tripoli in 1803.
   d. members of Congress who wanted the U.S. to declare war on Britain.


50) Thomas Jefferson sent Lewis and Clark to the Louisiana Purchase to

   a. negotiate a treaty to buy the area from France.
   b. learn about the West and find a river route to the Pacific Ocean.
   c. negotiate trade agreements with the Indians.
   d. find the starting point of the Red River and possibly spy on Spain.


51) Although he planned to keep many Federalists in their government positions, Jefferson agreed to replace some Federalist officials with Republicans due to pressure from

   a. newspaper editors who condemned his position.
   b. Federalists who were unhappy with Jefferson.
   c. Republicans who had control of Congress.
   d. Federalists and Republicans.


52) Stephen Decatur and Oliver Hazard Perry

   a. served in the U.S. Navy.
   b. sailed under a flag inscribed, "Don't give up the ship!"
   c. defended Fort McHenry during the British bombardment.
   d. served aboard the USS *Constitution* that bombarded the city of Tripoli.


53) Lewis and Clark crossed the Great Plains with the help of their guide,

   a. York, the only expedition member who was of African descent.
   b. Sacagawea, a Shoshoni woman originally from the Rocky Mountains.
   c. a Shawnee religious leader known only as the Prophet.
   d. Sacagawea's Shoshoni brother.

54) The War of 1812 came to an end after

a. Jackson defeated the British in the Battle of New Orleans.
b. the British burned Washington and marched on Baltimore, bent on bombarding Fort McHenry.
c. U.S. and British diplomats decided to end the war.
d. Britain agreed to stop impressing American sailors, and the U.S. lifted its trade embargoes.

55) The result of the War Hawks' victory was that, for the first time in U.S. history,

a. Congress declared war.
b. a small American fleet defeated the mighty British navy.
c. privateers succeeded in waters where the U.S. Navy had failed.
d. the president served as commander-in-chief of the Army and the Navy.

56) The Lewis and Clark expedition was funded by

a. contributions from American citizens.
b. President Jefferson.
c. Congress.
d. Federalists from New England.

57) When Jefferson ordered Madison to withhold the commissions of the midnight judges,

a. William Marbury demanded that James Madison hand over his commission.
b. Marbury and Madison disagreed with Jefferson who turned the issue over to the Supreme Court.
c. Marbury set a precedent by establishing the principle of judicial review.
d. Marbury exercised his rights under the Judiciary Act of 1789.

58) Lewis and Clark's expedition across the American West and back was

a. marked by peace among all Indian groups that lived on the lands they crossed.
b. long, dangerous, difficult, and exhausting.
c. a long journey made easy due to the frontier experience of Meriwether Lewis.
d. chronicled in journals written by William Clark and Sacagawea.

59) The threat of an Indian-British alliance in the Great Lakes was weakened

a. when Britain signed the Treaty of Ghent.
b. when the War of 1812 shifted to the Mississippi River at New Orleans.
c. with the death of Tecumseh during the Battle of the Thames.
d. after Tecumseh traveled south to meet with leaders of the Creek nation.

60) John C. Calhoun and Henry Clay were Congressional leaders who wanted the U.S. to

a. declare war on Britain.
b. purchase Louisiana without first amending the Constitution.
c. repeal the Embargo Act.
d. allow New England to withdraw from the Union.

Call to Freedom

## ENHANCED QUESTIONS
**For each of the following, circle the letter of the best choice. Next, expand on the subject by answering the second question in the space provided.**

61) The most significant changes Jefferson made to Federalist policies concerned

a. appointments to the federal judiciary.
b. acquiring the Louisiana Territory and developing Washington.
c. military spending and taxes.
d. inauguration ceremonies and dinner parties.

What Federalist policies did Jefferson leave in place?

_____

_____

62) People opposed declaring War on Britain in 1812 because

a. they hoped to maintain friendly business relations with Britain and did not think the United States was prepared for war.
b. they had profited from the Embargo Act by smuggling goods to Britain.
c. they feared the British alliance with the Northwest Indians would close the Mississippi to U.S. ships.
d. they hoped that if the United States remained allied with Britain they would gain lands in Canada.

Why did other people support the war?

_____

_____

63) William Henry Harrison provoked the Creek to fight his army in the

a. Battle of the Thames.
b. Battle of Horseshoe Bend.
c. Battle of Lake Erie.
d. Battle of Tippecanoe.

How was the Shawnee chief Tecumseh affected by the outcome of this battle?

_____

_____

64) The Supreme Court's decision in Marbury v. Madison

    a. declared that the principle of judicial review was unconstitutional.
    b. established the principle of judicial review.
    c. resulted in a bitter feud between Jefferson and Marshall.
    d. forced Madison to give Marbury his judgeship.

How did this ruling affect the power and authority of the Supreme Court?

_____

_____

65) After Tripoli declared war on the United States,

    a. Oliver Hazard Perry's fleet patrolled the Mediterranean.
    b. the USS Philadelphia was captured and its sailors held hostage for ransom.
    c. Stephen Decatur led a force of U.S. Marines across the desert and attacked Tripoli.
    d. the USS Philadelphia bombarded the city of Tripoli.

How did differences between the U.S. and Tripoli resolve?

_____

_____

**Call to Freedom**

**Examine the image, and then answer the following questions.**

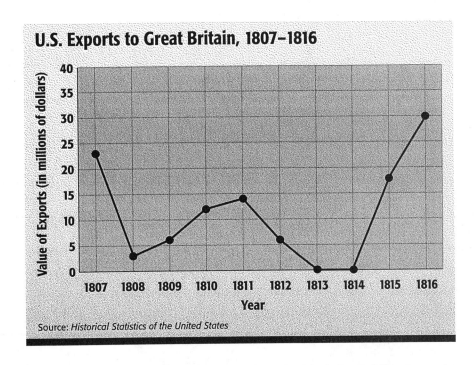

**U.S. Exports to Great Britain, 1807–1816**

Source: *Historical Statistics of the United States*

66) What was the value of U.S. exports to Great Britain in 1808?

_____

67) In what year between 1807 and 1816 was the value of exports to Great Britain the highest?

_____

68) In what year(s) between 1807 and 1816 was the value of exports to Great Britain the lowest? Why?

_____

SHORT ANSWER
**Write a brief answer for each of the following.**

69) Name four reasons why Napoleon changed his plans to build an American empire, and instead sold Louisiana.

_____

_____

_____

70) What factors motivated Indians and the British to ally against the United States in the Northwest Territory in the early 1800s?

_____

_____

_____

71) How and why did the British navy change their strategy in 1812?

_____

_____

_____

72) Explain how the demands of the Hartford Convention set a precedent in 1814.

_____

_____

_____

73) What spoken and unspoken messages did Jefferson convey in his first inaugural address?

_____

_____

_____

**ESSAY**
**On a separate sheet of paper, write an essay on one of the following.**

74) Describe the cultural diversity of New Orleans in the early 1800s, and explain how this community became the focal point of an international struggle for power during the War of 1812.

75) Agree or disagree with the following statement: "The Lewis and Clark Expedition ended Tecumseh's dreams." Explain your answer.

# ANSWER KEY

1) John Marshall

2) impressment

3) Toussaint L'Ouverture

4) Non-Intercourse Act

5) Battle of the Thames

6) embargo

7) Zebulon Pike

8) Red River

9) Fort Detroit

10) Battle of Horseshoe Bend

11) F
The Treaty of Ghent did not resolve these issues.

12) T

13) F
The United States paid tribute to all the Barbary States.

14) T

15) T

16) T

17) F
Tecumseh was not at the Battle of Tippecanoe.

18) T

19) F
The Louisiana Territory stretched west to the Rocky Mountains.

20) F
The first major change occurred when Jefferson and his fellow Republicans won.

21) c

22) b

23) b

24) d

25) a

26) c

27) d

28) b

29) c

30) a

31) d

32) a

33) b

**Call to Freedom**

# ANSWER KEY

34) b

35) c

36) a

37) d

38) c

39) b

40) d

41) c

42) a

43) d

44) d

45) c

46) b

47) a

48) c

49) d

50) b

# ANSWER KEY

51) d

52) a

53) b

54) c

55) a

56) c

57) d

58) b

59) c

60) a

61) c
Jefferson allowed many Federalist officials to keep their positions rather than replacing them with Republicans. In addition, he kept in place many Federalist policies such as the National Bank. Although he had once fought against the bank, he saw its practical uses once he was in office.

62) a
Many people supported the war because of what they perceived as Britain's insults to the United States. They felt that Britain was trying to keep the United States from becoming a powerful nation by encouraging the Indians to fight in the West and harassing U.S. ships. Some people also hoped that the war would increase the size of the nation.

63) d
The battle destroyed Tecumseh's village. Although Tecumseh was safe in the Creek nation, he lost the support he needed to create his dream of a great Indian confederacy.

Call to Freedom

# ANSWER KEY

64) b

As a consequence of its ruling on judicial review, the Supreme Court gained the power to declare legislation unconstitutional. This increased the power and authority of the court immensely.

65) b

The United States increased its military presence in the Mediterranean Sea, bombing Tripoli and attacking other Tripolitan towns. Faced with defeats, the ruler of Tripoli signed a peace treaty, agreed not to demand any more tribute, and returned his American hostages.

66) about 3 million

67) 1816

68) 1813 and 1814

69) Napoleon was about to go to war with Britain. The French had no troops in Louisiana because they had been busy fighting in Saint Domingue. Napoleon needed revenue to fight the British, which he hoped to gain by selling lands he could not protect. He also hoped that the United States would challenge to Britain's power in America.

70) As thousands of U.S. settlers poured into the Northwest Territory, Britain wanted to contain this rapid expansion and protect its interests in Canada without having to fight the United States. Thus, Britain allied with Northwest Territory Indians—who were angry about the provisions of the Treaty of Greenville and also resented the settlers encroaching on their lands—hoping that the Indians would be able to keep the United States in check.

71) After the U.S. Navy defeated British ships in one-on-one duels, the British were embarrassed and U.S. morale was improved. The British decided that instead of confronting U.S. ships directly, they would bring more ships to the American coast and began patrolling in large groups that the U.S. Navy could not confront. The British also blockaded American seaports and captured U.S. merchant ships.

72) New England Federalists who disliked the War of 1812 gathered in Hartford, Connecticut in what they called the Hartford Convention. More moderate members convinced the convention to send a delegation to President Madison, offering to support the war if measures were taken to increase the power of the states versus the federal government. However, other members wanted new England to withdraw from the United States entirely. The actions of the convention set a precedent for states to challenge the policies of the federal government.

73) In his inaugural address, Jefferson spoke about the United States's potential to become a great nation. He also presented his interpretation of the basic principles of the government and the rights of its citizens. He tried to calm Federalists' fears by explaining that he did not support mob rule and would not let party conflicts interfere with running the government fairly. In addition, Jefferson's plain dress and lack of formality solidified his association with the common people.

74) The busy seaport of New Orleans had a diverse heritage that mingled the cultures and languages of Africa, England, France and Spain with those of native Americans. Settlers, Indians, and fur traders relied on the Mississippi River and the New Orleans docks to handle their imports and exports. Jefferson feared that a French-occupied Louisiana would block the future westward expansion of the United States and would interfere with U.S. trade along the Mississippi. Therefore, the U.S. offered to buy New Orleans—an offer that resulted in the Louisiana Purchase. Napoleon's war with Britain was America's gain, until America became caught up in this international conflict and declared war on Britain. In 1814 the British defeated Napoleon in Europe and launched an offensive from their Caribbean bases against New Orleans—hoping to capture the city and take control of the Mississippi River. Thus, in 1815 New Orleans became the stage for the final battle between American and British forces in the United States. The U.S. victory in the Battle of New Orleans meant that this important city and its port would not be lost to a foreign power.

75) Students should explain that Tecumseh's dream was to unite the Indians of the Northwest Territory, the South, and the eastern Mississippi Valley into a single confederation to oppose the U.S. settlers who were living on lands that had belonged to the Indians for generations. As Tecumseh said, "The white people have no right to take the land from the Indians, because the Indians had it first." Those that agree with the statement might argue that although Lewis and Clark were instructed to establish peaceful relations with American Indians, their expedition proved that settlers could travel across the West to the Pacific Ocean. Their findings drove many more settlers into the region and convinced the U.S. government that the area was worth protecting. Tecumseh's goals for his nation stood in the way of the United States taking advantage of the land that it claimed. Students who oppose this statement might point out that Lewis and Clark were sent to make peace with the Indians and their dependence on the Indians for help made them respect Indians even more. They were sent on a scientific mission that did not set policy. The conflict between the U.S. and Britain started the wars on the frontier, and these wars weakened the Indian alliance. Tecumseh's loss at Tippecanoe and death at the Battle of Thames ended his dreams.

Call to Freedom

# Chapter 11 A New National Identity

**MATCHING**
**In the space provided, write the term or the name of the person that best fits the description. Choose your answers from the list below. Not all answers will be used.**

Whig Party
Indian Removal Act
Simón Bolívar
kitchen cabinet
American System

Rush-Bagot Agreement
Bureau of Indian Affairs
Nicholas Biddle
Democratic Party
Treaty of Dancing Rabbit Creek

Adams-Onís Treaty
Hudson River school
Tariff of Abominations
National Republican Party

1) _____ viewed by southern leaders as another example of the federal government's power over the states

2) _____ limited naval power on the Great Lakes for both the United States and British Canada

3) _____ political organization formed by supporters of Andrew Jackson

4) _____ authorized the removal of Indians who lived east of the Mississippi River

5) _____ President Jackson's informal group of trusted advisers

6) _____ the use of high tariffs to pay for internal improvements

7) _____ artists who celebrated the beauty of the American landscape in their work

8) _____ revolutionary fighter nicknamed "The Liberator"

9) _____ political organization that supported the idea of a weak president and a strong legislature

10) _____ ceded more than 10 million acres of Choctaw land to the state of Mississippi

**TRUE/FALSE**
**Write T if a statement is true or F if it is false. If a statement is false, explain why.**

11) _____ Jackson chose John C. Calhoun as his vice-president in 1832 because Calhoun shared Jackson's views on nullification.

_____

12) _____ American Indian cultures had no written language until 1821.

_____

13) _____ Spain ceded present-day Texas to the United States in the Adams-Onís Treaty of 1819.

_____

14) _____ The Cumberland Road opened up transportation between Albany and Buffalo, and linked the Great Lakes region to New York City.

_____

15) _____ As the Creek walked the Trail of Tears, almost one fourth of the people died because of disease, lack of food, and harsh weather.

_____

16) _____ The independent countries of Central America make up a region known as Latin America.

_____

17) _____ The *Last of the Mohicans* is one of the "Leatherstocking Tales."

_____

18) _____ The Cumberland Road, America's first federal road project, was also called the National Road.

_____

19) _____ Westward expansion and economic prosperity created a building boom in the Jacksonian era.

_____

Call to Freedom

20) _____ To weaken the power of the Second Bank of the United States, Jackson moved most of its funds to state banks which his opponents nicknamed "pet banks."

_____

**MULTIPLE CHOICE**
**For each of the following, circle the letter of the best choice.**

21) Due to the North's growing population, slave states in 1819 had

a. more power than free states in the House of Representatives.
b. more power than free states in the Senate.
c. equal power in the Senate and more power in the House.
d. equal power in the Senate and less power in the House.

22) The purpose of public nominating conventions was to

a. encourage women and free African Americans to become more active in politics.
b. encourage voters to become more active in politics.
c. allow more voter input in the selection of presidential and vice presidential candidates.
d. change voting rights to allow more white men to participate in the selection of presidential and vice presidential candidates.

23) The United States and Britain disagreed over control of the waterways between the U.S. and Canada because

a. the Treaty of Ghent declared that Britain could maintain its fleet there until 1840.
b. both wanted to maintain fishing rights over the Great Lakes area.
c. both wanted harbor rights to forts and trading communities along the Great Lakes.
d. the U.S. Navy had defeated the British navy after the Treaty of Ghent was signed.

24) After the Illinois government ordered the removal of all Indians from the state,

a. Black Hawk attacked a militia led by Isaiah Stillman.
b. the Sauk lived side-by-side with white settlers in Saukenuk.
c. Black Hawk's followers killed three delegates of a peace convention sent under a white flag to Saukenuk.
d. Sauk forces attacked U.S. troops as they attempted to retreat across a river.

25) Southerners opposed protective tariffs because

a. they distrusted President Adams's upper-class culture and feared he was out of touch with their needs.
b. according to the Constitution, tariffs were "null, void . . . nor binding" upon the states.
c. the region had little industry and relied heavily on imported goods.
d. they had doubts about using federal money for internal improvements in the North.

26) Almost all new buildings in the Jacksonian era used

    a. Greek and Roman architectural styles.
    b. the "Georgian" style.
    c. a unique style of architecture that showed that the United States was a better republic than ancient Greece and Rome.
    d. the architectural designs of Thomas Paine, Thomas Jefferson, and Thomas Cole.

27) More white men gained suffrage in the 1820s and 1830s because many states

    a. withdrew voting rights held by women and free African men.
    b. eliminated property ownership as a qualification for voting.
    c. began holding public nominating conventions that allowed more people to vote.
    d. allowed southern slaveholders to determine who could vote at the polls.

28) The 1828 presidential campaign focused heavily on

    a. the candidates' personalities.
    b. the issue of suffrage.
    c. boundary disputes between settlers and Indians.
    d. the issue of nullification.

29) Indians in the Northwest Territory stopped resisting white settlement on their lands after

    a. Sauk leaders signed the Treaty of Dancing Rabbit Creek.
    b. Congress passed the Indian Removal Act.
    c. the Sauk were removed to Indian Territory.
    d. the Black Hawk War.

30) The National Republican Party was formed by people who

    a. had supported Jackson during the First Seminole War.
    b. approved of Monroe's message of patriotism and good will.
    c. backed President Adams.
    d. viewed the Monroe Doctrine as "indecent declarations."

31) Jackson established Indian Territory in order to

    a. gain the fertile lands of the Lower South for U.S. farmers.
    b. remove the Sauk from Illinois after the Black Hawk War.
    c. establish boundaries for the Seminole within the Florida Everglades.
    d. remove the Choctaw and the Cherokee from the fertile lands of the Mississippi Delta.

32) Jackson's supporters were mostly

    a. National Republicans.
    b. farmers and southern slaveholders.
    c. southern Whigs and Democrats.
    d. independent farmers from Tennessee and Kentucky.

33) Catharine Maria Sedgwick, the most successful female author of her era, was

a. influenced by Puritan teachings that she advocated in "A New England Tale."
b. an unmarried woman who challenged commonly held prejudices about women.
c. also a portrait painter who studied under John Singleton Copley.
d. the first to use fictional characters to represent American ideals.

34) "Liberty and Union, now and forever, one and inseparable!" reflected

a. Van Buren's stance during the presidential campaign of 1836.
b. John C. Calhoun's disagreement with Jackson.
c. Daniel Webster's opposition to nullification.
d. the Whigs' response to Democrats who endorsed "Tippecanoe and Tyler too."

35) Supporters of states' rights believed that

a. federal power over the states was unconstitutional.
b. voters had the right to nullify any state law which did not apply to them.
c. federal power should equal the power of the states.
d. state power should be greater than federal power.

36) The Bureau of Indian Affairs was

a. created by Congress to oversee federal policy toward American Indians.
b. created by President Jackson to administer the Indian Removal Act.
c. administered by state governments with approval from Congress.
d. established after Black Hawk signed the Treaty of Dancing Rabbit Creek.

37) Jackson rewarded some of his supporters with governments jobs, a practice known as

a. the American System.                    c. Jacksonian Democracy.
b. the spoils system.                      d. a "corrupt bargain."

38) Henry Clay believed that internal improvements linking various regions of the country would

a. benefit the Second National Bank that loaned money to investors and western settlers.
b. curb inflation and help the nation recover from the Panic of 1837.
c. make trade easier and create a national economy.
d. encourage states and individuals to invest in roads, turnpikes and canals.

39) The Georgia militia began attacking Cherokee towns after

a. the Supreme Court ruled against the Cherokee.
b. Samuel Worcester sued the state of Georgia.
c. President Jackson authorized the militia to remove the Cherokee to Indian Territory.
d. gold was discovered on the Cherokee's land in Georgia.

40) Jackson vetoed legislation to renew the Second National Bank's charter because

    a. he believed that the bank's original charter was unconstitutional.
    b. of his long-running feud with Chief Justice John Marshall.
    c. he believed that the Bank allowed the wealthy to influence the government.
    d. the elastic clause gave him the presidential power to veto banking legislation.

41) The First Seminole War began when

    a. General Jackson and his troops invaded Florida without presidential authorization.
    b. President Monroe sent U.S. troops under Jackson to secure the Florida border.
    c. Jackson overthrew the Spanish governor of Florida.
    d. Jackson ordered the execution of two British citizens whom he suspected of aiding the Seminole.

42) Under the American System, the construction of the Erie Canal was paid by

    a. private investors.               c. Congress.
    b. the citizens of New York.        d. the Second Bank of the United States.

43) President Adams's public support in the South declined when he introduced proposals to

    a. allow Maine to join the Union as a free state.
    b. prohibit slavery in territories or states formed south of the 49th parallel.
    c. expand federal funding of roads, canals, scientific research, and education.
    d. require that all state legislatures fund the cost of building the National Road.

44) Britain wanted to restrain other Europeans nations' influence in the Americas in the early 1820s because Britain

    a. feared the loss of trade that would result it European nations colonized South America.
    b. wanted to protect its colonies in Central America and Mexico.
    c. had close trade relations with most of the independent Latin American countries.
    d. was still recovering from war with France.

45) The state banks' practice of offering credit to people buying land resulted in

    a. increased expansion in the West.
    b. inflation.
    c. a decrease in inflation as additional settlers helped expand western trade.
    d. increased westward expansion and inflation.

46) In the Adams-Onís Treaty of 1819 that the United States made with Spain, the United States

    a. gave up its claims to present-day Texas.
    b. ceded Florida to Spain.
    c. won $5 million of its citizens' claims against Spain.
    d. agreed to remove U.S. troops from Florida.

47) Before they were removed from their lands, the Chickasaw lived in

a. Florida.
b. Illinois.

c. upper Mississippi.
d. southern Alabama.

48) Although many people supported the idea of unifying the country through internal improvements, they had doubts about

a. whether canals and roads were really necessary.
b. funding these projects with money gained from a protective tariff.
c. how these improvements would unite people from different regions.
d. how long-lasting new roads would be.

49) The Monroe Doctrine

a. encouraged Simón Bolívar to lead many Latin American countries in their fight for independence.
b. prevented Latin American governments from gaining too much international power.
c. protected Latin American countries from internal conflicts.
d. has played a significant role in shaping U.S.–Latin American relations.

50) Shortly after Van Buren took office, the country experienced a

a. strong economy unprecedented since Monroe's presidency.
b. period of peace that journalists named "the Era of Good Feelings."
c. financial crisis, called the Panic of 1837, that led to a severe economic depression.
d. revival of interest in Georgian architecture due to the publication of Asher Benjamin's *Practical House Carpenter.*

51) One of the largest canal projects was the Erie Canal which

a. connected Columbus, Ohio with Vandalia, Illinois in 1850.
b. ran from Cumberland, Maryland, to Wheeling in present-day West Virginia.
c. made Charleston, South Carolina "the New York of the South."
d. ran from Albany to Buffalo, New York.

52) The writer who first popularized American historical fiction was

a. Catharine Maria Sedgwick.
b. James Fenimore Cooper.

c. Washington Irving.
d. George Caleb Bingham.

53) Opothleyaholo tried to organize an armed resistance to the forced removal of the

a. Creek from Alabama.
b. Choctaw from Mississippi.

c. Seminole from Florida.
d. Chickasaw from Georgia.

54) Most canal construction in the early 1800s took place in the

    a. South.
    b. Southeast.

    c. Northeast.
    d. Great Lakes region.

55) President Monroe's Secretary of State was

    a. John Quincy Adams.
    b. Henry Clay.

    c. John Tyler.
    d. Martin Van Buren.

56) Thomas Cole was the leader of the

    a. National Republican Party.
    b. Whig Party.

    c. Senate during Jackson's presidency.
    d. Hudson River school.

57) The first American Indians to be removed to Indian Territory were the

    a. Sauk from Illinois.
    b. Choctaw from Mississippi.

    c. Creek from Alabama.
    d. Chickasaw from Georgia.

58) One of the first American writers to gain international fame for his use of satire was

    a. Washington Irving.
    b. James Fenimore Cooper.

    c. William Wirt.
    d. Nicholas Biddle.

59) U.S. officials sympathized with revolutions in Latin America because

    a. U.S. trade with these countries increased after they won their independence.
    b. the U.S. hoped to acquire Florida and Mexico from Spain.
    c. these anticolonial struggles seemed similar to the American Revolution.
    d. the U.S. hoped to acquire Mexico from Spain.

60) The presidential campaign of 1840 was won by the

    a. National Republicans.
    b. Democrats.

    c. Republicans.
    d. Whigs.

Call to Freedom

# ENHANCED QUESTIONS

**For each of the following, circle the letter of the best choice. Next, expand on the subject by answering the second question in the space provided.**

61) When South Carolina passed a resolution claiming nullification of the 1828 and 1832 tariffs, President Jackson

    a. asked John C. Calhoun of South Carolina to resign as vice president.
    b. accepted Calhoun's voluntary resignation as vice president.
    c. threatened to send U.S. troops into South Carolina to enforce federal laws.
    d. asked Congress to expel South Carolina from the Union.

How did Congress and South Carolina resolve this issue?

_____

_____

62) In 1821 Britain wanted to issue a joint statement with the United States warning

    a. Spain not to interfere with Latin America.
    b. Europe not to interfere with Latin America.
    c. revolutionaries not to interfere with Latin America.
    d. Europe not to interfere with British and U.S. interests in North and South America.

How did John Quincy Adams and James Monroe respond to this proposal?

_____

_____

63) In Worcester v. Georgia the Supreme Court declared that the Cherokee Nation wasPresident

    a. ruled by a government system inspired by the U.S. Constitution, and therefore a free and independent nation under the rights and privileges of the Constitution.
    b. a distinct community in its own territory in which the laws of Georgia can have no force.
    c. a foreign nation and did not have to abide by state laws.
    d. a domestic dependent nation that must obey state laws.

What was Jackson's reaction to this ruling? What was the significance of his reaction?

_____

_____

64) When the House of Representatives had to determine the winner of the 1824 presidential election, Speaker of the House Henry Clay influenced the vote by backing

a. John Quincy Adams.  
b. Andrew Jackson.  

c. William Henry Harrison.  
d. Martin Van Buren.  

How did this situation affect the winner's presidency and Clay's career?

_____

_____


65) The Second Seminole War began when the Seminole

a. began harboring runaway slaves.  
b. refused to sign a treaty promising to leave Florida within three years.  
c. leader Osceola called upon the Seminole to resist removal by force.  
d. attacked U.S. forces at the Withlacoochee River in 1842.  

How did the outcome of this war affect the Seminole's desire to remain in Florida?

_____

_____

Call to Freedom

## GRAPHIC IMAGE QUESTIONS
**Examine the image, and then answer the following questions.**

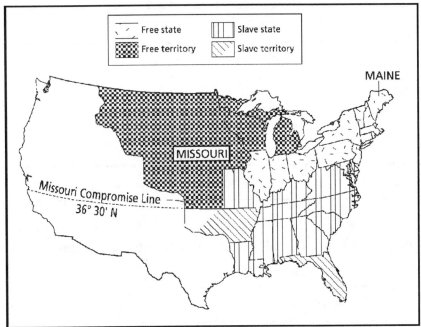

The Missouri Compromise

66) After the Missouri Compromise, how many slave territories were there?

_____

67) What latitude line marked the division between the free and slave states in the Missouri Compromise?

_____

68) After the Missouri Compromise, how many slave states and how many free states were there?

_____

## SHORT ANSWER
**Write a brief answer for each of the following.**

69) Why were political changes in the 1820s and 1830s known as "Jacksonian Democracy?"

_____

_____

_____

70) How did the Convention of 1818 benefit the United States?

_____

_____

_____

71) Explain why and how Cherokee society resembled white society.

_____

_____

_____

72) What two important rulings did John Marshall make in McCulloch v. Maryland?

_____

_____

_____

73) How did the Missouri Compromise settle the dispute between free states and slave states?

_____

_____

_____

**ESSAY**
**On a separate sheet of paper, write an essay on one of the following.**

74) How did the works of writers and artists such as Wirt, Cole, Cooper, Irving, and Sedgwick reflect the national identity and character that evolved during the Era of Good Feelings?

75) Describe how Henry Clay's desire for national unity affected America's policies on slavery and internal improvements during his years of service as Senator, Speaker of the House, and Secretary of State.

Call to Freedom

ANSWER KEY

1)   Tariff of Abominations

2)   Rush-Bagot Agreement

3)   Democratic Party

4)   Indian Removal Act

5)   kitchen cabinet

6)   American System

7)   Hudson River school

8)   Simón Bolívar

9)   Whig Party

10)  Treaty of Dancing Rabbit Creek

11)  F
     Calhoun resigned from the vice presidency in 1832 to support his home state of South Carolina in its nullification fight. Jackson condemned nullification, and threatened to send U.S. troops into South Carolina to enforce federal laws. Van Buren became vice president in 1832.

12)  T

13)  F
     Spain ceded Florida to the United State in the Adams-Onís Treaty, while the U.S. gave up its claims to present-day Texas.

14)  F
     The Erie Canal accomplished this.

15)  F
     The Cherokee walked the Trail of Tears.

16) F

Latin America refers to the countries of Central and South America.

17) T

18) T

19) T

20) T

21) d

22) c

23) b

24) b

25) c

26) a

27) b

28) a

29) d

30) c

31) a

32) b

Call to Freedom

33) b

34) c

35) d

36) a

37) b

38) c

39) d

40) c

41) a

42) b

43) c

44) c

45) d

46) a

47) a

48) c

49) b

50) d

51) d

52) b

53) a

54) c

55) a

56) d

57) b

58) a

59) c

60) d

61) c
The two sides reached a compromise. Congress agreed to gradually lower the tariffs over several years. South Carolina leaders agreed to enforce the tariffs, although they continued to insist that nullification was legal.

62) b
Adams and Monroe put together a statement, which became known as the Monroe Doctrine, declaring that North and South America were off limits to future colonization by any foreign power. They also declared that the U.S. government would consider any European countries' attempts to colonize or interfere with newly independent Latin American countries to be a hostile act.

63) b

Jackson supported Georgia in defying the Court's ruling. By not enforcing the Court's decision, Jackson was violating his constitutional oath as president to uphold the laws of the land.

64) a

Adams appointed Clay as secretary of state. This appointment and the allegations that Adams and Clay had made a "corrupt bargain" weakened Adams's congressional and public support during his presidency.

65) c

After the U.S. government gave-up fighting the Seminole, some Seminole chose to migrate to Indian Territory. However, many Seminole remained on tribal lands in Florida where they still live today.

66) two

67) 36° 30'

68) 12 slave, 12 free

69) Changes in voting rights and the creation of nominating conventions in the 1820s and 1830s gave many voters more influence over who was elected president. These changes occurred as Jackson campaigned for president in 1824, 1828, and 1832.

70) This treaty gave the U.S. fishing rights off parts of the Newfoundland and Labrador coasts, established the border between the United States and Canada at the 49th parallel as far west as the Rocky Mountains, and gave the United States and Canada joint occupation of Oregon.

71) Many Cherokee believed that they could avoid conflict with settlers by adopting practices similar to those of white society. The Cherokee invited missionary societies to establish schools and to teach Cherokee children to read and write English. The Cherokee created a government system inspired by the U.S. Constitution, established the first writing system among American Indian cultures, and published a newspaper in both English and Cherokee.

72) Marshall ruled that the elastic clause allowed Congress to establish the Second Bank of the United States. This ruling was a broad interpretation of the implied powers of Congress. He also ruled that because federal law was superior to state law, Maryland could not tax or otherwise interfere with the Bank.

73) The Missouri Compromise allowed Missouri to enter the Union as a slave state while Maine joined as a free state. It also declared that slavery would be prohibited in any new territories or states formed north of the 36° 30' line, which ran along Missouri's southern border.

74) The spirit of national pride that developed during the Era of Good Feelings was reflected in the art of the Hudson River school. The artists from this school drew landscapes that glorified American history and the beauty of the frontier. After William Wirt wrote about the heroes of the Revolution in order to encourage American pride, most American writers used fictional characters to represent American ideals. Irving believed that Americans should learn from the past and be cautious about the future. Cooper's stories promoted patriotism and national pride. Sedgwick encouraged pride and self-esteem in her unmarried female readers when she argued that not all women had to get married. She also tried to present stories of Pilgrims as realistically as possible. These developments in literature and art contributed to the creation of a new national American identity.

75) Kentucky Representative Henry Clay proposed the Missouri Compromise, which settled a Congressional dispute on how to bring states into the Union—as slave states or free states. Clay's proposal was motivated by his desire to maintain the unity of the country. In 1824 Clay proposed a protective tariff to boost domestic industries and to discourage citizens from buying foreign goods. He believed that the federal government should use the proceeds from this tariff for internal improvements such as better roads and canals that would link the various regions of the country, making trade easier. His support of what became known as the American System resulted in the construction of the Cumberland Road, the Erie Canal, turnpikes, and similar projects. As Speaker of the House during a tie-breaking vote that determined the presidency in 1824, Clay's desire for unity led him to back John Quincy Adams over Andrew Jackson, who was popular with slaveholders. Clay became Secretary of State under Adams, whose support of federal funding for roads and canals mirrored Clay's.

# Chapter 12 The North and the South

## MATCHING
**In the space provided, write the term or the name of the person that best fits the description. Choose your answers from the list below. Not all answers will be used.**

Harriet Jacobs
folktales
Eli Whitney
yeomen
planters

John Deere
spirituals
Samuel Morse
textiles
Francis Cabot Lowell

Industrial Revolution
Cyrus McCormick
mass production
technology
interchangeable parts

1) _____ large-scale southern farmers who owned more than 20 slaves

2) _____ built the first U.S. textile mill with spinning and weaving operations in one factory

3) _____ oral stories that contained a moral

4) _____ small landowning farmers in the South

5) _____ cloth

6) _____ tools and machinery designed to produce goods

7) _____ enslaved person who worked in a doctor's house and eventually escaped North

8) _____ the making of large numbers of identical goods more efficiently

9) _____ designed a steel plow that more effectively cut through thick soil and tough grass

10) _____ invented a new machine for removing seeds from short-staple cotton

## TRUE/FALSE
**Write T is a statement is true or F if it is false. If a statement is false, explain why.**

11) _____ In 1840 President Van Buren granted a 10-hour work day to textile workers, artisans, and government employees.

_____

12) _____ The first manufacturing success of the Industrial Revolution was in the production of steamboats.

_____

13) _____ The majority of white southerners owned more than 20 slaves.

_____

14) _____ Eli Whitney introduced the idea of interchangeable parts and mass production for muskets, an idea that would later revolutionize the manufacturing of other products.

_____

15) _____ By the 1830s most families who lived in cities were able to install water pumps inside their houses instead of relying on public pumps on street corners.

_____

16) _____ Wages at the Lowell mill were much better than women could earn teaching or doing domestic work in the early 1800s.

_____

17) _____ Spirituals were emotional Christian songs that blended African and European traditions.

_____

18) _____ The Industrial Revolution was a period of rapid growth in the use of machines in manufacturing and production.

_____

19) _____ Violent slave revolts were relatively rare.

_____

20) _____ Industry grew rapidly in the South during the 1840s.

_____

**MULTIPLE CHOICE**
**For each of the following, circle the letter of the best choice.**

21) The Transportation Revolution was a period of rapid growth in the

 a. use of turnpikes to get products to market during the 1800s.
 b. use of steam engines that powered boats and railroad trains during the late 1700s.
 c. technological discoveries that improved travel in Britain during the late 1700s.
 d. speed and convenience of transportation in the United States during the early 1800s.

22) Workers could more easily assemble muskets and replace defective parts quickly if the muskets

 a. had interchangeable parts.
 b. were mass produced.
 c. were produced in factories rather than in the homes of gunsmiths.
 d. were tested before being shipped to major consumers such as the U.S. government.

23) Shipping by steamboat made it practical for shipping goods from

 a. cities to farms.
 b. eastern textile mills to midwestern consumers.
 c. the North to the South.
 d. from western producers to eastern markets.

24) Telegraphs grew in use after a telegraph reported the

 a. race between the *Tom Thumb* and a horse-drawn railcar.
 b. results of the Democratic convention of 1844.
 c. first voyage of the *Clermont*.
 d. strike at the Lowell mill in 1836.

25) In the late 1700s many U.S. mill owners found it difficult to attract people to work in factories because

 a. few young men and women were mechanically minded.
 b. many people found factory work boring and repetitive.
 c. young women could earn more money working as teachers or as domestic help.
 d. the work was often dangerous and the hours were long.

26) Charleston, Savannah, and New Orleans grew into major port cities as a result of the

 a. major road network that connected these cities to smaller, inland cities.
 b. importance of international and domestic cotton trade.
 c. canals that connected these cities to inland plantations.
 d. abundance of poor white laborers who loaded and unloaded the trading ships.

27) Southern popular fiction of the early 1800s tended to

  a. romanticize southern life.
  b. increase white southerners' fear of a violent slave rebellion.
  c. portray the cultural and literary pursuits of urban white southerners.
  d. appeal more to yeomen than to wealthy white slaveholders.

28) The first textile mill using the Lowell System was built in

  a. Waltham, Massachusetts, in 1813.      c. Boston, Massachusetts, in 1793.
  b. Lowell, Massachusetts, in 1823.       d. Springfield, Massachusetts, in 1807.

29) The most important unit of slave communities was the

  a. church.                               c. spiritual.
  b. family.                               d. folktale.

30) The growth of factories resulted in

  a. fewer jobs for women.
  b. higher salaries for women.
  c. longer hours and lower salaries for workers hired by craftspeople.
  d. higher profits for craftspeople who made goods by hand.

31) The Cotton Belt extended from

  a. Virginia to Georgia.                  c. Maryland to Tennessee.
  b. South Carolina to East Texas.         d. Virginia to Texas.

32) A mechanical reaper that made harvesting faster and more efficient was designed by

  a. Eli Whitney.                          c. John Deere.
  b. Cyrus McCormick.                      d. Dr. Rush Nutt.

33) The cotton gin that sparked a boom in cotton production was the result of

  a. Joseph R. Anderson's life-long interest in crossbreeding varieties of cotton.
  b. Robert Fulton's investments in a Massachusetts textile mill that depended on the production of cotton.
  c. Eli Whitney's visit to a Georgia plantation where he learned that such a machine was needed.
  b. Elias Howe's ownership of a Louisiana plantation that produced short-staple cotton.

34) Morse code was the name given to a system

  a. using a series of short and long electric pulses that represented letters and numbers.
  b. developed by Samuel Morse for use by clipper ships at sea.
  c. developed by Robert Fulton for navigators of steamboats.
  d. of telegraph instructions relayed to engineers of railroad trains.

Call to Freedom

35) In the 1830s and 1840s, some workers in skilled trades began forming trade unions—

  a. political parties made up of artisans—to change laws and win government support.
  b. companies owned and operated by artisans—to steer profits away from management.
  c. mobs of dissatisfied workers—to stage strikes until union demands were met.
  d. organizations of artisans in a particular trade—to improve working conditions.

36) To convince business owners to listen to them, workers sometimes staged strikes,

  a. illegally closing the factory until employers were willing to negotiate.
  b. destroying machines and equipment, thus disabling the factory.
  c. refusing to work until employers met union demands.
  d. working for other companies until the original employer raised salaries.

37) The locomotive *Tom Thumb* was built by

  a. Eli Whitney.
  b. Peter Cooper.
  c. Tredegar Iron Works.
  d. the Springfield Armory.

38) The domestic slave trade increased because

  a. importing slaves became illegal in 1812.
  b. major port cities held frequent slave auctions that attracted buyers throughout the South.
  c. growing and harvesting cotton and other southern crops required a large number of field workers.
  d. planters became increasingly convinced that religion justified their holding slaves.

39) Iceboxes and iron cookstoves began appearing in middle class homes in the

  a. 1830s.
  b. 1840s.
  c. 1850s.
  d. 1860s.

40) Parliament passed laws making it illegal for machine plans or skilled mechanics to leave Britain because

  a. overpopulation increased the demand for more textile mills in Britain.
  b. textile mills had replaced small-scale manufacturing methods in France and Spain.
  c. the growth of cities depended on the textile industry.
  d. Britain hoped to keep its industrial secrets and maintain an economic advantage over other countries.

41) Early strikes by union members were not very successful because

  a. few workers belonged to labor unions until the 1870s.
  b. employers rarely hired workers whom they suspected of being union members.
  c. the courts and police usually supported companies against striking union members.
  d. factory owners closed plants whenever there was a strike.

42) The United States had more locomotives hauling more freight than in any other country in the world by

    a. 1845.               c. 1855.
    b. 1850.               d. 1860.

43) In the 1850s more women were able to work out of their homes if they owned a machine designed by

    a. Sarah Bagley.            c. Lucy Breckinridge.
    b. Isaac Singer.             d. Cyrus McCormick.

44) Ships such as *America* and *Flying Cloud* were

    a. steamboats built by Robert Fulton's company for ferry service on the Hudson River.
    b. clipper ships that helped fill the need for fast ocean shipping.
    c. a common sight on the Mississippi River by 1840.
    d. able to move quickly against the current and did not rely on winds.

45) Slaves' style of worship blended many aspects of traditional African religions with those of

    a. Buddhism.            c. Islam.
    b. Catholicism.           d. Christianity.

46) By making workers sign special contracts with longer hours, company officials

    a. produced more textiles than any other nation in the world.
    b. were able to open more factories that doubled work opportunities for people in New England.
    c. avoided laws in some states that required a ten-hour workday.
    d. were able to pay workers higher salaries while saving on production costs.

47) On August 9, 1807,

    a. Robert Fulton successfully sent the *Clermont* up the Hudson River.
    b. the *Tom Thumb* proved its power during a race against a horse-drawn railcar.
    c. Morse code tapped out the message, "What hath God wrought?"
    d. Eli Whitney assembled random pieces into a working musket.

48) The first successful textile mill in the United States was established in

    a. 1793 at Pawtucket, Rhode Island.
    b. 1769 by Richard Arkwright.
    c. Waltham, Massachusetts, by Francis Cabot Lowell.
    d. Lowell, Massachusetts, by Samuel Slater.

Call to Freedom

49) In the late 1700s the South's major cash crops were

a. rice and tobacco.
b. tobacco and indigo.
c. tobacco, rice, and indigo.
d. corn, tobacco, and rice.

50) By 1840 U.S. railroad companies had built

a. about 1,000 miles of track.
b. 1,000 more miles of track than existed in all of Europe.
c. more than 30,000 miles of track, linking New York City with Chicago.
d. 5,000 miles of track and established connections between every major city in the eastern United States.

51) Manufacturing in the U.S. grew more slowly than in Britain because

a. investors did not develop factories outside New England.
b. most U.S. apprentices lacked mechanical skills.
c. Americans preferred farming to manufacturing.
d. American mills lacked mass-produced machinery that made British mills profitable.

52) Yeomen differed from planters in that they owned less land and

a. did not earn enough money to buy slaves.
b. tended to work side by side in the fields with their slaves, if they owned any.
c. seldom sold slaves on the domestic slave market.
d. often allowed slave families to remain together for generations.

53) Clipper ships were introduced because

a. their beautiful designs captured the fancy of American investors.
b. steamboats were unable to carry enough fuel to cross the oceans.
c. Americans needed a ship that could be easily mass produced.
d. they could carry cargoes more quickly than steamships.

54) In the late 1850s, Chicago was the site of

a. John Deere's large factory that produced 1,000 plows a year.
b. Isaac Singer's factory that made Singer a millionaire by 1858.
c. Cyrus McCormick's large factory that was one of the first to use new improvements in steam-engine technology for manufacturing.
d. Eli Whitney's factory that surpassed the Springfield Armory in the production of muskets.

55) Dishonest slave traders sometimes kidnapped free African Americans from the North and

a. sold them into slavery in the South.
b. reunited them with their families in the South.
c. forced them to perform domestic work in the slave traders' homes.
d. transported them to the West Indies to work on sugar plantations.

56) Most free African Americans who lived in southern cities worked

    a. as skilled artisans.                    c. as domestic laborers.
    b. in factories.                            d. in barber shops.

57) Steamboat travel led to reductions in shipping rates

    a. only on luxury goods.
    b. of 90 percent for upstream travel and 75 percent for trips downstream.
    c. of 15 percent for upstream travel and 10 percent for trips downstream.
    d. but raised the price of the labor needed to carry it.

58) A device that sends and receives pulses of electrical current through a wire is a

    a. telegraph.                      c. telegraph receiver.
    b. telegraph key.                  d. telegraph cable.

59) On large plantations most slaves were

    a. under the control of a driver who was also a slave.
    b. expected to work 12-14 hours per day, seven days a week.
    c. assigned to specific jobs, with the majority working in the fields.
    d. assigned to the household or the field at around the age of six.

60) The average female employee in the Lowell mills

    a. was between 13 and 15 years old.
    b. earned between $12 and $14 a day.
    c. was a young unmarried woman from a local farm.
    d. came from either Massachusetts or New Hampshire.

## ENHANCED QUESTIONS
**For each of the following, circle the letter of the best choice. Next, expand on the subject by answering the second question in the space provided.**

61) One of the most active figures in the labor union movement was

    a. Sarah Bagley.                    c. Harriet Jacobs.
    b. Catherine Greene.              d. Lucy Breckinridge.

How did she contribute to the union movement in 1844 and 1845?

_____

_____

Call to Freedom

62) The Industrial Revolution first took place in the manufacture of

a. steamboats.

c. textiles.

b. muskets.

d. farming equipment.

How did James Hargreaves and Richard Arkwright influence the growth of this industry?

_____

_____

63) Hinton Rowan Helper warned southerners that the region

a. was overdependent on the labor system of slavery.
b. relied too heavily on cotton as a cash crop.
c. was falling behind the North by not industrializing.
d. was raising more cash crops than it could adequately process.

Who was Joseph R. Anderson and what role did he have in trying to correct this problem?

_____

_____

64) Cotton's drawback as a crop was that

a. it pulled many nutrients from the soil.
b. it grew well only in the Cotton Belt.
c. its seeds had to be imported from Mexico.
d. it could not be grown side-by-side with food crops such as wheat and corn.

How did people who studied scientific agriculture respond to this problem?

_____

_____

65) Nat Turner and his followers killed almost 60 white people in Virginia because

a. Turner's family was sold to a sugar planter in Louisiana.
b. recently enacted slave codes prevented Virginia slaves from learning to read or write.
c. Turner planned to establish a free society on land that belonged to planters in the region.
d. Turner believed that God had called on him to overthrow slavery.

What happened during the revolt, and what were its results?

_____

_____

## GRAPHIC IMAGE QUESTIONS
**Examine the image, and then answer the following questions.**

### Transportation Methods of the Mid-1800s

| TYPE OF TRANSPORTATION | AVERAGE SPEED | SHIPPING COSTS |
| --- | --- | --- |
| Roads | 2 miles per hour by wagon 6–8 miles per hour by stagecoach | $0.12 per ton per mile |
| Canals | 1.5–5 miles per hour | $0.045 per ton per mile |
| Steamboats | around 20 miles per hour | $0.007 per ton per mile |
| Clipper Ships (Ocean Travel) | 11.5–17 miles per hour (depending on weather) | $10.00 per ton for transatlantic shipment |
| Railroads | around 20 miles per hour (including stops) | $0.06 per ton per mile |

Source: George Rodger Taylor,
*The Transportation Revolution, 1815 to 1860*

66) How much did it cost to ship something by stagecoach?

_____

67) What was the fastest way to ship something? What was the cheapest way to send something?

_____

68) Why might a merchant ship goods by railroad rather than by steamboat?

_____

## SHORT ANSWER
**Write a brief answer for each of the following.**

69) Why did Great Britain experience an Industrial Revolution in the mid-1700s?

_____

_____

_____

Call to Freedom

70) Why were the first textile mills built in New England?

_____

_____

_____

71) How did the Lowell system differ from the Rhode Island system?

_____

_____

_____

72) How did white ministers and enslaved people differ in their interpretation of the Bible's view of slavery?

_____

_____

_____

73) Describe how slaves resisted slaveholders' attempts to control every aspect of their lives.

_____

_____

_____

**ESSAY**
**On a seperate sheet of paper, write an essay on one of the following.**

74) Describe a typical day in the life of an enslaved field worker, an enslaved household worker, and an enslaved skilled worker on a southern plantation after the invention of the cotton gin.

75) Explain why manufacturing grew slowly in the United States, and how the Industrial Revolution changed the way many people in the Northeast lived and worked after 1812.

# ANSWER KEY

1)  planters

2)  Francis Cabot Lowell

3)  folktales

4)  yeomen

5)  textiles

6)  technology

7)  Harriet Jacobs

8)  mass production

9)  John Deere

10) Eli Whitney

11) F
Only federal government workers gained the 10-hour workday. Most other working men and women continued to put in 12–14 hours, 6 days a week.

12) F
The first success was in the manufacture of textiles.

13) F
The majority of white southerners did not own slaves.

14) T

15) F
A few wealthy families were able to install water pumps inside their houses.

16) T

**Call to Freedom**

ANSWER KEY

17)  T

18)  T

19)  T

20)  F
The Industrial Revolution largely bypassed the South.

21)  d

22)  a

23)  d

24)  b

25)  b

26)  b

27)  a

28)  a

29)  b

30)  c

31)  b

32)  b

33)  c

34)  a

35)  d

36)  c

37)  b

38)  c

39)  a

40)  d

41)  c

42)  d

43)  b

44)  b

45)  d

46)  c

47)  a

48)  a

49)  c

50)  b

51)  c

52)  b

Call to Freedom

53) b

54) c

55) a

56) a

57) b

58) a

59) c

60) c

61) a
Bagley founded the Lowell Female Labor Reform Association in 1844. The next year she was elected vice president of the New England Workingmen's Association and ran the organization's effort to limit the workday to 10 hours.

62) c
James Hargreaves invented the spinning jenny, and Richard Arkwright invented the water frame. These two inventions increased the speed at which thread could be produced. The spinning jenny could be used in someone's home. However, the water frame required water and space to operate and to accomodate it, merchants built the first factories—textile mills.

63) c
In 1848 Anderson became owner of the Tredegar Iron Works in Richmond, Virginia. By 1860 he had turned Tredegar—the only large southern factory to make iron products—into one of the nation's most productive iron works.

64) a
Dr. Rush Nutt and others who experimented with cotton were part of a larger movement throughout the South that promoted scientific agriculture, or the use of scientific techniques to improve crop production. Some scientific agriculturists recommended crop rotation—periodically changing the types of crops grown on a particular piece of land—and increased research to better understand soil chemistry.

65) d

More than 100 slaves were killed in an attempt to put down Nat Turner's Rebellion, the most violent slave revolt in the United States. Turner was captured, brought to trial, and executed. After this rebellion, many states strengthened their slave codes to increase control over slaves, as the slave system continued to spread.

66) $0.12 per ton per mile

67) steamboats or railroads; steamboats

68) might need to ship goods to places that were not near rivers

69) As Britain's population grew, the demand for manufactured goods went up. Artisans—who traditionally crafted small numbers of goods by hand in their shops—could not meet this new demand, and people began looking for ways to use machines to produce items more quickly and efficiently. This process led to the Industrial Revolution, a period of rapid growth in the use of machines in manufacturing and production.

70) The area had many of the conditions necessary for a thriving factory system—an available labor pool and merchants with money willing to invest in building new mills. In addition, the region had an inexhaustible supply of water power in its thousands of rivers and streams.

71) The Rhode Island system was Samuel Slater's approach to spinning thread and dividing the work into simple tasks. Slater and his partners encouraged families to move to Pawtucket—the location of Slater's mill—and hired entire families, assigning children to the simplest jobs. Francis Cabot Lowell developed a different kind of factory system. He employed young, unmarried women from local farms to work at spinning and weaving operations under one roof. This combination of employing young women and of spinning thread and weaving cloth in one mill became known as the Lowell system.

72) White ministers often tried to use religion to support the institution of slavery, preaching that God wanted slaves to obey slaveholders. However, slaves themselves noted that the Bible also implied that all people are equal in the eyes of God. They came to see themselves as God's chosen people, much like the Hebrew slaves in ancient Egypt, who had faith that they would someday live in freedom.

Call to Freedom

73) Enslaved people maintained their own religious beliefs and practices. They sometimes worked slower to protest increased hours in the field, or ran away to avoid an angry slaveholder. Although some ran away permanently, others left for only short periods of time, and sometimes returned voluntarily. Two planned slave rebellions—one led by Gabriel Prosser in 1800 and one led by Denmark Vesey in 1822—were stopped before they could be carried out. Few slaves resorted to violent resistance, as Nat Turner did in 1831. Other ways of retaining control over their own lives meant brightening up their assigned clothing, picking berries to improve their food rations, and keeping their own gardens and chickens. To maintain their cultural heritage, they passed down family histories and African customs and told folktales that encouraged them to survive and win their freedom.

74) On large plantations, most slaves were assigned to specific jobs, with the majority working in the fields. Women, men, and children over the age of about 10 began their day at sunup working in the gang system—everyone laboring at the same task—and worked until sundown. Poor weather and illness did not stop the work, nor did a meal break; field workers sometimes ate, standing at their hoes. They wore very poor clothing. When the day's work was done, they went home to a dirt-floor cabin which often had a leaky roof and few furnishings. Slaves who worked as cooks, maids, nurses, or butlers around the planter's house were at the service of the planter's family 24 hours a day. They usually received better food and clothing than field hands, but often worked longer hours. Skilled workers labored at such jobs as blacksmithing and carpentry. Sometimes the planters allowed them to hire out their services to other people. In this way, some skilled slaves earned enough money to buy their freedom. Until they were free, however, they labored at their skill at the planter's demand. Sometimes field hands, household workers, and skilled workers had time to tend their own gardens, fish, and collect berries. Out of the watchful eye of the slaveholder, they also worshipped, sang, and told folktales to their children, enabling enslaved parents and children to celebrate their cultural heritage while they survived under slavery. Whether laboring in the field, in the house, or in a blacksmith shop, all enslaved people lived in fear of punishment.

75) As late as 1808 there were only 15 cotton mills in the entire country. Americans preferred farming to manufacturing. In addition, few people had sufficient capital to invest to build a factory. The Embargo of 1807 and the War of 1812 encouraged the expansion of manufacturing. Both events prevented consumers from buying British goods and revealed America's dependence on foreign producers. American manufacturers seized the opportunity to expand their factories, sell more goods, and increase their profits. To find and keep workers, Samuel Slater and his partners created the Rhode Island system that required families to move to Pawtucket where the entire family might work in the mill. Francis Cabot Lowell acquired laborers by building a large mill in Lowell, Massachusetts and recruiting young, unmarried women from local farms. These young women became known as the "Lowell girls." Young women who might have taught school or worked as a housekeeper moved to Lowell and worked in the mill, paying $1.25 a week for room and board. Young women from across New England came to work at the Lowell mills. Many female workers welcomed the opportunity to earn money and to associate with other women. However, as factories became more common, male and female workers began to object to their long, tiring work day with its mechanical dangers. During the 1840s the Lowell Female Labor Reform Association and the New England Workingmen's Association became politically active, and began fighting for workplace reforms.

# Chapter 13 New Movements in America

## MATCHING

**In the space provided, write the term or the name of the person that best fits the description. Choose your answers from the list below. Not all answers will be used.**

utopian community
American Anti-Slavery
Society
Ralph Waldo Emerson
middle class
abolition

Josiah Quincy
Seneca Falls Convention
Margaret Fuller
emancipation
tenements

Thomas Gallaudet
Second Great Awakening
American Colonization
Society
Samuel Gridley Howe

1) _____ meeting that launched the organized women's rights movement

2) _____ established the first free U.S. school for the hearing-impaired

3) _____ group that demanded immediate emancipation and racial equality for African Americans

4) _____ dirty, overcrowded, and poorly built housing

5) _____ group of people working to establish a perfect society on Earth

6) _____ freedom from slavery

7) _____ prison reformer who asked that young offenders be given different punishments than adults

8) _____ social and economic level between the wealthy and the poor

9) _____ complete end to slavery

10) _____ period of widespread evangelism during the 1790s

## TRUE/FALSE

**Write T if a statement is true or F if it is false. If a statement is false, explain why.**

11) _____ The most famous conductor on the Underground Railroad was Harriet Tubman.

_____

Call to Freedom

12) _____ William Holmes McGuffey was the leading voice for education reform in the mid-1800s.

_____

13) _____ Sarah Grimké, Lucretia Mott, and Elizabeth Cady Stanton were the most important leaders of the women's movement in the mid-1800s.

_____

14) _____ The American Colonization Society was formed to send freed African Americans to start colonies in Africa.

_____

15) _____ The Seneca Falls Convention and the Declaration of Sentiments marked the first time that American women organized for their rights as a group.

_____

16) _____ Ralph Waldo Emerson, Emily Dickinson, and John Greenleaf Whittier were important figures in the transcendentalist movement.

_____

17) _____ Prior to the arrival of new Catholic immigrants, most people living in the United States were Protestants.

_____

18) _____ The works of Nathaniel Hawthorne, Herman Melville, and Edgar Allan Poe were recognized by Europeans as distinctly American in style and content.

_____

19) _____ Frederick Douglass published the *Liberator* and helped found the American Anti-Slavery Society.

_____

20) _____ Between one and two hundred thousand Irish and German immigrants arrived in the United States between 1840 and 1860.

---

**MULTIPLE CHOICE**
**For each of the following, circle the letter of the best choice.**

21) The most popular poet of the mid-1800s was

   a. John Greenleaf Whittier.          c. Emily Dickinson.
   b. Henry Wadsworth Longfellow.       d. Walt Whitman.


22) Cities grew rapidly during the mid-1800s due to

   a. immigration and the migration of rural inhabitants to urban areas.
   b. the growth of the middle class.
   c. the enriched cultural life available in cities.
   d. an increase in adequate public services such as police and fire protection.


23) The New York African Free School began educating New York City's African American

   a. 1820.          b. 1832.          c. 1848.          d. 1787.


24) One of the most important antislavery publications of the mid-1800s was

   a. *American Slavery As It Is,* by Theodore Weld and the Grimké sisters.
   b. *North Star,* by Frederick Douglass.
   c. *Clotel,* by William Wells Brown.
   d. *Incidents in the Life of a Slave Girl,* by Harriet Jacobs.


25) The common-school movement got its name from

   a. providing girls schools and boys schools with the same books.
   b. building all schools the exact same way.
   c. the effort to have all children, regardless of their class or background, educated in a common place.
   d. educating free African Americans in the South just like white children.


26) Former slaves who contributed to the abolitionist cause were

   a. Horace Mann, Margaret Fuller, and Henry David Thoreau.
   b. Josiah Quincy, Angelina Grimké, and Charles Finney.
   c. Lucretia Mott, Walt Whitman, and Elizabeth Cady Stanton.
   d. Frederick Douglass, Sojourner Truth, and Harriet Tubman.

Call to Freedom

27) "What I must do is all that concerns me, not what the people think," wrote

a. Walt Whitman in *Leaves of Grass.*
b. Henry David Thoreau in *Walden.*
c. Ralph Waldo Emerson in "Self-Reliance."
d. John Greenleaf Whittier in *Poems Written During the Progress of the Abolition Question.*


28) During the 1840s, more than 1 million people died of starvation and disease in Ireland as a result of

a. a cholera epidemic.
b. a potato blight.
c. unsanitary living conditions in urban tenements.
d. crop failures and an inadequate clean water supply.


29) One of the most important African American leaders of the 1800s was

a. David Walker.
b. Henry Highland Garnet.
c. Frederick Douglass.
d. Robert Purvis.


30) The textbook most often used in public schools in the mid-1800s was

a. McGuffey's *Reader.*
b. *The Pilgrim's Progress.*
c. the *New England Primer.*
d. the Bible.


31) Organizers of the Seneca Falls Convention wrote a

a. Declaration of Sentiments modeled on the language of the Magna Carta.
b. Declaration of Sentiments modeled on the language of the Declaration of Independence.
c. Declaration of Rights modeled on the language of the Bill of Rights.
d. Declaration of Rights modeled on the language of the Virginia Declaration of Rights.


32) Angelina and Sarah Grimké joined the antislavery movement after they

a. rejected the views of their southern, slaveholding family.
b. attended the World Anti-Slavery Convention in London.
c. heard Sojourner Truth's convincing lecture in Philadelphia.
d. met William Lloyd Garrison, who hired them to edit the *Liberator.*


33) Some white northerners opposed the abolition movement because they

a. thought slavery was a good way to protect African Americans.
b. thought that slavery was essential for the southern economy and culture.
c. did not believe in equal treatment for African Americans, and thought that freed slaves would take jobs away from white northerners.
d. opposed colonizing African Americans in Liberia.

34) The romantic movement drew upon the idea that

      a. all social change should be motivated by religious faith.
      b. only love could solve social problems.
      c. reason, not emotion, should motivate true art.
      d. each individual brings a unique perspective to the world.

35) Many leaders of reform movements were

      a. poor white women.           c. enslaved African Americans.
      b. poor white men.             d. middle class women.

36) Two leading male supporters of the women's movement were

      a. Horace Mann and Ralph Waldo Emerson.
      b. William Lloyd Garrison and Frederick Douglass.
      c. Robert Owen and John Fairfield.
      d. Horace Greeley and Theodore Weld.

37) The Perkins Institute, a school for blind people, was established by

      a. Samuel Gridley Howe.       c. Catharine Beecher.
      b. Thomas Gallaudet.          d. Mary Lyon.

38) Most Irish immigrants settled in towns and cities in

      a. midwestern states.
      b. Ohio, Michigan, and Wisconsin.
      c. Massachusetts, New York, Pennsylvania, and New Jersey.
      d. New England.

39) The abolitionists' goal of emancipation was very difficult to achieve because of

      a. southern opposition to the Underground Railroad.
      b. racism, fear, and the South's economic dependence on slavery.
      c. northern opposition to the colonization movement.
      d. David Walker's justification of force to resist oppression, a view that frightened many white Americans.

40) Poet Emily Dickinson

      a. established a utopian community in New Harmony, Indiana.
      b. participated in the Brook Farm experiment.
      c. was one of the most popular romantic poets during her lifetime.
      d. published only two poems during her lifetime.

41) In the 1800s, Lucy Stoners were women who

    a. kept their maiden names after they married.
    b. believed women and men should receive equal pay for equal work.
    c. opposed the women's rights movement.
    d. believed that women should try to influence society in the home, not in public.


42) The first college to accept African Americans was

    a. Harvard.        b. Dartmouth.        c. Oberlin.        d. Avery.


43) Many native-born American citizens felt threatened by immigrants because

    a. immigrants tended to be more violent than native-born Americans.
    b. immigrants tended to be Protestants.
    c. immigrants wanted their native languages taught in public schools.
    d. of their different cultural and religious backgrounds, and the economic competition they presented.


44) The American romantic writer who created the modern detective story was

    a. Nathaniel Hawthorne.        c. Ann Sophia Stephens.
    b. Edgar Allan Poe.        d. Herman Melville.


45) A leading reformer in the temperance movement was

    a. Abraham Lincoln.        c. Lyman Beecher.
    b. Harriet Beecher Stowe.        d. Catharine Beecher.


46) The greatest accomplishment of the women's rights movement of the mid-1800s was the

    a. presentation of the Declaration of Sentiments to the New York legislature.
    b. attendance of hundreds of women at the Seneca Falls Convention.
    c. recognition given Angelina Grimké by the Massachusetts legislature.
    d. active involvement of thousands of women in women's rights issues.


47) One of the most vocal opponents of the African colonization movement was

    a. Elijah Lovejoy.        c. George Fitzhugh.
    b. David Walker.        d. Robert Purvis.


48) German immigrants were most likely to

    a. work as artisans in towns and cities in the Northeast.
    b. work as laborers in Chicago.
    c. become farmers in Ohio, Michigan, and Wisconsin.
    d. establish businesses in towns and cities in Ohio and Pennsylvania.

49) Which group encouraged people to follow their personal beliefs, rely more on their own judgment, and rise above the material things in life?

    a. transcendentalist                 c. Shaker communities
    b. utopian communities            d. romantic artists and writers

50) The region that maintained the most schools in the early 1800s was

    a. the West.                         c. the Middle Atlantic states.
    b. the South.                       d. New England.

51) *Woman in the Nineteenth Century* was written in 1845 by

    a. Emily Dickinson.               c. Catharine Beecher.
    b. Margaret Fuller.               d. Ann Sophia Stephens.

52) The New York Tribune became a strong voice for abolition under the leadership of editor

    a. William Lloyd Garrison.        c. Horace Greeley.
    b. John Greenleaf Whittier.       d. Lyman Beecher.

53) Know-Nothings wanted to

    a. elect only native-born citizens to public offices.
    b. prevent Protestants from moving out of unskilled jobs and into better ones.
    c. require immigrants to live in the United States for 10 years before they could become citizens.
    d. exclude Catholics from public office.

54) In 1840 the American Anti-Slavery Society split over the role of

    a. women in the antislavery movement.
    b. free African Americans in the movement.
    c. former slaves in the movement.
    d. foreigners and immigrants in the movement.

55) The purpose of organizations such as the American Temperance Society and the American Temperance Union was to

    a. educate people about the negative effects of alcohol.
    b. outlaw the sale of alcohol.
    c. urge people to give up or to limit the consumption of alcohol.
    d. prevent interstate trade of alcohol.

56) Robert Purvis was one of the leading organizers of the

a. American Anti-Slavery Society, which appealed to Americans' sense of religious principles and conscience.
b. Underground Railroad, a network of people who arranged transportation and hiding places for fugitive slaves.
c. American Colonization Society, which established a colony on the west coast of Africa.
d. Second Great Awakening, which signaled "nothing else than a new beginning of obedience to God."

57) By 1855 African Americans were allowed to attend white schools in

a. New York City.
b. Philadelphia.
c. Boston.
d. Chicago.

58) Many Catholic, Jewish, and Protestant immigrants came from

a. Germany to escape persecution and government control.
b. Ireland to build canals and railroads or to work as miners.
c. Ireland to escape famine and to become farmers in the American Midwest.
d. Germany to work as merchants, supervisors, and clerks in northeastern cities.

59) One of the most important leaders of the Second Great Awakening was

a. Lyman Beecher.
b. Charles Grandison Finney.
c. Henry Highland Garnet.
d. Charles Remond.

60) The social reform effort that encouraged people to use self-discipline to stop drinking hard liquor was the

a. common-school movement.
b. women's rights movement.
c. transcendentalist movement.
d. temperance movement.

## ENHANCED QUESTIONS
**For each of the following, circle the letter of the best choice. Next, expand on the subject by answering the second question in the space provided.**

61) Nativists were

a. Protestants who feared losing their jobs to Catholics.
b. native-born Catholics and Protestants who opposed German immigrants.
c. U.S. citizens who opposed immigration.
d. native-born citizens who feared losing their jobs to Irish immigrants.

How politically successful were nativists in the 1850s?

_____

_____

62) The rise of industry and growth of cities in the Northeast offered new opportunities for

    a. people who owned their own businesses or worked in skilled occupations.
    b. the working class to establish businesses of their own.
    c. immigrants who qualified for jobs held by skilled craftspeople.
    d. the poor to attain wealth doing work that other people avoided.

    Describe this growing social and economic class of people.

    _____

    _____


63) Neal Dow was one of several reformers in the temperance movement who

    a. discouraged women from participating in the movement.
    b. wanted to outlaw the sale of alcohol.
    c. lectured that people who drank alcohol were disobeying God's laws and should not be admitted as members of churches.
    d. wanted immigrants to take a temperance pledge before entering the country.

    How successful was Dow in spreading his message?

    _____

    _____


64) During the early 1800s abolitionists disagreed about

    a. the degree of equality that African Americans should have in society.
    b. when the end to slavery should take place in the United States.
    c. equal rights for enslaved Africans and free African Americans.
    d. whether African Americans were justified in using force to resist oppression.

    How did Robert Finley respond to this disagreement?

    _____

    _____


65) The fight for women's rights was turned into a political movement by

    a. Lucy Stone.            c. Dorthea Dix.
    b. Elizabeth Cady Stanton.     d. Susan B. Anthony.

    How successful was this leader in gaining new rights for women?

    _____

    _____

Call to Freedom

# GRAPHIC IMAGE QUESTIONS
**Examine the image, and then answer the following questions.**

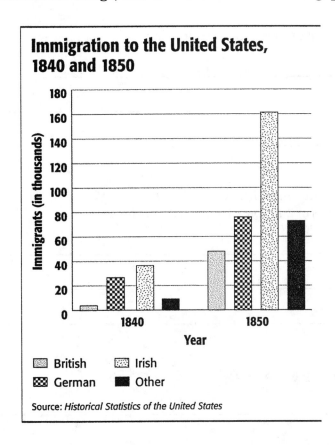

**Immigration to the United States, 1840 and 1850**

Immigrants (in thousands)

Year

British    Irish
German    Other

Source: *Historical Statistics of the United States*

66) What was the smallest immigrant group to the United States in 1850?

_____

67) By about how many thousands did the number of German immigrants to the United States increase between 1840 and 1850?

_____

68) By about how many thousands did the numer of Irish immigrants to the United States increase between 1840 and 1850?

_____

## SHORT ANSWER
**Write a brief answer for each of the following.**

69)  What challenges did cities face as a result of their rapid development?

_____

_____

_____

70)  When and why did Dorothea Dix and Angelina Grimké speak before the Massachusetts legislature? Which speaker initiated reform that spread to the national level?

_____

_____

_____

71)  For what reasons did some Americans oppose slavery?

_____

_____

_____

72)  How did women's involvement in other reform movements affect the women's rights movement?

_____

_____

_____

73)  What were the three main goals of the women's rights movement?

_____

_____

_____

Call to Freedom

**ESSAY**
**On a separate sheet of paper, write an essay on one of the following.**

74) Explain why the teachings of the Second Great Awakening launched changes in society. Then compare how the Second Great Awakening influenced transcendentalists and reform movement activists to develop different views about improving society.

75) Describe how Horace Mann, Catharine Beecher, Emma Willard, and Mary Lyon contributed to education reform in the mid 1800s. Also explain how women and African Americans were especially affected by reforms.

# ANSWER KEY

1) Seneca Falls Convention

2) Thomas Gallaudet

3) American Anti-Slavery Society

4) tenements

5) utopian community

6) emancipation

7) Josiah Quincy

8) middle class

9) abolition

10) Second Great Awakening

11) T

12) F
Horace Mann was the leading voice for education reform.

13) F
Lucy Stone, Susan B. Anthony, and Elizabeth Cady Stanton were the most important.

14) T

15) T

16) F
Important figures in this group were Emerson, Margaret Fuller, and Henry David Thoreau.

17) T

18) T

19) F
William Lloyd Garrison published the *Liberator* and helped found the American Anti-Slavery Society.

20) F
More than 3 million people immigrated from Ireland and Germany during this time.

21) b

22) a

23) d

24) a

25) c

26) d

27) d

28) b

29) c

30) a

31) b

32) a

33) c

34) d

35) d

36) d

37) a

38) c

39) b

40) d

41) a

42) c

43) d

44) b

45) c

46) d

47) b

48) c

49) a

50) d

Call to Freedom

51) b

52) c

53) a

54) a

55) c

56) b

57) c

58) a

59) c

60) d

61) c
Nativists formed the Know-Nothing Party that won several state elections during the 1850s.

62) a
This middle class was a social and economic level between the wealthy and the poor.

63) b
Dow's efforts resulted in the Maine Law of 1851 which made selling alcohol illegal in the state. Banning the sale of alcohol became a major goal of reformers. By 1855, twelve other states had laws banning liquor.

64) a
Finley started the American Colonization Society because he thought that sending freed African Americans to Africa would prevent conflicts between the races in the United States. The society established the colony of Liberia where 12,000 African Americans eventually settled.

65) d

Organizing a system to cover every area of New York State, Anthony collected more than 6,000 signatures to petition for a new property rights law. In 1860 the state legislature passed a law giving married women ownership of their wages and property.

66) British

67) about 50,000

68) about 120,000

69) Cities were noisy and crowded. Urban residents, particularly immigrants, often lived in tenements. Epidemics were common because cities lacked clean water, public health regulations, or sanitary ways to dispose of garbage and human waste. Cities also became centers of criminal activity due to inadequate police protection. Fire protection was also poor.

70) In 1838 Grimké became the first woman to speak before a legislature in the United States. She addressed both the issue of slavery and the question of women's role in politics. In 1841 Dix visited a jail and reported her findings in a fiery speech calling for better treatment of mentally ill people. The legislature responded by creating special facilities for mentally ill people, separating them from criminals. Dix's reform efforts resulted in the establishment of more than 100 state hospitals for mentally ill people.

71) Some groups, such as the Quakers, opposed slavery on religious grounds. Some ministers of the Second Great Awakening believed that slavery was morally wrong. Other opponents held to the political philosophy that all people are created equal.

72) Women who participated in the abolitionist movement discovered that they had to defend a woman's right to speak in public. Abolitionists' defense of women's role in the antislavery movement led them to write and speak about equal rights for women. With improved education and the experience of working together in reform associations, women gained some of the skills and tactics necessary to effectively organize.

73) Women sought equal educational opportunities, equal pay for equal work, and the abolishment of laws that negatively affected women, such as laws that prevented women from voting or sitting on juries, and laws that prevented married women from having control over their property.

74) Leaders of the Second Great Awakening taught that each individual was responsible for his or her own salvation and that sin was avoidable. Charles Finney called on converts to perform good deeds in their communities. Transcendentalists sought spiritual inspiration from sources other than Christian religion, yet their focus on self-discovery, self-reliance, and personal accountability mirrored the same teachings that renewed believers throughout the country. Transcendentalists attempted to change society from within by changing themselves. Their greatest contributions were their writings that taught others how to achieve a simpler, less materialistic life. Some transcendentalists lived apart from society in order to focus on perfecting their individual natures. Others formed utopian communities that allowed people to pursue spiritual and cooperative lifestyles that were unavailable in the larger society. Social reformers, on the other hand, attempted to change society by changing the views and circumstances of people other than themselves. In an effort to change society, reformers in the temperance movement urged other people to abstain from alcohol, and tried to make the sale of alcohol illegal. Educational reformers broadened educational opportunities for poor children, women, and African Americans. Anti-slavery activists succeeded in raising awareness about the injustices of slavery. Overall, the Second Great Awakening motivated many Americans to change themselves and society without revolution, violence, bloodshed, or rebellion against the government.

75) Horace Mann, the leading voice for education reform, supported the common-school movement, which was the effort to have all children, regardless of class or background, educated in a common place. Mann became Massachusetts's first secretary of education in 1837. His accomplishments included doubling the state's school budget, increasing teachers' salaries, extending the school year, and establishing the first school for teacher training. His writings and ideas spread throughout the nation, and influenced Latin America and Europe as well. His work set the standard for educational reform throughout the United States. Catharine Beecher became one of the most effective women's educational reformers during the early 1800s when few women could obtain an education beyond grade school. Beecher established an all-female academy in Hartford, Connecticut and wrote several well-known essays including *An Essay on the Education of Female Teachers*. Women's educator Emma Willard started the first college-level institution for women in the United States, the Troy Female Seminary. 1837, Massachusetts educator Mary Lyon founded Mount Holyoke Seminary for women. African American students benefited from the common school movement as their existing schools grew, and as cities such as Philadelphia and Boston opened new elementary schools for them. In 1855 Boston began allowing African American students to attend white schools. Also, in the 1830s Oberlin college in Ohio began admitting African Americans and became the first co-educational institution in the United States.

# Chapter 14 Westward Expansion and War

**MATCHING**
**In the space provided, write the term or the name of the person that best fits the description. Choose your answers from the list below. Not all answers will be used.**

| | | |
|---|---|---|
| Tejanos | Bear Flag Revolt | Gadsden Purchase |
| Donner party | prospect | manifest destiny |
| *empresarios* | Mexican Cession | annex |
| forty-niners | Sam Houston | Sutter's Fort |
| Stephen F. Austin | mountain men | Susanna Dickinson |

1) _____ some of the first non-American Indians who journeyed to the Rocky Mountains and beyond

2) _____ declared California an independent republic

3) _____ to take control of

4) _____ colony near the Sacramento River

5) _____ people hoping to find California gold and strike it rich

6) _____ agents who agreed to bring settlers to Texas

7) _____ first president of the Republic of Texas

8) _____ trapped by Sierra Nevada snows on the California Trail

9) _____ to search for gold

10) _____ strip of land that included the southern parts of present-day Arizona and New Mexico

**TRUE/FALSE**
**Write T is a statement is true or F if it is false. If a statement is false, explain why.**

11) _____ Once a year Tejanos met to trade and socialize in an event known as the rendezvous.

_____

12) _____ Most supporters of manifest destiny ignored the fact that American Indians and people of Spanish descent had been living in the West for centuries.

_____

13) _____ Texas became an independent republic in December 1845.

_____

14) _____ Stephen F. Austin brought some of the first American settlers to Texas.

_____

15) _____ The vast majority of California gold miners soon became wealthy land owners.

_____

16) _____ In 1821 a revolutionary army led by Father Hidalgo defeated the Spanish and declared Mexico an independent nation.

_____

17) _____ As a result of the California Gold Rush, San Francisco grew more rapidly than any other city in the world between 1848 and 1850.

_____

18) _____ Santa Anna's 3,000 soldiers fought against some 189 Texan soldiers at the Alamo.

_____

19) _____ In 1849 nearly 100,000 gold-seekers flocked to California in what is know as the California Gold Rush.

_____

20) _____ The Oregon Trail stretched more than 2,000 miles from Independence, Missouri to Santa Fe, New Mexico.

_____

## MULTIPLE CHOICE
**For each of the following, circle the letter of the best choice.**

21) "Fifty-four forty or fight!" referred to the

    a. U.S. claim that the Rio Grande marked the southern border of Texas.
    b. slogan on the flag created by Californians during the Bear Flag Revolt.
    c. U.S. negotiations with Mexico for the Gadsden Purchase.
    d. disputed northern boundary of Oregon Country.

22) Californios were

    a. Mexican citizens living in California.
    b. Spanish colonists in California.
    c. gold-seeking immigrants who came to California in 1849.
    d. forty-niners who declared California an independent republic.

23) The continental boundaries of the United States were finally fixed with the

    a. Gadsden Purchase.
    b. Mexican Cession.
    b. annexation of Texas.
    c. Treaty of Guadalupe Hidalgo.

24) Settlers came to Utah to

    a. prospect for gold.
    b. escape economic hardship.
    c. gain religious freedom.
    d. establish trading centers near the gold strikes.

25) "I shall never surrender or retreat," said

    a. William Travis after Santa Anna's troops surrounded the Alamo.
    b. General Zachary Taylor, claiming California for the United States.
    c. General Winfield Scott at Mexico City.
    d. Santa Anna during the 88-hour bombardment of Veracruz.

26) The Mormon Church leader who led his followers to Utah was

    a. Joseph Smith.
    b. Brigham Young.
    c. Father Hidalgo.
    d. Marcus Whitman.

27) A U.S. Army officer who became a popular hero during the Mexican War was

    a. Stephen Kearny.
    b. Robert Stockton.
    c. John C. Frémont.
    d. Zachary Taylor.

28) The Texan who sent out a call for all Texans to take up weapons against the Mexican government was

    a. William Travis.
    b. Juan Seguín.
    c. Moses Austin.
    d. Stephen F. Austin.

29) Between 1849 and 1853 some 24,000 young men migrated to California from

    a. Mexico.
    b. Central America.
    c. China.
    d. eastern Europe.

30) American merchants were allowed to trade in the Southwest after

    a. Mexico gained independence from Spain in 1821.
    b. Bernardo de Gálvez made peace with the Apache Indians in the late 1700s.
    c. Nicholas Trist negotiated the Treaty of Guadalupe Hidalgo in 1848.
    d. James Gadsden negotiated the Gadsden Purchase in 1853.

31) The capital of the Republic of Texas was

    a. San Antonio.
    b. Houston.
    c. Santa Fe.
    d. El Paso.

32) In 1830 the Church of Jesus Christ of Latter-Day Saints was founded in

    a. Utah by Father Hidalgo.
    b. Salt Lake City by Brigham Young.
    c. western New York by Joseph Smith.
    d. Nauvoo, Illinois by Moses Austin.

33) In the 1840s new settlers replaced the mountain men on the frontier because of

    a. John Jacob Astor's economic losses during the Panic of 1837.
    b. the Adams-Onís Treaty with the Flathead, Nez Percé, and Shoshoni Indians.
    c. boundary disputes between Britain, Russia, Spain, and the United States.
    d. overtrapping and the declining demand for beaver pelts.

34) General Kearny's troops were guided toward San Diego by explorer and army scout

    a. Kit Carson.
    b. John C. Frémont.
    c. Davy Crockett.
    d. Jim Bridger.

35) Texans defended the Alamo during the

    a. Mexican Revolution.
    b. Mexican War.
    c. Texas Revolution.
    d. Bear Flag Revolt.

36) When Mormon pioneers settled near the Great Salt Lake, Utah was part of

    a. the Republic of Texas.
    b. Mexico.
    c. the United States.
    d. Great Britain.

37) In the early 1840s the population of California was made up primarily of

    a. Americans.
    b. Californios.
    c. Mexicans.
    d. American Indians.

38) The majority of American settlers in Texas came from

    a. southern states.                   c. present-day New Mexico.
    b. the Great Lakes region.          d. New York and Illinois.

39) Santa Anna charged almost 400 Texan soldiers with treason and had them executed after the

    a. Texan assault on Veracruz.        c. Battle of Goliad.
    b. United States annexed Texas.    d. Battle of San Jacinto.

40) Many Americans headed west to Oregon Country after losing their jobs, their savings, and their homes during the

    a. Bear Flag Revolt.                c. Texas Revolution.
    b. Panic of 1837.                  d. Mexican War.

41) The Bear Flag Revolt began when

    a. Commodore Sloat seized California for the United States.
    b. Californios created a flag featuring a star and a grizzly bear.
    c. Californios declared California an independent republic.
    d. American settlers near Sutter's Fort revolted against Mexican rule.

42) Tejanos were

    a. Spanish settlers in Texas.       c. American settlers in Texas.
    b. Mexican settlers in California.   d. Indians and mestizos in Texas.

43) Manuel Lisa, Jim Bridger, and Jedediah Smith were

    a. Californios.                   c. mountain men.
    b. defenders of the Alamo.        d. army scouts.

44) President Polk bypassed General Taylor for General Winfield Scott as commander of an invasion of southern Mexico because

    a. Taylor's army had won no victories against Santa Anna.
    b. Polk believed Taylor couldn't win the war and felt threatened by Taylor's popularity among the American people.
    c. Taylor seized Monterey without Polk's permission.
    d. Taylor ignored Polk's order to return to Washington from Mexico City.

45) Texans who defended the Alamo were led by

    a. Stephen F. Austin.          c. William Travis and Jim Bowie.
    b. Sam Houston.             d. Jim Bridger and Davy Crockett.

46) German immigrant Levi Strauss gained his fortune in California by

    a. making durable denim work pants.
    b. operating laundries that had steady customers from the mining camps.
    c. guiding settlers across the Sierra Nevada on the California Trail.
    d. operating a sawmill and trading post at Sutter's Fort.

47) The pro-slavery Whig from Virginia who wanted to extend the political power of the southern slave states by annexing Texas was

    a. James K. Polk.           c. William Henry Harrison.
    b. Andrew Jackson.        d. John Tyler.

48) In 1845 diplomat John Slidell tried to

    a. negotiate a peace treaty with Mexico before Polk called him back to Washington.
    b. purchase California and New Mexico for $30 million.
    c. prevent a massive U.S. assault on Mexico City.
    d. purchase the southern parts of present-day Arizona and New Mexico for $10 million.

49) The principle Mormon settlement in the West was

    a. the mission of Waiilatpu.     c. Salt Lake City.
    b. Lisa's Fort.             d. Santa Fe.

50) In exchange for land in Texas, American settlers had to

    a. become Mexican citizens.
    b. stop practicing polygamy and become members of the Catholic Church.
    c. obey Mexican laws and serve in the Mexican army.
    d. become Mexican citizens, obey Mexican laws, and be loyal to the Catholic Church.

51) Texans forced Santa Anna to sign a treaty recognizing Texas's independence after the Battle of

    a. San Jacinto.          c. Gonzales.
    b. Goliad.              d. Monterrey.

52) Skunk Gulch, Hangtown, Git-Up-and-Git, and Dry Gulch were

    a. fur-trading posts on the Columbia River.
    b. California mining camps.
    c. settlements in the Willamette Valley.
    d. Mexican trading posts along the Santa Fe Trail.

53) Mexican officials agreed to the Treaty of Guadalupe Hidalgo after

    a. Veracruz fell to the U.S. Army.    c. U.S. troops captured Mexico City.
    b. the Battle of San Jacinto.      d. Santa Anna was captured.

54) One of the earliest U.S. settlements in Oregon Country was

a. Lisa's Fort, established by Manuel Lisa.
b. Astoria, a fur-trading post founded by John Jacob Astor.
c. Sutter's Fort, established by Swiss immigrant John Sutter.
d. Waiilatpu, a mission established by Marcus and Narcissa Whitman.


55) Congress declared war on Mexico during the presidency of

a. Polk.                           c. Harrison.
b. Jackson.                        d. Tyler.


56) Many Chinese immigrants in California

a. made their fortunes and returned home.     c. worked as woolen spinners and weavers.
b. owned placer mines.                        d. started laundries.


57) During the Texas Revolution, the commander in chief of the Texas army was

a. Juan Seguín.                    c. Sam Houston.
b. Stephen F. Austin.              d. Jim Bowie.


58) Most California gold miners were

a. Californios and European immigrants.       c. mestizos and American families.
b. young, unmarried American men.             d. Tejanos and Mexican War veterans.


59) One of the earliest Rocky Mountain explorers who blazed trails for future generations was

a. Manuel Lisa.                    c. John C. Frémont.
b. Marcus Whitman.                 d. George Donner.


60) The colony called Sutter's Fort was established by an immigrant from

a. Mexico.                         c. China.
b. Germany.                        d. Switzerland.

# ENHANCED QUESTIONS

**For each of the following, circle the letter of the best choice. Next, expand on the subject by answering the second question in the space provided.**

61) The Treaty of Guadalupe Hidalgo

a. resolved Mexican claims to Texas and ceded much of Mexico's northern territory to the United States.
b. required the United States to pay Mexico $5 million for the Mexican Cession.
c. resolved Mexican claims to California and Oregon and established the boundaries of the Mexican Cession.
d. recognized Texas as an independent nation and ceded "land in abundance" to Texas settlers.

What lands were included in the Mexican Cession?

_____

_____

62) The southern branch of the Oregon Trail became known as the

a. Sierra Nevada Trail.          c. Snake River Trail.
b. California Trail.              d. Platte River Trail.

How did the Santa Fe Trail differ from this trail and the Oregon Trail?

_____

_____

63) Mormons were members of the

a. Catholic Church.              c. Protestant Christian faith.
b. Jewish faith.                 d. Church of Jesus Christ of Latter-Day Saints.

Describe the trail that Mormons and other immigrants took West.

_____

_____

64) The Alamo was

    a. headquarters for Mexican government officials in Texas.
    b. an adobe church in the villa of El Paso.
    c. an old Spanish mission in San Antonio.
    d. the capital of the Republic of Texas.

Why did "Remember the Alamo!" become a rallying cry for the Texas Revolution?

_____

_____

65) The Mexican republic was created by

    a. the Mexican Constitution of 1824.
    b. revolutionaries led by Iturbide.
    c. Spanish viceroy Bernardo de Gálvez.
    d. Indians and mestizos who revolted against Spanish rule.

What were the borders of the Mexican republic?

_____

_____

Call to Freedom

# GRAPHIC IMAGE QUESTIONS

**Examine the image, and then answer the following questions.**

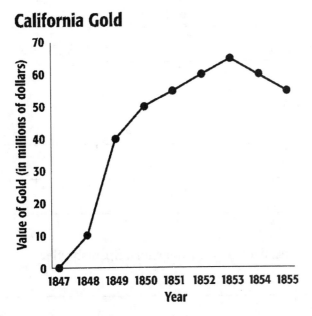

**California Gold**

Source: *Statistical Abstract of the United States,* 1892

66) In what year was the most gold mined?

_____

67) About how much more gold was mined in 1855 than in 1849?

_____

68) How did the amount of gold mined change after 1853?

_____

## SHORT ANSWER
**Write a brief answer for each of the following.**

69) Define manifest destiny and explain how its supporters justified their beliefs.

_____

_____

_____

70) Describe the successes and failures of Marcus and Narcissa Whitman.

_____

_____

_____

71) What did the Mormons accomplish in the West?

_____

_____

_____

72) Why did Father Hidalgo lead Indians and mestizos in a revolt against Spanish rule?

_____

_____

_____

73) Why did conflicts arise between Mexican officials and American settlers in Texas?

_____

_____

_____

**ESSAY**
**On a seperate sheet of paper, write an essay on one of the following.**

74) What was life like on the Oregon Trail?

75) What was life like in mining camps and towns during the California gold rush?

Call to Freedom

ANSWER KEY

1) mountain men

2) Bear Flag Revolt

3) annex

4) Sutter's Fort

5) forty-niners

6) *empresarios*

7) Sam Houston

8) Donner party

9) prospect

10) Gadsden Purchase

11) F
Mountain men met in the rendezvous.

12) T

13) F
In December 1845 Texas became a state.

14) T

15) F
The vast majority of miners did not become rich.

16) F
Father Hidalgo began a revolt but was defeated and executed in 1811. In 1821 officer Agustín de Iturbide defeated the Spanish and declared Mexico an independent nation.

17) T

18) T

19) T

20) F
The Santa Fe Trail ran from Independence, Missouri, to Santa Fe, New Mexico. The Oregon Trail stretched more than 2,000 miles across the northern Great Plains and the Rocky Mountains, then forked at the Snake River in present-day Idaho. Most settlers followed the northern branch to Oregon. The southern branch became known as the California Trail.

21) d

22) b

23) a

24) c

25) a

26) b

27) d

28) d

29) c

30) a

31) b

32) c

Call to Freedom

33) d

34) a

35) c

36) b

37) d

38) a

39) c

40) b

41) d

42) a

43) c

44) b

45) c

46) a

47) d

48) b

49) c

50) d

51)  a

52)  b

53)  c

54)  b

55)  a

56)  d

57)  c

58)  b

59)  a

60)  d

61)  a

The Mexican Cession included the present-day states of California, Nevada, and Utah, and parts of Arizona, Colorado, New Mexico, Kansas, Oklahoma, and Wyoming.

62)  b

The Santa Fe Trail ran from Independence, Missouri, to Santa Fe, New Mexico. Unlike the Oregon and California Trails, the Santa Fe Trail was not often used as a migration route, but as a trade route.

63)  d

The route that thousands of Mormons traveled was called the Mormon Trail. Mormons fleeing persecution in the East and the Midwest were joined by immigrants from Great Britain and Scandinavia. The Mormon Trail closely paralleled the Oregon Trail.

64)  c

In 1836, some 189 Texan soldiers at the Alamo were surrounded by Santa Anna's 3,000 soldiers. When the Mexican army attacked the Alamo on March 6, the Mexicans killed all the Texans, sparing only the lives of the few women and children.

ANSWER KEY

65) a

Its borders stretched beyond those of present-day Mexico to include the current U.S. states of Arizona, California, Nevada, New Mexico, Texas, and Utah. The republic also contained parts of what are now Colorado, Kansas, Oklahoma, and Wyoming.

66) 1853

67) about $15 million more

68) It declined.

69) Manifest destiny was the belief that the United States was meant to expand across the continent to the Pacific Ocean and that nothing could stop such growth from taking place. Belief in manifest destiny encouraged Americans to build settlements beyond the borders of the United States. Many Americans reasoned that taking land away from Mexicans and American Indians was acceptable because these groups had not put the land to good use. Others argued that American settlers would improve the West by spreading democracy to the peoples they conquered.

70) The Whitmans traveled to Oregon Country of the Pacific Northwest to convert the local Cayuse Indians to Christianity. In part their mission failed because the Whitmans wanted the Cayuse to give up their traditional customs, as well as change their religion. However, many settlers gained rest and shelter at the Whitmans' Waiilatpu mission. In 1847 settlers brought measles to the Cayuse, and an epidemic killed many Cayuse children. Blaming the Whitmans, a group of Cayuse attacked the mission and killed the Whitmans and more than 10 other people.

71)  In the dry climate where water was valuable, Mormons developed a code whereby the first person to use water had full rights to its use. However, the water had to be used for beneficial purposes such as farming, mining, or manufacturing. In any dispute over water use, the good of the community would outweigh the interests of individuals. Young's new approach helped the Mormons make the desert bloom with crops. It also created the basis for modern water laws throughout the West.

72) Hidalgo and his followers hoped that independence would lead to better living conditions for many poor Indians and mestizos living in New Spain. Hidalgo also wanted to abolish slavery, end unfair taxes on Indians, and take riches away from wealthy colonists to give to poorer ones.

73) Mexico required settlers in the province of Coahuila y Tejas to become citizens, obey Mexican laws, and be loyal to the Catholic Church. American settlers rarely followed Mexican laws or conditions of settlement. Many newcomers brought slaves, even though Mexico had abolished slavery. When Mexican officials learned that Stephen F. Austin was encouraging Texans to organize a separate Mexican state government, they imprisoned him for a year and a half. After his release, Austin encouraged Texans to take up weapons against the Mexican government.

74) The pioneers' journey usually began in late spring, and lasted for six to eight months. Most of the groups were young families who traveled in wagon trains and faced great obstacles. Shortages of food, water, and supplies were a constant problem. Pioneers also faced rough weather and natural barriers such as rivers and mountains. Pioneers traveled from dawn until dusk, with many adults walking much of the way to conserve their animals' strength. At the end of each day, women unpacked wagons, cooked dinner, cleaned up, washed and mended clothes, and tended to children. Men looked after livestock, hunted for food, and scouted the trail ahead. Along the way, American Indians often helped pioneers by acting as guides or by supplying food in exchange for trade goods.

75) Gold mining was a difficult, time-consuming effort. Early miners frequently banded together to prospect for gold. In the days before courts were established, competition for claims led to many arguments, even violent disputes. Most miners were placer miners who used pans, a rocker/cradle device, or a sluice box to wash gold nuggets out of loose rock and gravel along rivers and streams. To extract gold from hard rock, mining companies dug shafts and tunnels to reach gold deposits buried in the hills. Mining camps sprang up wherever a number of people gathered to look for gold, and disappeared when the gold ran out. Miners of many cultural backgrounds filled the camps. Some miners observed an informal system of law and order while others lived rowdy and often dangerous lives. The few women who lived in mining camps made good money cooking meals, washing clothes, and operating boardinghouses. However, most miners were young, unmarried men. All had to pay high prices for basic necessities because the large amounts of gold in circulation caused severe inflation in California.

# Chapter 15 A Divided Nation

**MATCHING**
**In the space provided, write the term or the name of the person that best fits the description. Choose your answers from the list below. Not all answers will be used.**

| | | |
|---|---|---|
| Roger B. Taney | James Buchanan | Charles Sumner |
| secession | Constitutional Union Party | Henry Clay |
| Abraham Lincoln | Colonel Robert E. Lee | Preston Brooks |
| popular sovereignty | Henry Ward Beecher | Free-Soil Party |
| Jefferson Davis | Harriet Beecher Stowe | |

1) _____ wrote the powerful antislavery novel *Uncle Tom's Cabin*

2) _____ victor in the 1860 presidential race

3) _____ allowed voters in a particular territory to decide whether they wanted to ban or permit slavery

4) _____ led the squad of U.S. Marines that captured John Brown at Harpers Ferry

5) _____ Kentucky senator who proposed the Compromise of 1850

6) _____ Chief Justice who wrote the majority opinion in the *Dred Scott* decision

7) _____ the act of formally withdrawing from the Union

8) _____ party formed in 1848 by antislavery northerners when Democrats and Whigs refused to address the slavery issue

9) _____ Mississippi senator whom delegates of seven seceded states elected as president of their new nation

10) _____ retired from politics after a southern congressman beat him unconscious in the Senate chamber

## TRUE/FALSE
**Write T if a statement is true or F if it is false. If a statement is false, explain why.**

11) _____ The Fugitive Slave Act made it a federal crime to assist runaway slaves and allowed slaves to be arrested in states and territories where slavery was legal.

_____

12) _____ The popularity of Lincoln's Freeport Doctrine helped get him elected to the Senate in 1858.

_____

13) _____ Four political parties—Northern Democrats, Southern Democrats, Republicans, and Whigs—had presidential candidates in the election of 1860.

_____

14) _____ The victor in the 1848 presidential election had no political experience and had never voted in any election.

_____

15) _____ John Brown's murder of five pro-slavery men who lived along Pottawatomie Creek in eastern Kansas became known as the Pottawatomie Massacre.

_____

16) _____ The Republican Party was formed in 1854 to prevent the spread of slavery to the West.

_____

17) _____ John Brown's raid also became known as the Sack of Lawrence.

_____

18) _____ The Free-Soil Party endorsed the Wilmot Proviso.

_____

19) _____ In 1857 the U.S. Supreme Court ruled that Congress had no right to ban slavery in the territories.

_____

20) _____ As a result of the Kansas-Nebraska Act, Congress approved the construction of a railroad from Chicago to the Pacific in 1854.

_____

## MULTIPLE CHOICE
**For each of the following, circle the letter of the best choice.**

21) The political party focused exclusively on respecting the Constitution, preserving the Union, and enforcing the nation's laws was called

    a. the Republican Party.     c. the Free-Soil Party.
    b. the Democratic Party.     d. the Constitutional Union Party.

22) Although Franklin Pierce was from New England, southerners trusted him because he

    a. promised to honor the Compromise of 1850 and enforce the Fugitive Slave Act.
    b. had fought alongside Jefferson Davis and Winfield Scott in the Mexican War.
    c. promised to start the Pacific railroad from New Orleans rather than Chicago.
    d. had attended southern schools and understood the South's economic concerns.

23) Congress approved the Compromise of 1850 only after

    a. Henry Clay agreed to allow California to enter the Union as a slave state.
    b. Texas agreed to surrender its land claims in Utah and New Mexico.
    c. Millard Fillmore became president when Taylor died in office.
    d. Daniel Webster delivered a stirring speech in support of compromise.

24) The Supreme Court ruled that Dred Scott was not free because

    a. Scott was not a U.S. citizen.
    b. his status, as free or slave, depended on the laws of Missouri where his owner lived.
    c. he was, until death, the property of Dr. and Mrs. John Emerson and their descendants.
    d. he had not been given his freedom while living in free territory.

25) After nearly 60 northern Democrats voted for the Kansas-Nebraska bill,

    a. citizens attended protest meetings and sent anti-Nebraska petitions to Congress.
    b. southern Democrats refused to cooperate with them.
    c. only seven of them retained their House seats in the next election.
    d. the Northern Democratic party fell apart completely during the 1860 election.

26) The question of whether California would be admitted to the Union as a free state or a slave state

a. was the primary argument in the Lincoln-Douglas debates.
b. led Stephen Douglas to introduce a bill in Congress that would divide the state according to the restrictions of the Missouri Compromise.
c. was answered by Stephen Douglas in what became known as the Freeport Doctrine.
d. led Henry Clay to offer a series of proposals to address all of the current issues of sectional disagreement.

27) Some northerners reacted to the hanging of John Brown by

a. celebrating his death with speeches against violence.
b. passing laws to outlaw abolition meetings.
c. freeing their slaves.
d. mourning his death by ringing church bells and draping public buildings in black.

28) Stephen Douglas introduced the Kansas-Nebraska bill after southern senators

a. agreed to abandon their plan for a southern railroad route if the new territory west of Missouri was opened to slavery.
b. promised to support his plan if he would support a railroad route from New Orleans across Texas to southern California.
c. agreed to side with President Taylor on the California question.
d. promised to honor the Compromise of 1850 and the Fugitive Slave Act.

29) While the South Carolina secession convention was underway, a plan to save the Union was introduced in Congress by

a. Alexander Stephens.        c. John Bell.
b. John J. Crittenden.        d. John C. Breckinridge.

30) Democrats lost support in the north when the public learned about U.S. plans to

a. acquire the slave territory of Cuba.
b. send weapons to pro-slavery citizens in eastern Kansas.
c. expand the Fugitive Slave Act by raising commissioners' fees from $10 to $50 for each suspected fugitive they returned to the South.
d. prevent fugitive slaves from crossing into Canada to avoid the reach of the Fugitive Slave Act.

31) In what became known as the Freeport Doctrine, Stephen Douglas upheld

a. the power of the Supreme Court to decide all matters pertaining to slavery.
b. popular sovereignty over the power of the Supreme Court.
c. his party's promise that slavery "shall grow no larger."
d. his party's pledge not to abolish slavery where it already existed.

Call to Freedom

32) The first state to formally withdraw from the Union was

    a. Mississippi.                          c. South Carolina.
    b. Alabama.                             d. Texas.

33) Eli Thayer formed the Massachusetts Emigrant Aid Company to help

    a. send weapons to free-soil settlers in Kansas.
    b. northern families move to Kansas and make the territory antislavery.
    c. settlers move from "Bleeding Kansas" to the safety of Nebraska.
    d. antislavery settlers purchase more land in Kansas and Nebraska.

34) The Whig Party fell apart completely because of the

    a. *Dred Scott* decision.             c. Compromise of 1850.
    b. rise of the Republican Party.       d. Kansas-Nebraska bill.

35) Although Winfield Scott was a southerner, he lost support in the South because he

    a. had freed all his slaves during the Mexican War.
    b. had spent most of his life on military duty outside the South.
    c. failed to come out in complete support of the Compromise of 1850.
    d. was strongly disliked by Zachary Taylor and John C. Calhoun.

36) The Fugitive Slave Act was enacted into law

    a. by Congress, as a part of the Compromise of 1850.
    b. in free states where special commissioners were paid by state legislatures.
    c. according to the requirements of the Kansas-Nebraska Act.
    d. by Congress, pending approval of state legislatures in free states.

37) The U.S. Constitution does not directly address the issue of

    a. slavery.                             c. sectionalism.
    b. secession.                         d. popular sovereignty.

38) After John Brown seized the federal arsenal in Harpers Ferry,

    a. enslaved African Americans from surrounding communities hastened to join him.
    b. he distributed arms and ammunition to slaves and free African Americans who enlisted in his army.
    c. he hoped slaves in the region would join him, but none did.
    d. a squad of U.S. Marines arrived to protect Brown's army from the southern militia.

39) The Confederate States of America was

a. established by the South Carolina legislature in December 1860.
b. a loosely organized, unofficial confederation of seven seceded states.
c. formed in 1861 by Jefferson Davis, Alexander Stephens, and Robert E. Lee.
d. a new nation with its own constitution and officials.

40) At their first presidential nominating convention, the Republican Party chose as their candidate

a. John C. Frémont.
b. Abraham Lincoln.
c. William Seward.
d. John J. Crittenden.

41) When California applied for statehood, the majority of its residents wanted California to enter the Union

a. as a slave state.
b. as a free state.
c. according to the requirements of the Missouri Compromise.
d. as a slave state only if New Mexico was admitted as a free state.

42) The U.S. Supreme Court ruled that Congress could not prohibit someone from taking slaves into a federal territory because

a. federal territories were ruled by popular sovereignty.
b. slaves were not citizens under the U.S. Constitution.
c. the status of slaves depended on the laws of each state.
d. slaves were considered property.

43) In 1854 Stephen Douglas introduced a bill in Congress that would divide the

a. Mexican Cession into two regions, one banning slavery and the other allowing it.
b. Mexican Cession into one territory with slavery allowed south of latitude 36° 30'.
c. remainder of the Louisiana Purchase into two territories, each to determine the slavery question by popular sovereignty.
d. remainder of the Louisiana Purchase into one territory with slavery prohibited north of latitude 36° 30'.

44) Lincoln's election to the presidency angered many southerners because Lincoln

a. did not campaign in the South and did not carry a single southern state.
b. won with less than 20 percent of the overall popular vote.
c. opposed the existence of slavery in new territories as well as in the South.
d. had boasted during a speech in Freeport, Illinois, that he would abolish slavery once in office.

Call to Freedom

45) Pennsylvanian James Buchanan was able to carry 14 of the 15 slave states in 1856 because

a. he campaigned more in the South than in any other region.
b. southerners considered Buchanan "as reliable as Calhoun himself" on the slavery issue.
c. he had avoided the Kansas-Nebraska controversy while serving as ambassador to Great Britain.
d. he defended South Carolina senator Andrew Pickens Butler during Brooks's and Sumner's fight in the Senate chamber.

46) Alarmed by the number of accused fugitive slaves who were returned to the South after 1850,

a. abolitionists stormed northern jails and freed dozens of accused fugitives.
b. thousands of African Americans in the North fled to Canada to avoid capture.
c. commissioners in the North refused to decide any case not tried by jury.
d. Martin R. Delany organized an emigrant aid company to help free African Americans.

47) The Democratic Party split in two in 1860 because

a. northern and southern members of the party refused to convene in either a southern or a northern city.
b. a party split seemed the only way to take votes from the Republican candidate.
c. Stephen Douglas refused to run on the same ticket with John C. Breckinridge.
d. northern and southern members of the party could not agree on a single candidate.

48) A South Carolina congressman resorted to violence in the Senate chamber in 1856 when a northern congressman

a. criticized the actions of pro-slavery people in Kansas and Nebraska.
b. directed personal insults at the President, other congressmen, and the state of South Carolina.
c. stated that the nation would be better off "were John C. Calhoun blotted from existence."
d. defended the right of John Brown to murder pro-slavery men at Pottawatomie Creek. move to Kansas.

49) The majority of the justices who heard the Dred Scott case

a. were from the South.
b. were from the North.
c. had either attended West Point with the Chief Justice, or had served under him during the Mexican War.
d. believed that a future Court ruling would prohibit states from banning slavery.

50) Many northerners who were otherwise indifferent to the troubles of slaves in the South

    a. were outraged by the *Dred Scott* decision.
    b. were so strongly influenced by *Uncle Tom's Cabin* that they began secretly sending money to help John Brown recruit, train, and supply a small army.
    c. objected to the lack of a trial by jury for accused fugitives, and the method of payment given commissioners.
    d. stormed a Boston jail in order to rescue accused fugitive Martin R. Delany.

51) During a stirring speech before Congress, Daniel Webster

    a. asked that the southern states be allowed "to separate and part in peace."
    b. demanded the admission of California "directly, without conditions, without qualifications, and without compromise."
    c. claimed that the admission of California as a free state would destroy the balance between the two sections of the country.
    d. criticized abolitionists for their agitation in the North, and scolded southerners who spoke for disunion.

52) Lincoln challenged Douglas to a series of debates in Illinois to

    a. gain voter recognition alongside his popular opponent.
    b. focus on the issue of race rather than on the extension of slavery.
    c. stress that the central issue in their campaign involved the abolishment of slavery in the South.
    d. stress that he was not in favor of social and political equality for African Americans.

53) After Preston Brooks beat Charles Sumner on the Senate floor,

    a. many people in the South nicknamed the attacker, "Bully Brooks."
    b. northerners tried to expel Brooks from the House of Representatives, but failed.
    c. Sumner was fined $300 and was expelled from the House of Representatives.
    d. Brooks and Sumner apologized to each other in front of members of the Senate.

54) Which presidential candidate opposed the spread of slavery but promised not to support abolishing it where it already existed?

    a. Stephen Douglas        c. John Bell
    b. Abraham Lincoln        d. John C. Breckinridge

55) Dred Scott sued for his freedom, saying that he had become free

    a. after his owner died.
    b. after purchasing his freedom from his owner.
    c. when he lived in free territory.
    d. when he moved from Missouri to Kansas.

56) John C. Calhoun asked Congress to allow the slave states to peacefully leave the Union if

a. California was admitted as a free state in 1850.
b. Dred Scott was declared free by the Supreme Court in 1857.
c. Stephen Douglas was elected president in 1860.
d. Abraham Lincoln was elected president in 1860.

57) Presidential candidate John C. Breckinridge was a slaveholder who

a. had served as a popular vice president under Franklin Pierce.
b. avoided taking a stand on the spread of slavery to the West.
c. pledged to lead the southern states out of the Union if a Republican were elected president.
d. did not believe a Republican victory in the election justified disunion.

58) "Beecher's Bibles" referred to

a. Kansas freesoilers who were former members of Reverend Henry Ward Beecher's New York congregation.
b. 50 rifles sent by Reverend Beecher and his congregation to freesoilers in Kansas.
c. members of John Brown's army recruited from Reverend Beecher's congregation.
d. 76 copies of *Uncle Tom's Cabin* sent from Reverend Beecher's congregation to pro-slavery members of Congress.

59) After hearing Dred Scott's petition for freedom, Taney ruled that

a. under the Constitution, free or enslaved African Americans had no rights in free territories.
b. the Missouri Compromise restriction on slavery north of 36° 30' was constitutional.
c. as a non-citizen, Scott did not have the right to file suit in federal court.
d. Congress had the right to ban slavery in the territories.

60) The last-minute effort to prevent southern states from seceding was called the

a. Compromise of 1850.
b. Charleston Compromise.
c. Wilmot Proviso.
d. Crittenden Compromise.

**ENHANCED QUESTIONS**

**For each of the following, circle the letter of the best choice. Next, expand on the subject by answering the second question in the space provided.**

61) An 800-member pro-slavery posse sacked Lawrence, Kansas in 1856

  a. to avenge the Pottawatomie Massacre.
  b. after a grand jury in Lawrence indicted pro-slavery government leaders for treason.
  c. because Lawrence was where leaders of the free-soil legislature lived.
  d. and murdered five leaders of the free-soil legislature who lived in Lawrence.

  How did people in Kansas respond to the Sack of Lawrence?

  _____

  _____

62) Harriet Beecher Stowe wrote her powerful antislavery novel

  a. after reading slave narratives and meeting fugitive slaves in Ohio where she lived.
  b. as a result of the cruelties of slavery she witnessed during her childhood in Louisiana.
  c. during a tour of the South where she witnessed the cruelties of slavery.
  d. after secretly interviewing hundreds of slaves in Louisiana and South Carolina.

  How was Stowe's novel viewed in the North and the South?

  _____

  _____

63) In 1860 some northerners and southerners, many of them former Whigs, formed the

  a. Free Soil Party.                    c. Anti-Secession Party.
  b. Constitutional Union Party.         d. Republican Party.

  What was this party's platform?

  _____

  _____

Call to Freedom

64) To aid the abolitionist cause, John Brown decided in 1858 to

a. burn Topeka, Kansas, seat of the pro-slavery Kansas legislature.
b. raid a federal arsenal in Virginia, arm local slaves, lead them to freedom, and kill or capture any white southerner who stood in the way of his plan.
c. burn the federal arsenal in Harpers Ferry, and lead local slaves to freedom in Canada.
d. raise an army to burn Topeka, then march to Harpers Ferry, seize federal weapons from the local armory, and incite a slave revolt that would sweep the South.

What happened when Brown attempted to carry out his plan?

_____

_____


65) In 1846 U.S. Representative David Wilmot introduced a proposal that

a. died in the Senate, where the North had more power.
b. met the approval of the House, which had a southern majority, but died in the Senate.
c. stated that voters in a particular territory could decide whether they wanted to ban or permit slavery.
d. stated that neither slavery nor involuntary servitude shall ever exist in any part of the Mexican Cession.

Name this proposal, and explain how it related to the issue of sectionalism.

_____

_____

| The Election of 1860 | | | |
| --- | --- | --- | --- |
| | Electoral Vote | Popular Vote | % of Pop. Vote |
| Lincoln | 180 | 1, 865, 593 | 39.8 |
| Douglas | 12 | 1, 382, 713 | 29.5 |
| Breckinridge | 72 | 848, 356 | 18.1 |
| Bell | 39 | 592, 906 | 12.6 |

66) What were the total number of electoral votes in the presidential election of 1860?

_____

67) Which candidate had the greatest number of electoral votes, and which candidate had the greatest percentage of the popular vote?

_____

68) Which candidate had the second greatest number of electoral votes? Which candidate had the second greatest percentage of the popular vote?

_____

**SHORT ANSWER**
Write a brief answer for each of the following.

69) Of the five main parts of the compromise proposed by Henry Clay, what actually became law in the Compromise of 1850?

_____

_____

_____

Call to Freedom

70) Why did Lecompton and Topeka both become seats of government in Kansas in 1855?

_____

_____

_____

71) What three issues were before the Supreme Court as it reviewed Dred Scott's case?

_____

_____

_____

72) How did Stephen Douglas respond when Lincoln pointed out that a contradiction existed between the Democrats' belief in popular sovereignty and the *Dred Scott* decision?

_____

_____

_____

73) How did a four-man contest work in Lincoln's favor during the 1860 presidential race?

_____

_____

_____

**ESSAY**
**On a separate sheet of paper, write an essay on one of the following.**

74) Describe the measures taken by Congress to negotiate conflicts over slavery and maintain the Union between 1850 and 1860. Include a discussion of the Wilmot Proviso, the Compromise of 1850, the Fugitive Slave Act, and the Kansas-Nebraska Act.

75) Describe how southern secessionists used U.S. Supreme Court decisions, the Constitution, and the Declaration of Independence in justifying their decision to secede from the Union. Also explain why southern secessionists believed that their only choice was to leave the Union in 1860 and 1861.

# ANSWER KEY

1) Harriet Beecher Stowe

2) Abraham Lincoln

3) popular sovereignty

4) Colonel Robert E. Lee

5) Henry Clay

6) Roger B. Taney

7) secession

8) Free-Soil Party

9) Jefferson Davis

10) Charles Sumner

11) F
   This act allowed slaves to be arrested even in areas where slavery was illegal.

12) F
   Douglas's Freeport Doctrine helped Douglas win the Senate seat in 1858.

13) F
   The four parties who nominated candidates in 1860 were the Northern Democrats, Southern Democrats, Republicans, and the Constitutional Union Party.

14) T

15) T

16) T

# ANSWER KEY

17) F
John Brown's raid refers to his attack on Harpers Ferry, Virginia in 1859.

18) T

19) T

20) F
The proposal to build the Pacific railroad was lost amid the controversy over the Kansas-Nebraska bill, and would not see Congressional approval until 1862.

21) d

22) a

23) c

24) b

25) c

26) d

27) d

28) a

29) b

30) a

31) b

32) c

33) b

34) d

35) c

36) a

37) b

38) c

39) d

40) a

41) b

42) d

43) c

44) a

45) c

46) b

47) d

48) b

49) a

50) c

Call to Freedom

# ANSWER KEY

51) d

52) a

53) b

54) b

55) c

56) a

57) d

58) b

59) c

60) d

61) c
First, John Brown decided it was his duty to avenge the attack on Lawrence. Brown led a company of seven along Pottawatomie Creek, pulled five pro-slavery men from their homes, and killed them in the Pottawatomie Massacre. During the months that followed the Sack of Lawrence and the Pottawatomie Massacre, Kansas collapsed into a state of civil war. Around 200 people were killed during events in "Bleeding Kansas."

62) a
*Uncle Tom's Cabin* sparked outrage in the South where it was labeled a "filthy, lying book" and where Stowe was criticized for making up many scenes in the book. The book inspired many northerners to oppose slavery more strongly.

63) b
It recognized "no political principles other than the Constitution of the country, the Union of the states, and the enforcement of the laws."

ANSWER KEY

64) b

After two years of fundraising and recruiting, Brown had an army of only 22 men. After they seized the federal arsenal at Harpers Ferry, slaves were reluctant to join him. White southerners opened fire on Brown's men, killing eight. After the survivors barricaded themselves in the firehouse, U.S. Marines stormed the building and killed or captured the rest. Within six weeks, Brown and some of his men were convicted of treason, murder, and inciting slave rebellion, and were hanged on order of the court.

65) d

This proposal was called the Wilmot Proviso, and demonstrated the growing sectionalism over the issue of slavery in the United States.

66) 303

67) Lincoln

68) Breckinridge, Douglas

69) California entered the Union as a free state. The rest of the Mexican Cession was divided into two territories in which the status of slavery would be decided by popular sovereignty. Texas surrendered its land claims in exchange for federal financial assistance. The slave trade was abolished in the nation's capital. A new fugitive slave law was enacted.

70) The first territorial legislature was located at Lecompton. After thousands of pro-slavery men crossed the border from Missouri, voted in Kansas, and returned home, the Lecompton legislature had an overwhelming pro-slavery majority that quickly passed strong pro-slavery legislation. In response, antislavery Kansas boycotted the Lecompton legislature and created their own legislature in Topeka.

71) First, the Court had to rule on whether Scott was a U.S. citizen and thus able to sue in federal court. Second, the Court needed to decide if the time he lived on free soil made him free. Third, the Court had to determine if it was constitutional to prohibit slavery in parts of the Louisiana Purchase, a ruling that would affect the legality of the Missouri Compromise.

72) Douglas said he didn't think it mattered because the people have the lawful means to introduce it or exclude it as they please, for the reason that slavery cannot exist a day or an hour anywhere, unless it is supported by local police regulations." This response became known as the Freeport Doctrine.

73) The four-man contest was really a pair of two-man contests. Lincoln challenged Douglas for the North's electoral votes; Bell and Breckinridge competed for the South's electoral votes. As a result, Breckinridge and Bell split the electoral votes of all the slave states except Missouri, which Douglas won. Lincoln won the election with 180 of 183 electoral votes in the free states.

74) The issue of slavery had been a divisive issue in Congress since 1820 when the Missouri Compromise satisfied the South's intent to extend slavery beyond the slave states. The Wilmot Proviso, which failed to become law, demonstrated the growing sectionalism in Congress and in the country. In 1850 southern representatives such as Calhoun and Davis stated that the slave states could not remain in the Union if the balance of slave and free states was disturbed. Henry Clay proposed a compromise, called the Compromise of 1850, that called for admitting California as a free state but allowed the rest of the Mexican Cession was organized into two territories in which the issue of slavery would be decided by popular sovereignty. This satisfied southern states and kept them loyal to the Union. The Compromise of 1850 also produced a new slave law, the Fugitive Slave Act, that made it a federal crime to assist runaway slaves and allowed them to be arrested even in areas where slavery was illegal. This law enraged northerners, but pacified southerners who did not want their slaves to escape without capture.
A few years after this act was passed, northerners and southerners got into a conflict over whether the Pacific railroad would originate in free territory or slave territory. To settle this dispute, Stephen Douglas introduced what became the Kansas-Nebraska Act. This act proposed that the remainder of the Louisiana Purchase be divided into two territories in which slavery would be decided by popular sovereignty. This compromise satisfied the South's desire to open slavery in the remainder of the Louisiana Purchase. However, antislavery and pro-slavery settlers in Kansas soon clashed violently over the slavery issue.

75) In the *Dred Scott* decision Chief Justice Taney concluded that African Americans, whether slave or free, were not citizens under the U.S. Constitution. Taney pointed out that the Constitution's Fifth Amendment said no one could "be deprived of life, liberty, or property, without due process of law" and that slaves were considered property. This decision reinforced slaveholders' views that they had the legal right to own slaves, and the U.S. government should not interfere with their right. After John Brown's raid, southern whites—slaveholders and non-slaveholders alike—felt genuinely frightened by the prospect of another act of violence that would threaten their lives and property. Finally, Lincoln's victory in the 1860 presidential election convinced many southern whites that Republicans would move to abolish slavery in the South once they gained political power. Southerners feared that abolishing slavery would destroy the social and economic fabric of the South. In defending their proposal to secede, southerners pointed out that each of the original states had voluntarily joined the Union by holding a special convention to ratify the Constitution. Surely, they reasoned, states could also leave the Union by the same process—the will of a popular convention—whenever they wished. After South Carolina seceded in December 1860, six other states followed South Carolina in seceding from the Union. The seceded states formed a new nation dedicated to preserving the southern way of life.

# Chapter 16 The Civil War

**MATCHING**

**In the space provided, write the term or the name of the person that best fits the description. Choose your answers from the list below. Not all answers will be used.**

ironclads
Henry Bellows
Dorothea Dix
contrabands
Robert Anderson

William Tecumseh
Sherman
Thomas J. Jackson
J.E.B. Stuart
blockade runners

David G. Farragut
Copperheads
Clara Barton
Joseph E. Johnston

1) _____ Confederate general who led his cavalry completely around the Union lines in 1862

2) _____ nurse who became a captain in the Confederate army

3) _____ peace Democrats who opposed the war

4) _____ Union commander who refused to leave Fort Sumter

5) _____ earned the name "Stonewall" at the First Battle of Bull Run

6) _____ Union naval officer from Tennessee who sailed boldly past Confederate forts and captured New Orleans

7) _____ coordinated the efforts of tens of thousands of volunteers who served in the U.S. Sanitary Commission

8) _____ nurse whose work formed the basis for what would later become the American Red Cross

9) _____ small, fast vessels that delivered important supplies to the Confederacy

10) _____ escaped slaves

## TRUE/FALSE
**Write T if a statement is true or F if it is false. If a statement is false, explain why.**

11) _____ The last battle of the Civil War was fought April 9, 1865 at Appomattox Courthouse, Virginia.

_____

12) _____ African Americans were not allowed to serve as soldiers in the Union army until 1863.

_____

13) _____ Kentucky, Maryland, and Missouri voted against secession and did not join the Confederacy.

_____

14) _____ The Union victory in the First Battle of Bull Run dashed Confederate hopes of quickly and easily winning the war.

_____

15) _____ American Indians fought on the side of the Union in the Battle of Pea Ridge.

_____

16) _____ The Battle of Antietam was the bloodiest single-day battle of the Civil War, and in U.S. military history.

_____

17) _____ The nearly 15,000 soldiers who took part in Pickett's Charge succeeded in destroying the center of the Union line at Gettysburg.

_____

18) _____ The largely pro-Union population of western Virginia formed their own state—West Virginia—in 1863.

_____

19) _____ About twice as many Civil War soldiers died of disease than died in combat.

_____

20) _____ With the capture of New Orleans, the Union gained complete control of the Mississippi River.

_____

## MULTIPLE CHOICE
**For each of the following, circle the letter of the best choice.**

21) The first major clash of Union and Confederate armies took place in July 1861 along a creek called

    a. Antietam, in Maryland.
    b. Bull Run, near Manassas, Virginia.
    c. Shiloh, in Tennessee.
    d. Chickahominy, near Richmond, Virginia.

22) The most important figure in the western theater was

    a. Ulysses S. Grant.
    b. David G. Farragut.
    c. John C. Pemberton.
    d. John B. Hood.

23) In 1863 President Lincoln expressed the Union's new sense of confidence and commitment in his

    a. First Inaugural Address.
    b. Second Inaugural Address.
    c. Gettysburg Address.
    d. Emancipation Proclamation.

24) The fort that controlled the entrance to Charleston harbor—one of the South's key seaports—was Fort

    a. Sumter.
    b. Henry.
    c. Donelson.
    d. Defiance.

25) The Emancipation Proclamation was an order that

    a. demanded immediate freedom for all African Americans enslaved by officers in the Confederate Army.
    b. freed all enslaved African Americans in the United States.
    c. freed all the Confederacy's slaves immediately.
    d. called for all slaves in areas rebelling against the Union to be freed on January 1, 1863.

Call to Freedom

26) General Robert E. Lee took charge of the Confederate army in Virginia

    a. after Lincoln called for 75,000 volunteers to suppress the southern rebellion.
    b. soon after he resigned from the U.S. Army in 1861.
    c. after General Joseph Johnston was severely wounded in the spring of 1862.
    d. as Union troops marched from Washington, D.C. into Virginia in June 1861.


27) The Civil War was the most costly conflict in American history, with around

    a. 300,000 Americans losing their lives.    c. 570,000 Americans losing their lives.
    b. 450,000 Americans losing their lives.    d. 620,000 Americans losing their lives.


28) Suspending habeas corpus allowed President Lincoln to silence the Copperheads by

    a. withdrawing constitutional protection against unlawful imprisonment.
    b. allowing the forcible draft of all able men into the army.
    c. excluding Copperheads from the draft that called all able men into the army.
    d. enforcing the Emancipation Proclamation in the Midwest as well as in the South.


29) After the fall of Fort Sumter, Lincoln

    a. put out a call for 75,000 men to enlist in the U.S. Army.
    b. called on state governors to provide a total of 75,000 militiamen to help put down the rebellion in the South.
    c. initiated the first of several drafts that enlisted 75,000 men in the Union army.
    d. invited men outside the seceded states to join a Union army that needed 75,000 soldiers.


30) News of the Emancipation Proclamation

    a. inspired General McClellan to employ a better strategy against Lee's army.
    b. pleased William Lloyd Garrison and his followers, who had argued for emancipation for more than two decades.
    c. came as a surprise to the U.S. Congress whose members had not sanctioned the act.
    d. displeased both northern Democrats and abolitionists who disliked the scope of the act.


31) Lee's army forced McClellan's army to retreat from the Richmond area as a result of the

    a. First Battle of Bull Run.    c. Seven Days' Battles.
    b. Second Battle of Bull Run.    d. Battle of Antietam.


32) In July 1862, Congress authorized the Union army to enlist African American volunteers as

    a. infantrymen.    c. scouts.
    b. cavalrymen.    d. laborers.


33) Union commanders set out to capture New Orleans after the Union victory

    a. in the Battle of Shiloh.    c. in the Battle of Pea Ridge.
    b. at Nashville.    d. at Fort Donelson.

34) Virginia, North Carolina, Tennessee, and Arkansas joined the Confederacy

   a. after Lincoln stated in his inaugural address that he intended to preserve the Union.
   b. to support the South Carolina militia in its attack on Fort Sumter.
   c. after Lincoln called for 75,000 militia members to fight the Confederate forces.
   d. when Robert E. Lee issued a call for volunteers to join the Confederate army.

35) As states chose sides in April 1861,

   a. Delaware's governor refused to send troops to help subdue the southern states.
   b. few slaveholders in Delaware supported secession.
   c. Delaware held a special secession convention before it seceded on April 23.
   d. the majority of slaveholders at Delaware's secession convention voted for secession.

36) Pope's army fell apart due to Lee and Jackson's daring maneuvers in the

   a. Seven Days' Battles.                    c. Second Battle of Bull Run.
   b. First Battle of Bull Run.                d. Battle of Gettysburg.

37) In early 1864, Lincoln entrusted supreme command of the Union armies in the East to

   a. Ulysses S. Grant.                        c. George Meade.
   b. William Tecumseh Sherman.                d. Irvin McDowell.

38) Lee hoped to gain international recognition for the Confederacy when he launched an
   offensive that ended in defeat at

   a. Vicksburg.                               c. Petersburg.
   b. Shiloh.                                  d. Gettysburg.

39) In 1861 the Confederate capital was moved from

   a. Charleston, South Carolina to Montgomery, Alabama.
   b. Montgomery, Alabama to Richmond, Virginia.
   c. Richmond, Virginia to Charleston, South Carolina.
   d. Montgomery, Alabama to Baltimore, Maryland.

40) During Sherman's March to the Sea, his destination was the port city of

   a. Charleston.                              c. Wilmington.
   b. New Orleans.                             d. Savannah.

41) Lee hoped that a victory on Union soil in 1862 would break northern morale and

   a. end the war quickly.
   b. convince Lincoln to rescind the Emancipation Proclamation.
   c. persuade European powers to offer aid to the South.
   d. encourage Maryland and Pennsylvania to join the Confederacy.

42) Targeting military as well as civilian economic resources to destroy an opponent's ability to fight is

a. cotton diplomacy.
b. total war.
c. habeas corpus.
d. guerilla warfare.

43) Starving residents and Confederate soldiers resorted to eating horses, dogs, and rats during the

a. Siege of Vicksburg.
b. Seven Days' Battles.
c. Siege of Petersburg.
d. spring of 1865.

44) Many volunteers who answered Lincoln's call for 75,000 troops were motivated by

a. higher salaries as soldiers than they would earn in northern factories.
b. the opportunity to serve under Mexican War heroes such as U.S. Grant.
c. hatred for slaveholders in the South.
d. a sense of duty to help preserve the government of the United States.

45) Through cotton diplomacy, the South tried to

a. finance the war with state allotments gained from cotton sales in Europe.
b. win foreign support, particularly from Great Britain.
c. break the northern blockade by shipping cotton to France.
d. gain the support of Copperheads who favored the continuation of slave labor in the South.

46) The Union navy wanted to blockade the South to

a. prove that the Union was in a superior position to conduct naval warfare.
b. prevent British ships from supplying arms and supplies to the Confederacy.
c. cut off trade that financed the Confederacy's war effort.
d. encourage naval officers to remain loyal to the Union.

47) In 1864 Sherman destroyed southern railways, bridges, crops, and livestock

a. on orders from Lincoln to "make Georgia howl."
b. in retaliation for Lee's invasion of Pennsylvania in 1863.
c. to speed the end of the war by breaking the South's will to fight.
d. to prove that his military skills exceeded those of McDowell, McClellan, Pope and Meade.

48) The 1861 draft led to resentment among poor southerners because

a. most poor southerners abhorred slavery and did not want to fight to support its existence.
b. the draft excluded those who owned a large number of slaves.
c. the majority of poor southerners did not have slaves at home to help their families raise crops and tend livestock.
d. the draft excluded men in border states that helped finance the war effort.

49) Many volunteers who willingly answered the south's call for troops were motivated by

    a. the attack on their homeland by northern outsiders.
    b. admiration for southern military leaders such as Lee, Jackson, and Stuart.
    c. the Confederate government's promise of a horse, a uniform, and ample rations for each man who enlisted.
    d. a chance to rise through the ranks and achieve prominence in the Confederate government.

50) More than 3,000 women served the Union as paid nurses under the leadership of

    a. Clara Barton.               c. Eliza Andrews.
    b. Sally Louisa Tompkins.      d. Dorothea Dix.

51) With the fall of Atlanta in 1864, the South lost

    a. its ability to wage total war against Sherman.      c. the war in the western theater.
    b. a vital railroad junction and center of industry.    d. the war in the eastern theater.

52) The Emancipation Proclamation received popular support in

    a. Italy.                c. France.
    b. Germany.          d. Britain and France.

53) American Indians who fought in the Battle of Pea Ridge

    a. hoped that Confederate leaders would grant the Indian nations greater independence than the Union had.
    b. were motivated by Lincoln's promise to grant land to Indians who fought for the Union.
    c. were labeled as contrabands by Union soldiers who fought beside them.
    d. won international attention for their bravery and their contributions to the Union cause.

54) Lee agreed to sign surrender documents at Appomattox Courthouse after

    a. Sherman threatened to wage total war on Virginia.
    b. realizing that his troops had no more will left to fight.
    c. receiving Grant's assurance that southern soldiers could keep their horses and weapons and not be tried for treason.
    d. receiving Jefferson Davis's telegram stating that "all is lost."

55) Many Copperheads were

    a. southern Democrats who opposed the war.
    b. northern Democrats who favored total war.
    c. northern abolitionists who opposed the pro-slavery views of Clement L. Vallandigham.
    d. midwesterners who sympathized with the South and opposed abolition.

56) The Union gained control of Kentucky and much of Tennessee with the

a. fall of Fort Henry and Fort Donelson and the surrender of Nashville.
b. surrender of Pemberton's forces to General Grant at Vicksburg.
c. victory of Grant's outnumbered forces over the Confederates in the Battle of Shiloh.
d. surrender of Louisville and Nashville to Farragut's forces in 1862.

57) Some poor immigrants in the North who feared losing their jobs to African Americans after the war

a. attacked Union soldiers marching through Baltimore in 1861.
b. participated in antidraft riots in New York City in 1863.
c. seized an Erie Canal boat in 1864 and forced its crew to take them West where few African Americans lived.
d. disclosed the Underground Railroad's secret stations to agents seeking fugitive slaves.

58) Union voters re-elected Lincoln in a landslide after the

a. Emancipation Proclamation went into effect.
b. Battle of Gettysburg.
c. capture of Atlanta.
d. capture of Savannah.

59) For most of the war, the 180,000 African American soldiers who fought with the Union

a. received less pay than their white counterparts.
b. competed for inclusion in the 54th Massachusetts Infantry.
c. served with distinction in the western theater.
d. were allowed to vote in Congressional elections but not in the presidential election of 1864.

60) Clashes between Union and Confederate forces took place as far west as

a. Fort Smith, Arkansas.
b. Broken Bow, Nebraska.
c. El Paso, Texas.
d. Glorieta Pass, New Mexico.

**ENHANCED QUESTIONS**
**For each of the following, circle the letter of the best choice. Next, expand on the subject by answering the second question in the space provided.**

61) In 1861 Lincoln offered command of the Union forces to U.S. Army officer

a. William Tecumseh Sherman.
b. David G. Farragut.
c. Robert E. Lee.
d. J.E.B. Stuart.

Why did this officer decline Lincoln's request?

_____

_____

62) The first woman to receive a license to practice medicine was Dr.

    a. Dorothea Dix.                              c. Clara Barton.
    b. Elizabeth Blackwell.                 d. Mary Ashton Livermore.

How did she contribute to the care of Union soldiers?

_____

_____

63) In March 1861, Lincoln pledged that he would

    a. call for 75,000 volunteers to keep order in the South.
    b. declare war if the Confederacy seized federal property in the South.
    c. not attack the South or try to abolish slavery.
    d. not interfere with the Confederacy's plan to establish their own nation.

Describe the event on April 12, 1861, that changed Lincoln's purpose.

_____

_____

64) During the clash of the ironclads in Hampton Roads, Virginia,

    a. Confederate naval officers mocked the *Merrimack* as "a tin can on a shingle!"
    b. John Ericsson's design for a rotating gun turret helped the *Virginia* defeat the *Monitor*.
    c. the *Virginia* bombarded the *Monitor* with powerful cannons, forcing it to withdraw.
    d. the *Monitor* forced the *Virginia* to withdraw.

What was the significance of this naval battle?

_____

_____

65) As Lee's army crossed into Maryland in September 1862, Union soldiers

    a. stumbled across a copy of Lee's battle plan wrapped around some cigars.
    b. captured three of Hood's infantrymen who disclosed Lee's battle plan.
    c. in Sharpsburg, Maryland overheard the war conference between Lee and Jackson.
    d. hid in a Confederate supply wagon where they discovered Lee's battle maps.

Describe the results of this Union advantage in the battle that soon followed.

_____

_____

Call to Freedom

## GRAPHIC IMAGE QUESTIONS
**Examine the image, and then answer the following questions.**

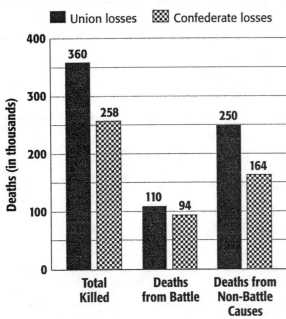

**Lives Lost in the Civil War, 1861–1865**

■ Union losses  ▨ Confederate losses

Source: *Encyclopedia of American History*

66) Which side suffered the greatest number of deaths in the Civil War?

_____

67) Did the Confederates suffer more deaths due to battle or non-battle causes?

_____

68) How many thousand more lives did Union forces lose in battle compared with Confederate forces?

_____

## SHORT ANSWER
**Write a brief answer for each of the following.**

69) Name the key advantages that the North and the South had at the beginning of the war.

_____

_____

_____

70) Describe Lincoln's strategy in announcing his intention to free the South's slaves.

_____

_____

_____

71) What was the strategic importance of the border states?

_____

_____

_____

72) What role did the 54th Massachusetts Infantry play in the war?

_____

_____

_____

73) Why did the Battle of Gettysburg represent a key turning point in the war?

_____

_____

_____

**ESSAY**
**On a separate sheet of paper, write an essay on one of the following.**

74) Describe the strategies of the North and the South as the war began. Explain how these strategies changed as Union leadership was transferred from different generals.

75) Describe the impact of the war on civilians and families in the North and in the South.

Call to Freedom

ANSWER KEY

1)  J.E.B. Stuart

2)  Sally Louisa Tompkins

3)  Copperheads

4)  Robert Anderson

5)  Thomas J. Jackson

6)  David G. Farragut

7)  Henry Bellows

8)  Clara Barton

9)  blockade runners

10) contrabands

11) F
Although Lee surrendered his troops to Grant at Appomattox Courthouse on April 9, 1865, no battle was fought on that day.

12) T

13) T

14) F
The First Battle of Bull Run was a Confederate victory.

15) F
The Indians fought on the side of the Confederacy in this battle.

16) T

17) F

General Picket lost his entire division in the unsuccessful charge.

18) T

19) T

20) F

The capture of Vicksburg earned the Union complete control of the Mississippi.

21) b

22) a

23) c

24) a

25) d

26) c

27) d

28) a

29) b

30) d

31) c

32) d

Call to Freedom

# ANSWER KEY

33)  a

34)  c

35)  b

36)  c

37)  a

38)  d

39)  b

40)  d

41)  c

42)  b

43)  a

44)  d

45)  b

46)  c

47)  c

48)  b

49)  a

50)  d

51)  b

52)  d

53)  a

54)  c

55)  d

56)  a

57)  b

58)  c

59)  a

60)  d

61)  c
Although Lee personally opposed slavery and secession, he felt his first loyalty was to his home state, Virginia.  He felt he could not fight against his birthplace and its people.

62)  b
In April 1861 Dr. Blackwell created the Women's Central Association of Relief.  Members of this group then helped pressure Lincoln to form the U.S. Sanitary Commission that sent volunteers, bandages, medicines, and food to Union army camps and hospitals.

63)  c
When federal troops refused to surrender Fort Sumter to South Carolina forces, Confederate guns opened fire on Fort Sumter.  The attack on Fort Sumter stunned the North and persuaded Lincoln to call for troops to put down the rebellion in the South.

# ANSWER KEY

64) d

The *Monitor*'s victory saved the Union fleet and ensured the continuation of the blockade. The clash of the ironclads also signaled a revolution in naval warfare—the days of wooden warships powered by wind were drawing to a close.

65) a

McClellan used the information to plan a counterattack against Lee's army. The Union army met the Confederates along Antietam Creek in Maryland. Although costly to both sides, Antietam was an important victory for the Union. Lee lost nearly a third of his troops, and his northward advance had been stopped.

66) Union

67) Non-Battle Causes

68) 16 thousand

69) The North had a much larger population, more money, a better railroad network for efficient movement of troops and supplies, and most of the nation's factories—particularly those that could produce uniforms, gunpowder, and weapons. The South had a large number of talented officers, and the advantage of defending itself on its own soil until the federal government and the northern people grew tired of the war.

70) Lincoln feared that such an act might weaken public support for the war. He also knew he lacked constitutional authority to abolish slavery on his own. He decided to use his power as commander in chief of the armed forces to issue a military order freeing slaves in areas controlled by the Confederacy—and waited until a strong Union victory allowed him to make his announcement from a position of strength.

71) Kentucky and Missouri dominated key stretches of the Ohio and Mississippi Rivers, respectively. Maryland and Delaware separated the federal capital of Washington from the rest of the North.

72) In July 1863, this regiment—consisting mainly of free African Americans—played a key role in the capture of Fort Wagner in South Carolina. The 54th became the most famous African American regiment of the war.

73) The Union victory—combined with Grant's capture of Vicksburg on the same day—renewed northern confidence that the war could be won.

74) The North's two-part plan was to blockade southern seaports to strangle the South's economy, and to gain control of the Mississippi River, dividing the Confederacy and cutting its internal communications. Many northern leaders also wanted to attack Richmond. The Confederacy's strategy was to defend itself against northern attacks and wear down the Union's will to fight. The main Confederate offensive plan focused on seizing Washington. The South also tried to win foreign support through cotton diplomacy. These strategies were carried out at sea, and in the eastern and western theaters. During the first two years of war, the North suffered from weak, hesitant leadership while the South's more capable leaders won victories at First and Second Bull Run, and in the Seven Days' Battles where the southern cavalry literally ran circles around the Union Army. Lincoln removed McDowell from command after his defeat at First Bull Run. In 1862 McClellan twice failed to take Richmond. When Pope's army fell apart at the Second Battle of Bull Run, Lee adopted a more aggressive strategy designed to take the war into the North. Again McClellan hesitated after the Union victory at Antietam, and Lincoln named Meade commander of Union forces in the East. Under Meade's leadership, the Union army turned the tide at Gettysburg while Grant was achieving the North's strategic goals in the western theater.

   After the summer of 1863, the South abandoned its offensive strategy while the North—spurred by victories and stronger leaders—intensified its offense. The South was weakening not in ability, but in resources: money, men, and supplies. Its early victories had failed to gain the foreign support that would have helped finance the war. The North discovered that its strategy of taking control of the Mississippi River was not enough; the North had to advance into the heart of the Confederacy with a mighty offensive in the eastern theater. Impressed with Grant's successes in the West, President Lincoln transferred him to the critical eastern theater and made him supreme commander. While Grant and Lee faced each other during the siege of Petersburg, Sherman waged total war on Georgia—a strategy that broke the South. [General Sheridan simultaneously waged total war on Virginia by destroying the Shenandoah Valley, the breadbasket of the Confederacy.] Lee did not have the resources to continue fighting, and was compelled to surrender to Grant in April, 1865. The North's strategy to blockade the South had also succeeded. However, its aggressive leadership on land led more to total victory than did the blockade.

Call to Freedom

75) The Civil War split the nation on a personal as well as national level. Especially in the border states, members of the same family often joined opposing sides. Even President Lincoln's wife had four brothers who fought for the Confederacy. These differences added to the anxiety that civilians and families at home suffered during four years of war. Families in the North suffered separation from loved ones who fought far away, on foreign soil, in a climate they were unaccustomed to. Families on both sides suffered when their loved ones were captured and held as prisoners of war in such places as Andersonville [and Elmira] where conditions were deplorable. In the South, the Union blockade took a heavy toll on civilians. The value of Confederate money dropped as prices of daily necessities such as food, clothing, and medicine rose dramatically. Basic items such as bread became too expensive for most people to afford. Civilians on both sides also adapted to new roles by performing vital tasks in factories and other areas. When northern farmers and industrial workers left for war, women replaced them at their work. In the South, women ran farms and plantations. African American families were often pawns of war as they waited to see which side would win—and which side would decide their future. In the South, enslaved people continued to work in towns and on plantations, hoping for a Union victory but living in uncertainty. Poor people in the North were frightened by the possibility of a Union victory that might result in a migration of freed African Americans who would seek jobs in the North. Poor people in the South detested a "rich man's war, a poor man's fight" when the draft forced men to leave their families to fight for the continuation of an institution—slavery—that they did not embrace. People in the South also suffered as their homeland was devastated by war. At war's end, bitterness still lingered in both the North and the South, while the South's lands and economy lay in ruins. Peace at Appomattox did not guarantee internal peace for northern and southern families who lost loved ones to civil war, or for southerners who lost their homes and heritage to a conquering enemy.

# Chapter 17 Reconstruction

**MATCHING**

**In the space provided, write the term or the name of the person that best fits the description. Choose your answers from the list below. Not all answers will be used.**

| | | |
|---|---|---|
| Radical Republicans | sharecropping | Reconstruction Acts |
| *Plessy* v. *Ferguson* | Compromise of 1877 | Civil Rights Bill of 1875 |
| George Washington Cable | Fifteenth Amendment | Jim Crow laws |
| Thaddeus Stevens | Freedmen's Bureau | |
| Redeemers | Thirteenth Amendment | |

1) _____ ended Reconstruction by removing the last federal troops from the South

2) _____ gave African American men the right to vote

3) _____ laws that enforced segregation in the southern states after 1881

4) _____ wrote novels about the African American community in New Orleans and protested racial prejudice in the South

5) _____ series of laws that required southern states to support the Fourteenth Amendment and give African American men the right to vote

6) _____ made slavery illegal throughout the United States

7) _____ separate-but-equal ruling that gave segregation the backing of the Supreme Court

8) _____ provided relief for poor African Americans and poor white Americans in the South

9) _____ allowed African Americans to sue private businesses for discrimination

10) _____ congressional minority led by Thaddeus Stevens and Charles Sumner

**TRUE/FALSE**
**Write T if a statement is true or F if it is false. If a statement is false, explain why.**

11) _____ The purpose of Reconstruction was to reunite the country and to build a southern society not based on slavery.

_____

12) _____ President Johnson's plan for Reconstruction was similar to Lincoln's proposed plan.

_____

13) _____ Congress required all state legislatures in the post-Civil War South to enact the Black Codes designed by Georgia governor Benjamin Perry.

_____

14) _____ The poll tax required all voters—African American men and white men—to pay a special tax before they could vote.

_____

15) _____ Because the 1863 Emancipation Proclamation had already abolished slavery throughout the United States, the Thirteenth Amendment of 1865 was declared unconstitutional.

_____

16) _____ The Fourteenth Amendment banned many former Confederate officials from holding state or federal offices.

_____

17) _____ During Reconstruction, no African Americans held public office in the former slave states.

_____

18) _____ Most Republicans in 1865 were moderates, while the Radical Republicans were a minority in Congress.

_____

19) _____ Many southern states that had been occupied by Union troops during the Civil War refused to elect new state legislatures under the Ten Percent Plan.

_____

20) _____ In 1865 Congress refused to allow the Freedmen's Bureau to provide relief to poor white southerners.

_____

## MULTIPLE CHOICE
**For each of the following, circle the letter of the best choice.**

21) The main purpose of Reconstruction was to

　　a. divide southern plantations among freedpeople and to found the Freedmen's Bureau.
　　b. reunite the country and to build a southern society not based on slavery.
　　c. grant citizenship to freedmen and to establish Republican legislatures in the South.
　　d. offer amnesty to southerners and to abolish slavery in former Confederate states.

22) Republicans in Congress in 1865 disapproved of southern representatives because

　　a. the representatives refused to divide their plantations among former slaves.
　　b. the representatives supported the Ten Percent Plan and the Republicans did not.
　　c. many of the representatives were former Confederate leaders.
　　d. many Republicans endorsed the Fifteenth Amendment and the representatives did not.

23) Benjamin Wade and Henry Davis proposed a Reconstruction plan that

　　a. Congress viewed as less strict than Lincoln's plan.
　　b. allowed only ten percent of southerners who had supported the Confederacy to vote.
　　c. President Johnson and the Radical Republicans supported.
　　d. Lincoln refused to sign into law.

24) Many white southerners referred to Northern-born Republicans who came South right after the war as

　　a. carpetbaggers.　　　　　　　　　c. Redeemers.
　　b. scalawags.　　　　　　　　　　　d. Radical Republicans.

25) By the end of 1865 all the southern states except Texas had

　　a. created new governments.　　　　c. passed Jim Crow laws.
　　b. established Black Codes.　　　　　d. enacted a poll tax.

26) Many scalawags were

a. sharecroppers who cheated landowners by taking more than their share of the crop.
b. small farmers who had supported the Union during the war and supported the Republicans during Reconstruction.
c. reformers who hoped to make money while rebuilding the southern economy.
d. mill workers who refused to support an agricultural economy.

27) Under the sharecropping system

a. poor African Americans and poor white Americans were able to buy land for the first time.
b. landowners charged sharecroppers a small fee (payable in cash) for the right to farm the land.
c. sharecroppers provided landowners with their labor in exchange for part of the crops.
d. sharecroppers became so prosperous that mill workers left the mills in order to farm.

28) Whose plan would have treated most leniently those Southerners who had supported the Confederacy?

a. Andrew Johnson's plan for Reconstruction
b. Abraham Lincoln's plan for Reconstruction
c. Benjamin Wade and Henry Davis
d. the Radical Republicans

29) Andrew Johnson assumed responsibility for Reconstruction after

a. Congress passed the Fifteenth Amendment.
b. carpetbaggers and scalawags undermined the efforts of the Freedmen's Bureau.
c. southern Democrats agreed to the Compromise of 1877.
d. John Wilkes Booth assassinated President Lincoln.

30) Republicans proposed the Fourteenth Amendment

a. after Federal troops were removed from the South.
b. to guarantee citizenship to freedpeople and American Indians.
c. after the Civil Rights Act of 1875 was declared unconstitutional.
d. to protect new laws enacted by the Civil Rights Act of 1866.

31) At the beginning of Reconstruction, most moderates in Congress

a. did not believe African Americans should receive fair treatment.
b. did not want the federal government to have to force the South to follow the Reconstruction laws.
c. wanted the federal government to require southern states to enact Black Codes.
d. protested that too many southern leaders still had Confederate sympathies.

32) Howard, Hampton, Fisk, and Tougaloo

    a. were African American colleges founded by the Freedmen's Bureau.
    b. were described by Mary Murfree in "The Dancin' Party at Harrison's Cove."
    c. wrote new lyrics to tradition spirituals that had been sung during generations of slavery.
    d. founded the Fisk Jubilee Singers in the late 1800s.

33) Wealthy southerners and former Confederate officials could not receive amnesty unless

    a. their Republican state legislatures agreed to pardon them for all war crimes.
    b. 10 percent of the voters in their state pledged an oath of loyalty to the United States.
    c. Johnson gave them a special presidential pardon.
    d. Federal troops were withdrawn from the South.

34) During the presidential election of 1868, African American votes

    a. contributed to a landslide victory for Andrew Johnson.
    b. helped Ulysses S. Grant and the "party of Lincoln" win a narrow victory.
    c. contributed to an overwhelming defeat for Horatio Seymour.
    d. were not counted in northern states under threats of violence from the Ku Klux Klan.

35) On January 31, 1865, at Lincoln's urging, Congress proposed the Thirteenth Amendment, which

    a. divided the South into five military districts.
    b. gave African American men the right to vote.
    c. banned many former Confederate officials from holding state or federal offices.
    d. made slavery illegal throughout the United States.

36) Thaddeus Stevens and Charles Sumner

    a. led the Radical Republicans, who wanted the federal government to be much more involved in Reconstruction.
    b. offered strong Congressional support for Johnson's Reconstruction plan.
    c. lost support among moderates when President Johnson criticized the Black Codes.
    d. led the commission that supported the election of Samuel J. Tilden by popular vote.

37) The impeachment proceedings against President Johnson

    a. resulted in a failure to convict him, which further increased his power as president.
    b. began with a vote in the Senate, followed by a trial in the House of Representatives.
    c. were carried out under the rules of the Constitution.
    d. gained national attention because of Johnson's popularity with Republicans.

38) The General Amnesty Act of 1872

   a. allowed African Americans to sue private businesses for discrimination.
   b. ended the impeachment proceedings against President Johnson.
   c. placed Radical Republicans in control of most southern states.
   d. allowed most former Confederates to hold public office.

39) Under Johnson's plan for Reconstruction,

   a. the president's cabinet appointed the governor, state officials, and members of Congress for each southern state.
   b. states that had set up their governments under Lincoln's plan were allowed to keep their governments in place.
   c. states governments set up under Lincoln's plan were declared unconstitutional under the Thirteenth Amendment.
   d. federal troops were removed from Arkansas, Louisiana, Tennessee, and Virginia.

40) The Fourteenth Amendment was opposed by

   a. African American voters and most Republicans.
   b. President Johnson and most Democrats.
   c. most citizens, with the exception of American Indians.
   d. Radical Republicans who sought reelection in 1866.

41) The Freedmen's Bureau helped more poor freedpeople than poor white southerners because

   a. financial aid for freedpeople was required by the Civil Rights Act of 1866.
   b. poor white southerners refused to accept help from the Freedmen's Bureau.
   c. Congress disqualified former Confederate soldiers and their families from aid.
   d. the Bureau's limited budget could not provide assistance for all poor people in the South.

42) Under the Fourteenth Amendment, guaranteed citizenship and equal protection under the law were rights denied to

   a. carpetbaggers and scalawags.          c. Ku Klux Klan members.
   b. most former slaves.                    d. American Indians.

43) Reconstruction governments

   a. refused to help the southern economy recover from the war.
   b. effectively prevented the growth of the Ku Klux Klan.
   c. built new railroads, hospitals, and prisons in the South.
   d. were largely controlled by Democrats.

44) After Reconstruction ended, Democrats known as Redeemers

 a. established Black Codes, primarily to prevent African American men from voting.
 b. cut budgets and taxes, eliminated social programs, and limited civil rights for African Americans.
 c. required literacy tests to prevent carpetbaggers and scalawags from voting.
 d. repealed Jim Crow laws that had been initiated by Radical Reconstruction governments.

45) What happened when so many farmers planted cotton after the war?

 a. The supply became too great and the price of cotton dropped.
 b. The price of cotton increased and farmers grew more prosperous.
 c. Banks and landlords pressured farmers to grow different crops.
 d. Textile mills found new and innovative ways to use the excess cotton.

46) Which industry was most successful in the New South?

 a. shipbuilding                      c. textiles
 b. agricultural machinery            d. steel

47) In the mid-1870s support for Reconstruction faded in the North

 a. even though Rutherford B. Hayes made Reconstruction a key issue in the 1876 election.
 b. where Redeemers had gained strength during Grant's presidency.
 c. after the Panic of 1873 hurt the Democratic Party.
 d. where people were growing concerned about economic problems and government corruption.

48) When Republicans chose Ulysses S. Grant as their presidential candidate in the election of 1868, Democrats chose

 a. Andrew Johnson.                   c. Samuel Tilden.
 b. Horatio Seymour.                  d. Rutherford B. Hayes.

49) In 1868 Republicans chose Ulysses S. Grant as their presidential candidate because he was

 a. a war hero with vast political experience.
 b. a moderate whose Reconstruction plan appealed to southern voters.
 c. a political outsider who supported the congressional plan for Reconstruction.
 d. an experienced politician who favored Lincoln's Ten Percent Plan.

50) During Reconstruction, voters elected

 a. more than 600 African American representatives to state legislatures and 16 to Congress.
 b. many African Americans to local offices in southern counties, but none to Congress.
 c. Andrew Johnson, Samuel Tilden, and Ulysses S. Grant as presidents.
 d. presidents who favored Radical Reconstruction in the South.

Call to Freedom

51) Who was unhappy about the wording of the Fifteenth Amendment?

a. African American activists who wanted American Indians to have the vote as well
b. women's rights activists who wanted the vote extended to women
c. activists such as William Lloyd Garrison, who did not want African American men to have the right to vote.
d. Radical Republicans, who did not think it was fair to extend the vote to African American men in the North.

52) Joel Chandler Harris, Mary Murfree, and George Washington Cable benefited from

a. new railroads that allowed their businesses to ship goods faster and farther than ever before.
b. textile mills that offered them an alternative to agricultural work.
c. southern interest in the folk ballads and dancing music they composed in the late 1800s.
d. national interest in stories about southern life.

53) One of the most important musical styles of the late 1800s was the

a. spiritual.                          c. Irish-American fiddle tune.
b. southern folk hymn.                 d. African folk ballad.

54) After Reconstruction ended, segregation was enforced by

a. Black Codes.                        c. Jim Crow laws.
b. the Compromise of 1877.             d. U. S. Supreme Court Justice John Marshall Harlan.

55) How did President Andrew Johnson react to the Reconstruction Acts?

a. He used his veto power to obstruct the efforts of Radical Republicans.
b. He broke the new laws by firing Secretary of War Edwin Stanton.
c. He traveled around the country arguing against the Reconstruction Acts.
d. He opposed the laws because he believed they gave too much power to the federal government.

56) During Reconstruction, the largest group of southern Republican voters were

a. northern-born carpetbaggers who sought political favors and fortune in the South.
b. African Americans who supported Reconstruction.
c. scalawags who wanted to overthrow Reconstruction legislatures.
d. Redeemers who wanted to limit the rights of African Americans.

57) The majority of laborers in southern cotton mills were

a. white women whose husbands sharecropped on mill-owned land.
b. white men, women, and children who worked 72-hour weeks.
c. African American men who saw industry as an alternative to sharecropping.
d. African American women and children.

58) The first large organizations run by freed African Americans were

    a. churches.
    b. cotton mills.
    c. public schools built by the Freedmen's Bureau.
    d. colleges for African American students.

59) Reconstruction ended in

    a. 1875, after Congress passed the Civil Rights Bill of 1875.
    b. 1869, after all southern legislatures agreed to follow the provisions of the Ten Percent Plan.
    c. 1877 when President Hayes removed the last federal troops from the South.
    d. 1870 when all the former Confederate states had rejoined the Union.

60) President Johnson believed that the Reconstruction Acts

    a. would deprive people "of life, liberty, or property without due process of law."
    b. would produce "a financial, political, and social revolution in the South."
    c. presented "a compromise worse by far for the nation than any other ever passed."
    d. used "powers not granted to the federal government or any one of its branches."

## ENHANCED QUESTIONS
For each of the following, circle the letter of the best choice. Next, expand on the subject by answering the second question in the space provided.

61) After the 1866 elections

    a. the Democrats gained control over the Senate.
    b. the Republican Party achieved a two-thirds majority in the House and Senate.
    c. the Democratic Party achieved a simple majority in the House and Senate.
    d. the Republican Party lost its majority in the House.

How did this situation affect the power of the president and his plan for Reconstruction?

_____

_____

62) The main purpose of the Ku Klux Klan was to

    a. drive Republicans out of the South and deny African Americans equal rights.
    b. protest the Civil Rights Bill of 1875 and deny the vote to African American men.
    c. organize riots in major southern cities such as Memphis and New Orleans.
    d. enforce Jim Crow laws in every southern state controlled by carpetbaggers.

How did the Klan pursue these goals?

_____

_____

Call to Freedom

63) The Republican Party controlled most southern governments during Reconstruction, partly because

a. most southerners were Republicans.
b. officials were appointed by Redeemers, most of whom were Republicans.
c. the Fourteenth Amendment banned many former Confederates from holding office.
d. terms for readmission to the Union required that governors appoint Republican officials.

Why did southern Democrats call the Republican officials carpetbaggers and scalawags?

_____

_____

64) In 1865 Congress was controlled by

a. moderate Republicans.
b. Radical Republicans.
c. the Redeemers.
d. Thaddeus Stevens and William Lloyd Garrison.

Why was the Democratic Party in the minority in 1865?

_____

_____

65) When Congress proposed increasing the powers of the Freedmen's Bureau in 1866,

a. President Johnson fired two cabinet officials without Senate approval.
b. President Grant went on a speaking tour to denounce Radical Reconstruction.
c. President Grant appointed a southern Democrat to head the Bureau.
d. President Johnson vetoed the bill.

How did the president explain his actions?

_____

_____

## GRAPHIC IMAGE QUESTIONS
**Examine the image, and then answer the following questions.**

### Cotton Production and Cotton Prices, 1876–1896

|  | Cotton Production (Acres of cotton harvested in millions) | Cotton Prices (Price per pound in cents) |
|---|---|---|
| **1876** | 12 | 9.5 |
| **1880** | 16 | 9.8 |
| **1884** | 17 | 9 |
| **1888** | 19 | 8.2 |
| **1892** | 18 | 8.2 |
| **1896** | 22 | 6 |

66) In which year was the greatest amount of cotton produced?

_____

67) In which year was the price of cotton lowest?

_____

68) In what year was the cost of cotton the highest?

_____

## SHORT ANSWER
**Write a brief answer for each of the following.**

69) Why did many freedpeople travel or relocate after the Civil War?

_____

_____

_____

Call to Freedom

70) What challenges did white southerners face after the Civil War?

_____

_____

_____

71) Why did sharecropping fail to help poor southerners buy their own land?

_____

_____

_____

72) Why was President Johnson's decision to fire Secretary of War Stanton viewed as grounds for impeachment?

_____

_____

_____

73) Why did African Americans view Black Codes as similar to slavery?

_____

_____

_____

## ESSAY
**On a separate sheet of paper, write an essay on one of the following.**

74) Describe how state legislatures deprived poor African Americans and white Americans of equal rights, education, and economic assistance during the late 1800s.

75) Explain how the Civil Rights of Act of 1875 and the Fourteenth Amendment did not prevent racial segregation in the South during the late 1800s. Describe the role of the U.S. Supreme Court in decisions affecting segregation.

# ANSWER KEY

1) Compromise of 1877

2) Fifteenth Amendment

3) Jim Crow laws

4) George Washington Cable

5) Reconstruction Acts

6) Thirteenth Amendment

7) *Plessy* v. *Ferguson*

8) Freedmen's Bureau

9) Civil Rights Bill of 1875

10) Radical Republicans

11) T

12) T

13) F
Each state had its own set of **Black Codes**.

14) T

15) F
The Emancipation Proclamation had freed slaves only in the Confederate states unoccupied by Union forces and allowed slavery to continue in the border states.

16) T

**Call to Freedom**

# ANSWER KEY

17) F

Voters elected African Americans to state legislatures and Congress during Reconstruction.

18) T

19) F

These states quickly elected new state legislatures.

20) F

Congress created the Freedmen's Bureau to provide relief for all poor people—black and white—in the South.

21) b

22) c

23) d

24) a

25) a

26) b

27) c

28) b

29) d

30) d

31) b

32) a

33)  c

34)  b

35)  d

36)  a

37)  c

38)  d

39)  b

40)  b

41)  d

42)  d

43)  c

44)  b

45)  a

46)  c

47)  d

48)  b

49)  c

Call to Freedom

50)  a

51)  b

52)  d

53)  a

54)  c

55)  d

56)  b

57)  b

58)  a

59)  c

60)  d

61)  b
This situation gave the Republicans the ability to override any veto of Johnson's, and resulted in a much harsher form of Reconstruction.

62)  a
The Klan used terror tactics and violence to threaten African Americans, white Republican voters, and public officials. Members of this secret society often wore disguises and attacked at night.

63)  c
Democrats viewed carpetbaggers as crooks who moved South to get rich, and scalawags as liars and cheats who betrayed the South by helping Radical Republicans. Since most government offices were held by northern or southern Republicans, Democrats referred to these officials as carpetbaggers and scalawags.

Call to Freedom

64) a

The Democratic Party's support was in the southern states not yet readmitted to the Union.

65) d

Johnson insisted that Congress could not pass any new laws until the southern states were represented in Congress. He also argued that the Freedmen's Bureau was unnecessary and that African Americans did not deserve any special assistance.

66) 1896

67) 1896

68) 1880

69) They traveled to find relatives, seek work, and make homes in African American communities. They also traveled because they now had the freedom to do so.

70) Many soldiers were disabled, their land or communities in ruins, their Confederate currency worthless, and food either scarce or expensive. Travel and communication were restricted because of the destruction of railroads, thereby causing citizens to feel isolated.

71) Sharecroppers whose crops failed could not pay their debts to the landowner or store owners. Many store owners and landowners also cheated sharecroppers. Therefore, sharecroppers were caught in a cycle of debt that often increased after each harvest.

72) Congress had recently passed an act preventing the president from removing cabinet officials without Senate approval. Johnson's decision broke the new law.

73) Black Codes greatly limited the freedom of African Americans by legislating where they could work and live, how they were to treat white people, where they could gather, and whether they could own guns.

74) Essays should indicate that poor white Americans and African Americans were hurt when state legislatures cut public funding for schools, got rid of social programs, used the poll tax and literacy tests to prevent people from voting.

75) Essays should indicate that after state governments began to legalize segregation with Jim Crow laws, the Supreme Court ruled that the Civil Rights Act of 1875 was unconstitutional and that the Fourteenth Amendment applied only to state governments. After that, the Supreme Court also backed segregation with its ruling in the case *Plessy* v. *Ferguson*.

Call to Freedom

# Chapter 18 The West

## MATCHING
**In the space provided, write the term or the name of the person that best fits the description. Choose your answers from the list below. Not all answers will be used.**

Mennonites       Gustavus Swift       Comstock Lode
Western Trail       open range       Treaty of Medicine Lodge
Chisholm Trail       Morrill Act       Homestead Act
Pacific Railway Acts       Fort Laramie Treaty       Battle of the Little Bighorn
range wars       Chisholm Trail       Bozeman Trail
bonanza

1) _____ gave government-owned land to small farmers

2) _____ public land on which cattle grazed

3) _____ provided loans and land grants to railroad companies in order to encourage railroad construction

4) _____ route running from Wyoming to Montana that was closed by the U.S. Army after Sherman negotiated with Red Cloud

5) _____ conflicts resulting from the competition between large and small ranchers for the use of public land for grazing

6) _____ 1867 agreement that required the southern Plains Indians to live on reservations

7) _____ large deposit of precious ore

8) _____ gave over 17 million acres of federal land to the states for the purpose of building colleges to teach agriculture and engineering

9) _____ popular cattle drive route that ran from San Antonio, Texas, to Abilene, Kansas

10) _____ agreement signed with the northern Plains Indians in 1851 that recognized Indian claims to land in the Great Plains and allowed the United States to build forts and roads through Indian lands

**TRUE/FALSE**
**Write T if a statement is true or F if it is false. If a statement is false, explain why.**

11) _____ For survival, Plains Indians depended on the horse and the buffalo.

_____

12) _____ Virginia City, Nevada, was a prosperous cattle town along the Western Trail.

_____

13) _____ Settlers raised Texas longhorns because they produced more meat than Spanish breeds.

_____

14) _____ Although shoot-outs were rare on the streets of most cattle towns, fights and disorderly behavior were common.

_____

15) _____ Living on reservations made buffalo hunting almost impossible for the Plains Indians.

_____

16) _____ Texas cattle herds grew during the Civil War after Texas ranchers began selling meat to the Confederate Army.

_____

17) _____ After the Civil War, Union General William Tecumseh Sherman was in charge of the western armies on the Great Plains.

_____

18) _____ The Apache, Comanche, Cheyenne, Arapaho, Pawnee, and Sioux lived on the Great Plains.

_____

19) _____ Most cowboys who drove longhorn cattle did not have to work very hard for their high wages.

_____

Call to Freedom

20) _____ The Pony Express went out of business because the transcontinental railroad transported people more quickly than the Pony Express.

_____

## MULTIPLE CHOICE
**For each of the following, circle the letter of the best choice.**

21) In 1859 Peter O'Riley and Patrick McLaughlin struck gold and silver at the Comstock Lode, which is

    a. in western Nevada.
    b. near present-day Denver, Colorado.
    c. in the Black Hills of Montana.
    d. in northern Idaho.

22) In the 1890s Hardy Powell began to teach farmers on the western Plains a method called

    a. exodusting.
    b. dry farming.
    c. sodbusting.
    d. homesteading.

23) Who first used the refrigerated railroad car to ship beef to eastern cities?

    a. Gustavus Swift
    b. Charles Goodnight
    c. Elizabeth Collins
    d. Joseph Glidden

24) Early explorers such as Stephen Long thought that the Great Plains

    a. contained precious ores as well as new strains of wheat originally from Russia.
    b. would support a cattle-ranching industry comparable to that of Texas.
    c. were suitable only for arid crops such as cotton and rye.
    d. were no better than a desert because of their barren landscape.

25) Conflicts with the Cheyenne and Arapaho began

    a. after the discovery of gold in present-day Colorado in 1858.
    b. in 1866 when the U. S. Army constructed forts along the Bozeman Trail.
    c. when white hunters began to slaughter thousands of buffalo in the 1870s.
    d. when the U.S. Army captured Geronimo in 1884.

26) Mechanical farming was advanced by equipment that was designed, built, and sold by

    a. James Oliver.
    b. Benjamin Singleton.
    c. Cyrus McCormick.
    d. John Wesley Powell.

27) Communities with churches and schools were

   a. rarely established on the Great Plains.
   b. established on reservations as required by treaties with the Plains Indians.
   c. an important part of life on the Plains.
   d. called boom towns because of their dependence on the cattle industry.

28) The Union Pacific and the Central Pacific took the lead in the race to complete the

   a. overland route of the Pony Express.
   b. transcontinental railroad.
   c. Chisholm Trail.
   d. first cattle drive from Texas to Montana.

29) To encourage people to move west, the Union Pacific

   a. advertised that it would take only four days to get there, instead of a month by wagon.
   b. organized wagon trains for settlers who went west on the Oregon Trail.
   c. signed a treaty with Red Cloud who promised safe homesteading for settlers arriving in North Dakota.
   d. offered jobs and machinery to immigrants who settled in Kansas.

30) In the West, concerns about safety and wages in the mines led to

   a. the closure of unsafe mines in Nevada and Colorado in the 1860s.
   b. the formation of miners' unions in the 1860s.
   c. range wars between cowboys and sheep ranchers.
   d. a series of federal laws in the 1870s that regulated working conditions.

31) As farming technology improved, the Great Plains became known as the

   a. sodbuster's folly.                    c. grazing ground of the longhorn.
   b. American Eden.                        d. breadbasket of the world.

32) Although he did not wish to fight the U.S. soldiers, Cheyenne chief Black Kettle

   a. saw 200 of his people attacked and killed in the Sand Creek Massacre in Colorado.
   b. attacked Colonel John M. Chivington's troops at Sand Creek.
   c. and Crazy Horse lured 82 cavalry troops into an ambush and killed them.
   d. defeated Custer and the Seventh Cavalry in the Battle of the Little Bighorn.

33) The Mennonites, a religious group from Russia,

   a. introduced dry farming to American settlers on the plains.
   b. taught Plains settlers how to build homes from bricks of sod cut out of the ground.
   c. introduced American farmers to a type of red wheat that grew well on the Plains.
   d. made up some 85 percent of the Union Pacific workforce.

34) The Panic of 1873 and the depression that followed it were started, in part, by

a. the collapse of the mine that Horace Greeley called "the richest and greatest in America."
b. railroad speculation and the collapse of Jay Cooke's banking firm.
c. Jay Gould's unsuccessful attempt to create a national railroad.
d. Nat Love's invention of barbed wire that threatened to topple the cattle kingdom.

35) In 1864 the U.S. Army led Navajo captives on a 300-mile desert march known as the

a. roundup of the vaqueros.         c. Ghost Dance.
b. shaman.                      d. Long Walk.

36) Many Plains families lived in sod houses because

a. sod houses were cheap, warm, and comfortable.
b. very little wood was available on the Plains.
c. sod houses were easier to maintain than wood or brick.
d. "houses built of sod" was a regulation imposed by the Homestead Act of 1862.

37) After Custer's soldiers discovered gold in the Black Hills in 1874,

a. the United States insisted that the Sioux sell their reservation land there.
b. Henry Comstock discovered one of the richest bonanzas in the West.
c. Henry Comstock sold his silver corporation for $11,000.
d. a boom town grew up around present-day St. Louis.

38) After ranchers moved more than a half million cattle from Texas onto the Plains in 1871,

a. ranchers discovered that winters on the Great Plains caused Texas Fever in longhorns.
b. the U.S. government began to charge ranchers for grazing rights on the open range.
c. the Cattle Kingdom soon stretched from Texas to Canada.
d. Texas Fever destroyed much of the Cattle Kingdom.

39) Lands once occupied by Plains Indians and buffalo herds became

a. vast reservations that provided ample hunting grounds for the Pawnee and the Sioux.
b. fenced with barbed wire by cowboys who established cattle ranches of their own.
c. sacred grounds where the Arapaho led a religious movement known as the Great Dance.
d. open range, or public land, on which huge herds of cattle grazed.

40) On May 10, 1869, a golden spike was driven at Promontory, Utah to mark

a. over 2 million tons of rails laid by Central Pacific crewmen on that day.
b. the completion of the transcontinental railroad fro Omaha to Sacramento.
c. the completion of the Union Pacific from Sacramento to Promontory.
d. the completion of the Central Pacific from Omaha to Promontory.

41) In 1890 many Sioux left Standing Rock Reservation in protest of

a. the U.S. government's requirement that the Nez Percé move to a reservation in Kansas.
b. the killing of Sitting Bull by reservation police.
c. the imprisonment of Geronimo and all Chiricahua Apache in Florida.
d. the killing of Crazy Horse after surrendering to the U.S. Army.

42) Immigrants came to the Great Plains looking for

a. economic opportunity.
b. an environment comparable to southern Europe.
c. gold in the Black Hills.
d. range rights for their sheep.

43) Professional hunters such as "Buffalo Bill" Cody shot thousands of buffalo to feed

a. soldiers in Sherman's western army.
b. Sioux Indians confined to reservations in the central Plains.
c. Chinese immigrants who built the Central Pacific across the Sierra Nevada.
d. workers on the Union Pacific as it crossed the Plains.

44) A rancher with range rights, or water rights,

a. often fenced his grazing lands to prevent cattle drives from using the water.
b. was required to provide water for U.S. soldiers and their horses and mules.
c. could eliminate competition by stopping farmers and other ranchers from using the  water.
d. could not prevent other ranchers from crossing rivers during roundups.

45) Crazy Horse and Sitting Bull defeated Custer and the Seventh Cavalry in

a. the Massacre at Wounded Knee.
b. the Battle of the Little Bighorn.
c. San Carlos, Arizona outside the Apache reservation.
d. 1886, ending the Pawnee armed resistance.

46) The most heavily used cattle drive route was the

a. Western Trail.
b. Chisholm Trail.
c. Oregon Trail.
d. Bozeman Trail.

47) Some 85 percent of the Central Pacific workforce were

a. Irish immigrants and Civil War veterans.
b. Chinese immigrants.
c. African Americans.
d. Mexican American vaqueros.

48) Cowboys branded young calves and horses during

    a. cattle drives.
    b. droughts.
    c. the spring roundup.
    d. the autumn roundup.

49) The northern Plains Indians were defeated when

    a. Kit Carson led U.S. troops against them in 1864.
    b. they were moved from northeastern Oregon to a reservation in present-day Idaho.
    c. Congress passed the Dawes General Allotment Act in 1880.
    d. Sitting Bull fled to Canada, and Crazy Horse was killed after surrendering to the U.S. Army.

50) Quanah Parker, the last of the Comanche war leaders, surrendered after

    a. "Buffalo Bill" Cody slaughtered all the buffalo on the Comanche hunting grounds.
    b. being outnumbered by the U.S. Army during a long chase across Idaho, Wyoming, and Montana.
    c. 5,000 soldiers captured Geronimo in 1886.
    d. the U.S. Army cut off the Comanches' access to food and water in 1875.

51) Early cowboys in the West borrowed many of their techniques from

    a. the Apache and Comanche who lived on the southern Plains.
    b. Mexican American vaqueros who had worked on ranches.
    c. Pawnee buffalo hunters.
    d. northern Plains Indians who tamed horses that had escaped from settlements.

52) Competition for use of the open range resulted in

    a. range wars among large ranchers, small ranchers, and farmers.
    b. conflicts between large ranchers and the Nez Percé Indians.
    c. decades of range wars between Nebraska sheep owners and Texas cattle owners.
    d. armed disputes between owners of the XIT Ranch and law official Wyatt Earp.

53) The Massacre at Wounded Knee marked the end of

    a. Geronimo's leadership of the Apache.
    b. negotiations between the Bureau of Indian Affairs and the Plains Indians.
    c. over 25 years of war on the Great Plains.
    d. Navajo reservations in present-day Arizona and New Mexico.

54) While Union Pacific workers faced harsh weather on the Great Plains,

    a. Central Pacific workers struggled to build the railroad across the Sierra Nevada range in California.
    b. Central Pacific workers faced Apache attacks in present-day Arizona.
    c. "the Casement Army" worked long, hard days laying rails across the rugged mountains of Idaho.
    d. Leland Stanford fired Chinese workers who refused to work for less than $5 a month.

Call to Freedom

55) One of the most important and dangerous duties of the cowboy was the

   a. spring roundup.
   b. autumn roundup.
   c. constant supervision of thousands of cattle within a 50-mile area.
   d. cattle drive.


56) Because few miners could afford stamping mills and smelters,

   a. the Comstock Lode was bought out by financiers Peter O'Riley and Patrick McLaughlin.
   b. mining became a big business as large companies bought up smaller claims.
   c. miners abandoned silver claims that did not prove to be bonanzas.
   d. they risked their lives underground where they labored for only $1.30 a day.


57) The Apache were fierce raiders famous for their ability to

   a. survive without horses on the northern Plains.
   b. hunt Plains buffalo with only a short bow and arrows.
   c. perform the Ghost Dance.
   d. survive in the desert.


58) In exchange for granting millions of acres of land to railroad companies, the U.S. government required railroads to

   a. give discounts to women to encourage them to move west.
   b. hire more European immigrants than Chinese ones.
   c. carry U.S. mail and soldiers at reduced rates.
   d. provide each western settler with 160 acres of land.


59) Acres of federal land set aside for Indians were known as

   a. reservations.                              c. vaqueros.
   b. bonanzas.                                  d. boom towns.


60) Many Union Pacific laborers were

   a. Chinese immigrants.
   b. Irish immigrants and Civil War veterans.
   c. soldiers who guarded the railroad against Indian attacks.
   d. peaceful Pawnee Indians.

## ENHANCED QUESTIONS
**For each of the following, circle the letter of the best choice. Next, expand on the subject by answering the second question in the space provided.**

61) In 1882 Gustavus Swift

a. invented barbed wire, which made it much easier to fence off large amounts of land.
b. blazed a cattle trail from Texas to New Mexico Territory.
c. used the refrigerated railroad car to carry refrigerated beef from packing plants to the big eastern markets.
d. invented a deep steel plow that enabled Plains farmers to break through the sod and plant grains that caused longhorns to thrive.

How did this affect the cattle industry? How was Chicago, Illinois, affected?

_____

_____

62) Benjamin Singleton led 20,000 to 40,000

a. Mennonites to North Dakota and Nebraska.    c. vaqueros to New Mexico Territory.
b. sodbusters to Oregon.    d. Exodusters to Kansas.

Who were these people? Why did they go west?

_____

_____

63) Reformers who felt that Indians would be better off if they adopted the ways of white people were hopeful when

a. Congress passed the Dawes General Allotment Act in 1887.
b. the Homestead Act was extended to include the Plains Indians in 1867.
c. the Fort Laramie Treaty replaced the Treaty of Medicine Lodge.
d. Congress passed the Morrill Act that allowed Indians to attend agricultural colleges.

How were Indians affected by this development?

_____

_____

64) The federal government helped the railroad companies by

a. allowing the Union Pacific and Central Pacific to lay track across Apache Indian reservations.
b. passing the Pacific Railway Acts in 1862 and 1864.
c. creating a national bank that loaned money at low interest to fledgling railroads.
d. establishing a national railroad headed by Jay Gould.

How did railroads benefit from this?

_____

_____


65) The U.S. government sent the peaceful Nez Percé Indians of northeastern Oregon to

a. help negotiate a treaty with Geronimo and the U.S. Army in Idaho.
b. Canada in exchange for Sitting Bull and his followers.
c. discuss policies of the Bureau of Indian Affairs with Sarah Winnemucca.
d. a reservation in present-day Oklahoma.

What incidents led to this situation?

_____

_____

Call to Freedom

## GRAPHIC IMAGE QUESTIONS
**Examine the image, and then answer the following questions.**

**Cost of Establishing a Farm in 1870**

| Item | Price |
|---|---|
| Land (per acre) | $3–$12 |
| Team (horses or oxen) | $300 |
| Wagon and yoke or harness | $150 |
| Plow | $25 |
| Cultivator and harrow | $45 |
| Combination reaper and mower | $252 |
| Other hand tools (ax, shovel, fork, rake, and scythe) | $50 |

66) What was the most expensive piece of farm equipment listed in the table?

_____

67) What was the least expensive single piece of equipment?

_____

68) What was the total cost for buying all the farm equipment in 1870?

_____

## SHORT ANSWER
**Write a brief answer for each of the following.**

69) Explain the discrimination that Mexican Americans and Mexican immigrants experienced in the mining industry.

_____

_____

_____

70) How did the transcontinental railroad affect growth and prosperity in the West?

_____

_____

_____

71) How did railroad companies help businesses in the West?

_____

_____

_____

72) How did settlers qualify for land granted by the Homestead Act?

_____

_____

_____

73) Why did the Cattle Kingdom decline in the 1880s?

_____

_____

_____

**ESSAY**
**On a separate sheet of paper, write an essay on one of the following.**

74) Explain the government's influence on how American Indians, African Americans, and immigrants adapted to life on the Great Plains.

75) Compare how ranchers and farmers were challenged by the environment of the Great Plains.

# ANSWER KEY

1) Homestead Act

2) open range

3) Pacific Railway Acts

4) Bozeman Trail

5) range wars

6) Treaty of Medicine Lodge

7) bonanza

8) Morrill Act

9) Chisholm Trail

10) Fort Laramie Treaty

11) T

12) F
Virginia City was a mining town near the Comstock Lode.

13) F
Longhorns were lean and tough. Settlers raised them because they adapted well to the environment.

14) T

15) T

16) F
Herds grew because Texas was isolated during the Civil War and was unable to sell cattle.

17) T

18) T

19) F
Most cowboys worked very hard for low wages.

20) F
The Pony Express went out of business because the telegraph sent messages faster.

21) a

22) b

23) a

24) d

25) a

26) c

27) c

28) b

29) a

30) b

31) d

32) a

33) c

34) b

35) d

Call to Freedom

# ANSWER KEY

36) b

37) a

38) c

39) d

40) b

41) b

42) a

43) d

44) c

45) b

46) a

47) b

48) c

49) d

50) d

51) b

52) a

ANSWER KEY

53)  c

54)  a

55)  d

56)  b

57)  d

58)  c

59)  a

60)  b

61)  c
This increased the national demand for beef and made cities such as Chicago famous for their meatpacking factories.

62)  d
Exodusters were African Americans who went west seeking land, economic opportunity, and equal rights. They were denied equal rights in the post-Reconstruction South.

63)  a
The Act split up reservation lands among individual Indians, then sold the lands that remained unalloted, thereby taking more land from them than all the wars. Indians also failed to become citizens as promised.

64)  b
These acts provided large land grants next to the railroad for every mile of track laid. The government also loaned money to railroad companies.

65)  d
After white settlers convinced the government to move the Nez Percé from their homelands, some angry young Nez Percé killed some settlers. The Nez Percé fled, were chased until they surrendered to the U.S. Army, and were then sent to Kansas.

66) team of horses or oxen

67) plow

68) $822

69) Although Mexican immigrants and Mexican Americans were skilled and experienced, they were often denied the better-paying jobs.

70) The transcontinental railroad increased the rate of economic and population growth, and encouraged settlement in remote areas by providing better transportation and selling farm land.

71) Railroads helped businesses ship items to and from the East more quickly.

72) Any adult who was a U.S. citizen or planned to become one could receive 160 acres of land if he or she paid a small registration fee and lived on the land for five years.

73) Having over 7 million cattle on the Great Plains drove down cattle prices, and depleted much of the prairie grass used for grazing. Severe winters killed many thousands of cattle, especially the new eastern breeds. Ranchers sold their cattle at low prices to pay their creditors, and many were financially ruined. Overall, low prices, harsh weather, and greater competition for grazing land ended the reign of the Cattle Kingdom.

74) Although the Great Plains was home to American Indians, they lost their land and livelihood when the government engaged them in warfare, broke its treaties, forced the Indians onto reservations, and allowed their buffalo herds to be destroyed. African Americans had more economic opportunities and rights on the Great Plains than in the South, where government actively discriminated against them. European immigrants benefited from government land grants, and were free to engage in any business they chose. Overall, government policy that discriminated against certain groups of people had an adverse effect on their adaptation to life on the Plains.

75) Both were challenged by sub-freezing temperatures and extreme heat, blizzards and tornadoes, and unusually severe winters. While farmers dealt with droughts, grasshoppers, and the challenge of home-building without much wood, ranchers benefited by driving the Longhorn cattle that needed very little water and could survive harsh weather. The cold winters also killed the ticks that caused Texas fever. Farmers received land from the government, and ranchers received grazing rights on the open range. However, farmers suffered when ranchers bought the range rights to water, and ranchers suffered when farmers used barbed wire to fence out the cattle. Sheep and cattle depleted much of the grasslands that led to the decline of the ranching industry, while farmers benefited from arid lands after dry farming techniques were introduced.

# Chapter 19 An Industrial and Urban Nation

## MATCHING
In the space provided, write the term or the name of the person that best fits the description. Choose your answers from the list below. Not all answers will be used.

Populist Party     patent     Eugene V. Debs
Greenback Party     suburbs     corporations
Bessemer process     steerage     Farmers' Alliance
Homestead Strike     National Grange     Pullman Strike
trust     Samuel Gompers     American Federation of Labor

1) _____ legal arrangement grouping together a number of companies under a board of directors

2) _____ residential neighborhoods outside of a central city

3) _____ social and educational organization for farmers

4) _____ organized individual national unions into a loose association

5) _____ exclusive right to manufacture or sell an invention

6) _____ area below deck on a ship's lower levels

7) _____ companies that sell shares of ownership called stocks

8) _____ result of Henry Frick's refusal to negotiate with the steelworkers' union

9) _____ leader of the American Railway Union

10) _____ British discovery that increased U.S. steel production

## TRUE/FALSE
Write T if a statement is true or F if it is false. If a statement is false, explain why.

11) _____ The Farmers' Alliance was more politically active than the National Grange.

_____

12) _____ Charles and J. Frank Duryea built the first practical motorcar in the United States.

_____

13) _____ Factories that focused on specialization suffered higher costs and decreased production.

_____

14) _____ The Immigration Restriction League was founded by nativists who demanded a literacy test for immigrants.

_____

15) _____ The depression triggered by the Panic of 1893 was caused by the national money system.

_____

16) _____ Thomas Alva Edison invented the "talking telegraph," or telephone, 15 years after telegraph wires connected the east and west coasts.

_____

17) _____ By the late 1800s, state governments formed benevolent societies to aid the poor.

_____

18) _____ By 1900 the combination of more farms and greater productivity led to overproduction and higher prices for crops.

_____

19) _____ In 1890 the federal government assumed control of immigration centers.

_____

20) _____ Collective bargaining was used by labor unions to negotiate for better wages and working conditions for all workers in a particular factory or industry.

_____

## MULTIPLE CHOICE
**For each of the following, circle the letter of the best choice.**

21) The Second Industrial Revolution was a period of explosive growth in

    a. the oil industry.                   c. manufacturing.
    b. the railroad industry.            d. commerce.

22) The leadership of Terence V. Powderly

    a. encouraged the U.S. government to support the American Railway Union after 1894.
    b. encouraged railroad workers to demonstrate in Haymarket Square.
    c. enabled the American Federation of Labor to organize individual unions into a powerful association.
    d. turned the Knights of Labor into the first truly national labor union in the United States.

23) To attract immigrants, railroad and steamship companies hired business agents who

    a. often painted unrealistic pictures of easy wealth and happiness in the United States.
    b. helped immigrants find lodging in urban settlement houses.
    c. distributed free tickets to people willing to travel in steerage or on immigrant trains.
    d. served as interpreters between factory managers and foreigners seeking employment.

24) Orville and Wilbur Wright's first flight at Kitty Hawk, North Carolina, was made possible in part by the type of engine invented by

    a. Edwin L. Drake.              c. Dr. Benjamin Silliman, Jr.
    b. Nikolaus A. Otto.            d. Mikola Tesla.

25) Railroad workers and the railroad industry were aided most by the inventions of

    a. Elisha Otis.                 c. Charles and J. Frank Duryea.
    b. Frederick Law Olmsted.        d. George Westinghouse and Granville T. Woods.

26) Immigrants' poverty and lack of education were protested by

    a. labor unions who bargained for the rights of skilled laborers.
    b. nativists who claimed these factors would negatively affect American society.
    c. political leaders entrusted with providing benevolent aid to the poor.
    d. middle-class Americans who moved to suburbs outside of central cities.

27) After Oliver Kelley toured the South in 1866, he and several other government clerks founded the

    a. National Grange, to improve farmers' living standards.
    b. Colored Farmers' Alliance that grew to include more than 1 million members.
    c. Grand State Alliance, to improve economic conditions for poor Texas farmers.
    d. Populist Party, to provide farmers with greater democracy and voice in government.

Call to Freedom

28) Most new immigrants settled in

a. settlement houses that provided education and child care.
b. cities where unskilled industrial jobs were plentiful, but low-paying.
c. communities that preserved their language and customs.
d. the West where they worked as farm laborers or as tenant farmers.

29) In the late 1800s farmers' problems most often involved

a. unfair railroad rates and railroad monopolies.
b. resistance to mechanized farming.
c. money issues such as debt, credit, and low prices.
d. wholesalers, brokers, grain buyers, and grain elevator operators who profited at farmers' expense.

30) After Congress passed the Sherman Antitrust Act,

a. legislation against monopolies was strictly enforced.
b. the U.S. government began to break up monopolies held by Andrew Carnegie and John D. Rockefeller.
c. the Act was difficult to enforce because it did not clearly define a monopoly.
d. monopolies were declared legal in they did not involve several states.

31) Frederick Law Olmsted promoted the idea of preserving green areas in cities when he designed

a. Hull House in Chicago.
b. the company town of Pullman, Illinois.
c. Lincoln Park in Chicago.
d. Central Park in New York City.

32) The Interstate Commerce Commission

a. lacked any real power to enforce its regulations.
b. forced short railroad lines not to discriminate in favor of big shippers.
c. provided uniform national regulations over trade between states.
d. controlled legislation that regulated rates for the use of railroads and grain elevators.

33) The organization that limited its membership to skilled workers was the

a. Knights of Labor, founded by Uriah Stephens.
b. American Railway Union, under the order of George Pullman.
c. American Steelworkers Union, as required by Henry Frick.
d. AFL, under the leadership of Samuel Gompers.

34) To increase the amount of silver purchased for coinage, Congress

a. passed the Bland-Allison Act over President Hayes's veto.
b. passed the Sherman Silver Purchase Act.
c. voted against the Sherman Silver Purchase Act proposed by William Henry Harrison.
d. inflated the money supply with paper dollars not backed by gold or silver.

35) In 1876 Nikolaus A. Otto invented an engine powered by

    a. electricity.                      c. gasoline.
    b. oil.                             d. kerosene.

36) Farmers who hoped to raise prices, increase their income, and more easily pay their debts were in favor of

    a. regulating railroad rates in favor of big shippers.     c. the gold standard.
    b. coining silver to create inflation.               d. coining silver to decrease inflation.

37) Among urban African American communities, churches

    a. led by women members became the centers of social and political life.
    b. declined in the late 1800s as benevolent societies gained strength.
    c. raised money to build settlement houses, establish schools, and publish newspapers.
    d. sponsored classes in citizenship and U.S. government.

38) Free coinage meant

    a. paper money was worth a specific amount in gold or silver.
    b. coin had a fixed ratio in gold.
    c. coin had a fixed ratio in gold or silver.
    d. money and coin had a fixed ratio in gold or silver.

39) Trusts often tried to

    a. eliminate competition by lowering prices for consumers.
    b. reduce inflation by raising prices for consumers.
    c. regulate production and eliminate competition.
    d. regulate production and lower prices for consumers.

40) Opportunities for immigrants in the United States

    a. often exceeded those that they had in the land of their birth.
    b. rarely equaled those that they had in the land of their birth.
    c. increased after the U.S. government established immigrant processing centers.
    d. decreased as suburbs began to replace urban neighborhoods.

41) The political party that supported government ownership of railroads, telephone and telegraph systems was the

    a. Democratic Party.                c. Populist Party.
    b. Republican Party.              d. Greenback Party.

Call to Freedom

42) After 1880 many of the nation's buildings, highways, and railroads were built by

    a. old immigrants.
    b. new immigrants.
    c. native-born Americans.
    d. skilled and unskilled workers who belonged to the Knights of Labor.

43) Frederick W. Taylor's time-and-motion studies encouraged scientific management that

    a. led to a decrease in specialization.
    b. decreased the cost of labor, and improved working conditions.
    c. encouraged managers to strictly enforce the eight-hour workday.
    d. encouraged managers to see workers as parts of the production process, not as individuals.

44) The Populist Party and organized farmers' parties ended after

    a. William Jennings Bryan's defeat in the 1896 election.
    b. McKinley's defeat in the 1896 election.
    c. the election of Grover Cleveland in 1892.
    d. James B. Weaver's defeat in the 1892 election.

45) Jane Addams encouraged educated, monied social workers to live at Hull House to

    a. provide child care and kindergarten instruction for the children of immigrants.
    b. to put into practice some of the theories they learned in school.
    c. supervise the young immigrant women who lived there.
    d. teach classes in citizenship, music, art, and English.

46) By 1900, 40 percent of Americans lived in

    a. rural areas.             c. settlement houses.
    b. cities.                 d. company towns such as Pullman, Illinois.

47) In the late 1800s charities received millions of dollars from philanthropists who

    a. also supported the Knights of Labor and the AFL.
    b. also established the eight-hour day and safe working conditions for laborers in their factories.
    c. had immigrated from Europe to make their fortune in America.
    d. believed that the wealthy had a duty to take care of the poor.

48) Mary Harris Jones was called "Mother" Jones by

    a. poor workers whose rights she fought to protect.
    b. immigrants at Ellis Island where she conducted interviews for the U.S. government.
    c. opponents of child labor at the Homestead Steel works.
    d. children of immigrant mothers who lived with her at Hull House.

49) After Mikola Tesla invented alternating current,

    a. George Westinghouse invented the first electric light bulb.
    b. the electric generator replaced the gasoline engine as a power source.
    c. electricity could be transmitted over long distances.
    d. kerosene could be more easily refined from oil.

50) Oil became a big business in Pennsylvania, Ohio, and West Virginia after

    a. Silliman discovered how to refine oil into gasoline.
    b. Edwin L. Drake proved that it was possible to pump oil from the ground.
    c. Rockefeller established the Standard Oil Company.
    d. Rockefeller offered rebates to state-owned railroads that shipped his products.

51) During the Homestead Strike, a gun battle erupted between the

    a. state militia and the steel workers.
    b. steel workers and the militia after Pinkerton detectives arrested the strikers.
    c. militia and the Pinkerton detectives whom management hired to break the union.
    d. Pinkerton detectives and the steel workers who were locked out of the plant.

52) The city that grew from 30,000 residents to 1.7 million residents within 50 years was

    a. Chicago.
    b. New York.
    c. Omaha.
    d. Des Moines.

53) In order to provide some uniform national regulations over trade between states, Congress

    a. created the Interstate Commerce Commission in 1873.
    b. passed the Interstate Commerce Act in 1887.
    c. supported the Supreme Court in the case *Munn* v. *Illinois*.
    d. established the gold standard in 1873.

54) William Jennings Bryan of Nebraska ran for president as a

    a. Populist with a free silver coinage platform.
    b. Republican with a gold standard platform.
    c. Republican with a free silver coinage platform.
    d. Democrat with a free silver coinage platform.

55) Immigration was favored by

    a. business leaders who wanted a large supply of low-wage workers.
    b. labor unions in the West.
    c. nativists who supported the AFL.
    d. grange leaders who favored mechanized farming.

56) By 1880, one fourth of all farms were

    a. owned by native-born Americans.    c. rented by tenants.
    b. owned by immigrants.    d. controlled by grain cooperatives.

57) Inventors were invited to live and work in a "scientific village" started by

    a. George Westinghouse in Chicago.
    b. Thomas Alva Edison in Menlo Park, New Jersey.
    c. Alexander Graham Bell in Halifax, Nova Scotia.
    d. Orville and Wilbur Wright in Kitty Hawk, North Carolina.

58) Some immigrant communities formed

    a. Knights of Labor groups that worked to end child labor.
    b. granges, especially in midwestern cities and the West.
    c. settlement houses that provided room and board for families of workers killed in industrial accidents.
    d. benevolent societies to help others in cases of sickness, unemployment, and death.

59) To ensure that railroads charged fair rates and did not discriminate in favor of big shippers was the task of the

    a. Farmers' Alliance.    c. Populist Party.
    b. Interstate Commerce Commission.    d. National Grange.

60) After immigrants were interviewed and examined by Ellis Island officials,

    a. they were allowed to enter the country.
    b. sponsors showed them the way to designated lodging houses, and helped them find jobs.
    c. immigrants with contagious diseases were deported to their home country.
    d. they were admitted to the country as U.S. citizens.

Call to Freedom

333

# ENHANCED QUESTIONS

**For each of the following, circle the letter of the best choice. Next, expand on the subject by answering the second question in the space provided.**

61) The battle between Chicago police and union-led workers fighting for an eight-hour workday became known as the

    a. Pullman Strike.                      c. Haymarket Riot.
    b. Homestead Strike.                d. Second Industrial Revolution.

What role did the Knights of Labor play in this event? How was Knights' membership affected by the outcome?

_____

_____

62) In the late 1800s the U.S. government

    a. promoted free enterprise and laissez-faire capitalism.
    b. allowed free enterprise, and legislated against trusts.
    c. regulated the sale of corporate stocks in order to discourage laissez-faire capitalism.
    d. permitted corporations to form monopolies that discouraged free enterprise.

How did this policy affect entrepreneurs?

_____

_____

63) In 1882 Congress passed the Chinese Exclusion Act which prohibited Chinese people from

    a. joining labor unions.                c. becoming U.S. citizens.
    b. joining political parties.            d. immigrating to the United States for 10 years.

What was the significance of this act?

_____

_____

64) Farmers formed cooperative societies to sell their crops at higher prices while granges formed

    a. alliances with politicians who favored the gold standard.
    b. cooperatives to buy goods at lower prices and increase farmers' buying power.
    c. educational institutions that enrolled children of farmers in remote areas.
    d. social clubs that sponsored immigrant families in agricultural regions.

How successful were these efforts?

_____

_____


65) After Congress placed the United States on a gold standard,

    a. paper money was no longer worth a specific amount in gold.
    b. gold coins replaced silver coins as official U.S. currency.
    c. every dollar of paper money and every coin was worth a specific amount in gold.
    d. silver, rather than gold, backed the U.S. currency.

How did this act affect America's money supply?

_____

_____

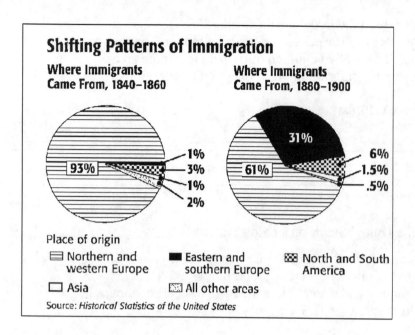

66) Which immigrant group experienced the greatest increase between the periods 1840–1860 and 1880–1890?

_____

67) What was the largest immigrant group in the period 1880–1900?

_____

68) Which immigrant group increased in population from 1% to 1.5% between the periods 1840–1860 and 1880–1890?

_____

**SHORT ANSWER**
Write a brief answer for each of the following.

69) Describe the impact of railroads on the U.S. economy in the late 1800s.

_____

_____

_____

70) Why did the Sherman Antitrust Act—designed to curb big business—work against railroad employees who went on strike against the Pullman Palace Car Company?

_____

_____

_____

71) Describe how Jane Addams and Ellen Gates Starr improved the lives of the poor in Chicago.

_____

_____

_____

72) Why did farmers organize the Farmers' Alliance and the Populist Party?

_____

_____

_____

73) Compare the characteristics of old immigrants and new immigrants.

_____

_____

_____

**ESSAY**
**On a separate sheet of paper, write an essay on one of the following.**

74) Describe how Cornelius Vanderbilt, Andrew Carnegie, and John D. Rockefeller used consolidation, vertical and horizontal integration, and trusts to form monopolies in the railroad, steel, and oil industries.

75) Explain how Charles Darwin's theory of natural selection influenced the U.S. government's role in big business, the growth of philanthropy and labor unions, and the lives of laborers and immigrants in the late 1800s.

ANSWER KEY

1) trust

2) suburbs

3) National Grange

4) American Federation of Labor

5) patent

6) steerage

7) corporations

8) Homestead Strike

9) Eugene V. Debs

10) Bessemer process

11) T

12) T

13) F
Specialization lowered costs and increased production.

14) T

15) F
Although some Americans blamed the money system, the depression had multiple causes.

16) F
Alexander Graham Bell invented the telephone.

Call to Freedom

# ANSWER KEY

17) F
Few government programs helped poor people. Private aid organizations formed benevolent societies.

18) F
This situation led to lower crop prices.

19) T

20) T

21) c

22) d

23) a

24) b

25) d

26) b

27) a

28) b

29) c

30) c

31) d

32) a

# ANSWER KEY

33) d

34) b

35) c

36) b

37) a

38) a

39) c

40) a

41) c

42) b

43) d

44) a

45) b

46) b

47) d

48) a

49) c

Call to Freedom

ANSWER KEY

50)  b

51)  d

52)  a

53)  b

54)  d

55)  a

56)  c

57)  b

58)  d

59)  b

60)  c

61)  c
Although Knights' leaders did not support the workers involved, several local chapters of the Knights did, and one arrested worker held a Knights membership card. Public opinion linked the Knights to the Haymarket Riot and its violence. As a result, membership in the Knights declined rapidly.

62)  a
Entrepreneurs, people who organize new businesses, had a great deal of freedom and many opportunities. Many entrepreneurs organized their businesses as corporations.

63)  d
This act was the first time an immigrant group was prohibited from entering the country. After the ban was extended into the early 1900s, the Chinese American population declined.

Call to Freedom

64) b

Cooperatives were often run by people inexperienced in business, and were opposed by banks, merchants, and railroads. As a result, most of the cooperatives fared poorly.

65) c

The money supply grew more slowly than the nation's population, resulting in deflation—a shrinking of the money supply and a general lowering of prices.

66) Eastern and Southern Europeans

67) Northern and Western Europeans

68) Asians

69) Railroads promoted western settlement. Large cities grew where major rail lines met. Manufacturers and farmers could get their products to market more rapidly by rail. Railroads and their related industries were one of America's largest employers.

70) After the American Railway Union supported the strikers by refusing to work on trains carrying Pullman cars, traffic on most of the Midwest's rail lines was halted because almost all trains carried Pullman cars. Railroad officials struck back by attaching Pullman cars to U.S. mail cars, ensuring that workers who stopped Pullman cars would be charged with the federal offense of interfering with the U.S. mail. The U.S. attorney general used the Sherman Antitrust Act to get the court order that stopped the strike. The attorney general argued that the workers were acting in restraint of trade.

71) In 1889 Addams and Starr founded Hull House, which focused on the needs of poor immigrant families. They established the first kindergarten and public playground in Chicago, worked for reforms such as child labor laws and the eight-hour work day for women, and taught English and U.S. government to help immigrants become citizens.

72) Farmers organized their own political organizations to increase their power. First locally, then regionally, they organized to elect candidates and achieve policies favorable to them. These organizations, which became known as the Farmers' Alliance, agreed to form a national political party known as the Populist Party to raise their issues to the national level.

Call to Freedom

# ANSWER KEY

73)  Arriving before the 1880s, most old immigrants—those from Britain, Germany, Ireland, and Scandinavia—spoke English, were Protestants, and had a skill. They settled often outside the cities, and became farmers. New immigrants were from southern and eastern Europe, and came to America seeking a better life, economic opportunities, and escape from political and religious persecution. Most settled in cities and worked at low-paying, unskilled, industrial jobs. They brought with them many new cultures and a variety of religious beliefs. Few spoke English well.

74)  Vanderbilt built his railroad empire by consolidating—buying smaller companies to form one large company—railroad companies and lines. Consolidation improved efficiency and travel time. This practice extended to his concept of building large central depots in big cities to centralize railroad services in urban areas. Carnegie succeeded in creating a steel monopoly through vertical integration—owning businesses involved in each step of a manufacturing process. He purchased the iron ore mines, coal fields, and railroads needed to supply and support his steel mills. Rockefeller practiced consolidation and vertical integration to build his oil monopoly. He also practiced horizontal integration, which means that he bought other companies in the same industry. By 1879 Rockefeller's companies controlled more than 90 percent of the U.S. oil-refining business. Rockefeller also formed a trust—a legal arrangement grouping together a number of companies under a board of directors. To make higher profits, trusts often tried to eliminate competition. Thus all three men used new business practices to make their own personal fortune, to build monopolies in their chosen fields, and to increase and improve services for consumers.

75) Darwin's theory of natural selection proposed that over time species evolved by adapting to their environments. Social Darwinists embraced Darwin's teaching and applied it to societies. They believed that government allowed the law of nature to work only when it practiced laissez-faire capitalism. According to Social Darwinists, government regulation of businesses threatened the "natural" economic order. Business leaders who built their economic empires by means of the Social Darwinist "survival of the fittest" practice of eliminating weaker competitors argued that they had gained great wealth because they were the fittest members of society. They used Social Darwinism to justify child labor, low wages, and unsafe working conditions for their employees, many of whom were poor, unskilled, immigrants. These employees had to demand fair labor practices by forming labor unions, striking, and holding demonstrations to show that they were as worthy of life and well-being as were their employers. Social activists such as Jane Addams fought against Social Darwinism by improving living conditions for the poor, and by living as an equal among the people she helped. Some business leaders believed that Social Darwinism meant the wealthy had a duty to take care of the poor, since nature pre-determined who would be poor and who would be rich. Carnegie and Rockefeller gave away millions of dollars to charity. Some critics of Social Darwinism argued that many entrepreneurs earned their fortunes through unfair business practices, not through natural selection. Citizens and small businesses demanded government action to control monopolies and restore competition. Government at the time continued to support big business. Even the Sherman Antitrust Act, designed to curb big business, worked against employees during the Pullman Strike. Government took no role in providing for the poor, and took only a self-protective role in processing the immigrants who planned to aid American industry by working long, hard hours to build and run the railroads, process the steel, and refine the oil. Government leaders and the wealthy who embraced Social Darwinism defended this system by saying that the division of classes—the wealthy and the poor—was the natural order of things, and that poor workers' demands were unrealistic and unacceptable.

# Chapter 20 The Spirit of Reform

**MATCHING**

**In the space provided, write the term or the name of the person that best fits the description. Choose your answers from the list below. Not all answers will be used.**

Federal Trade Commission    arbitration              Sixteenth Amendment
direct primary                  Susan Blow              Seventeenth Amendment
Underwood Tariff           political machines     Eighteenth Amendment
referendum                    Ida Tarbell              Nineteenth Amendment
Frances Willard           progressives         Ida B. Wells-Barnett

1) _____ allowed citizens to vote on approving laws already proposed by the state and local governments

2) _____ gave women in the United States the right to vote

3) _____ wrote many articles for *McClure's Magazine*

4) _____ introduced a version of the modern income tax on personal earnings

5) _____ investigated corporations and could issue restraining orders to prevent "unfair trade practices"

6) _____ guaranteed votes at election time through both legal and illegal methods

7) _____ allowed voters to choose candidates directly rather than relying on the choices of party leaders

8) _____ allows the federal government to pass direct taxes, such as the income tax

9) _____ allowed Americans to vote directly for U.S. senators

10) _____ wrote the book *A Red Record*, which reported lynching statistics for a three-year period

## TRUE/FALSE
**Write T if a statement is true or F if it is false. If a statement is false, explain why.**

11) _____ The Chinese Exclusion Act was extended indefinitely during Theodore Roosevelt's presidency.

_____

12) _____ Roosevelt transferred more land into government reserves than did President Taft.

_____

13) _____ Political bosses were political leaders who controlled elections through bribery and payoffs.

_____

14) _____ During the early 1900s, laws prevented immigrants from moving freely across the United States's borders with Mexico and Canada.

_____

15) _____ The U.S. Supreme Court forced Congress to pass laws in 1916 and 1919 that restricted child labor in the United States.

_____

16) _____ The Pendleton Civil Service Act established a merit system that affected almost 90 percent of government jobs in 1883.

_____

17) _____ Arguing that the president had a responsibility to become involved, Roosevelt brought striking coal miners and managers together for arbitration, a formal meeting to discuss and settle disagreements.

_____

18) _____ In 1874, reformers created the Women's Christian Temperance Union, which brought together women from many different backgrounds in the fight against alcohol.

_____

Call to Freedom

19) _____ The NAACP won the first of several important Supreme Court decisions when the Court outlawed the grandfather clause which had been used to prevent African Americans from voting.

_____

20) _____ Woodrow Wilson was the first president to consider conservation an important national issue.

_____

## MULTIPLE CHOICE
**For each of the following, circle the letter of the best choice.**

21) The Industrial Workers of the World (IWW) were led by

a. Samuel Gompers.
b. W.E.B. Du Bois.

c. Rufus Peckham.
d. Big Bill Haywood.

22) Which act strengthened federal laws against monopolies?

a. the Sherman Antitrust Act
b. the Clayton Antitrust Act

c. the Federal Reserve Act
d. the Underwood Tariff of 1913

23) The leader of the progressive crusade against child labor was

a. Florence Kelley.
b. Jane Addams.

c. Susan Blow.
d. John Dewey.

24) The National American Woman Suffrage Association was founded in 1890 by

a. Carrie Chapman Catt and Florence Willard.
b. Carry Nation and Florence Willard.
c. Elizabeth Cady Stanton and Susan B. Anthony.
d. Alice Paul and Susan B. Anthony.

25) In the 1880s Republican reformers came to be known as

a. muckrakers.
b. mugwumps.

c. bosses.
d. political machines.

26) Women who were denied access to male-dominated professions such as medicine and law

a. played a central role in the reform movements of the Progressive Era.
b. joined women's clubs that encouraged women to savor the sacred hearth of home.
c. became educators and college presidents of such institutions as Harvard and Johns Hopkins.
d. moved to southern and western states where women had more rights.

Call to Freedom

27) The 1901 New York State Tenement House Law

a. required tenement owners to live in their buildings.
b. required tenement owners to install toilets and running water in buildings that housed children under the age of 15.
c. outlawed the construction of dark and airless tenements.
d. was declared unconstitutional by the U.S. Supreme Court.

28) Which labor union had about 4 million members by 1920?

a. Women's Trade Union League (WTUL).
b. the Industrial Workers of the World (IWW).
c. the United Auto Workers (UAW).
d. the American Federation of Labor (AFL).

29) Labor unions, corporations, and all private citizens were promised a square deal by President

a. Roosevelt.
b. Taft.
c. McKinley.
d. Wilson.

30) The Crédit Mobilier of America's scandalous association with the Union Pacific Railroad was brought to the public's attention by

a. Lincoln Steffens.
b. Ida Tarbell.
c. the Memphis *Free Speech*.
d. the *New York Sun*.

31) The temperance leader who stormed into saloons with an ax was

a. Frances Willard.
b. Carry Nation.
c. Susan B. Anthony.
d. Elizabeth Cady Stanton.

32) Journalists who wrote about corruption in business and politics, hoping that their articles would lead to public awareness and reform, were nicknamed

a. mugwumps.
b. muckrakers.
c. bosses.
d. bull moose.

33) "The life of men and women is so cheap and property so sacred. . . . It is up to the working people to save themselves," said

a. Marie Van Vorst who posed as a poor woman to investigate conditions in a South Carolina textile mill.
b. Sadie Frowne of her 11-hour day in a garment factory in Brooklyn, New York.
c. union organizer Rose Schneiderman after the Triangle Shirtwaist Factory fire.
d. Florence Kelley to board members of the National Consumers' League.

34) Upton Sinclair's novel *The Jungle* influenced public opinion to such an extent that

a. Roosevelt persuaded Congress to pass the Pure Food and Drug Act.
b. many states passed minimum wage laws and maximum hour laws for women.
c. state legislatures passed mine and factory safety laws and new inspection regulations.
d. Wilson convinced Congress to pass the Keating-Owen Child Labor Act.

35) In the 1884 presidential election, dissatisfied mugwumps left the Republican Party and threw their support behind

a. Rutherford B. Hayes.
b. James A. Garfield.
c. Grover Cleveland.
d. Benjamin Harrison.

36) The group that helped African Americans find jobs and housing was the

a. Bull Moose Party.
b. National Consumers' League.
c. NAACP.
d. National Urban League.

37) The physical and spiritual cost to the men and women and children who bear the burden of America's industrial achievements was addressed by President

a. Taft.
b. Wilson.
c. Roosevelt.
d. Cleveland.

38) The unfair business practices of the Standard Oil Company were exposed by

a. Ida Tarbell.
b. Lincoln Steffens.
c. Upton Sinclair.
d. Ida B. Wells-Barnett.

39) Passed in December 1913, the Federal Reserve Act

a. strengthened federal laws against monopolies.
b. investigated corporations and could issue restraining orders to prevent "unfair trade practices."
c. created a banking system called the Federal Reserve.
d. brought the lowest tariff rates in many years.

40) Ulysses S. Grant's presidency was tainted when members of his administration were jailed for their part in the

a. Crédit Mobilier scandal.
b. Tammany Hall election.
c. Boston ballot box scandal.
d. Whiskey Ring.

Call to Freedom
349

41) Leading reformers Jane Addams and John Dewey belonged to the

    a. National Association for the Advancement of Colored People.
    b. National Urban League.
    c. National Child Labor Committee.
    d. National Consumers' League.


42) The president who doubled the number of national parks, created 16 national monuments, and established 51 wildlife refuges was

    a. Cleveland.             c. Roosevelt.
    b. Taft.                 d. Wilson.


43) The Wisconsin Idea, which became a model for other state governments, was

    a. Governor Robert La Follette's program of reform.
    b. John Patterson's system of council-manager government.
    c. Mayor Samuel Jones's argument for government as an instrument of progress.
    d. Susan Blow's proposal that public kindergartens teach basic social skills.


44) Many progressive reforms were put into place by the impressive legislative record of President

    a. Hayes.             c. Cleveland.
    b. Arthur.           d. Wilson.


45) The Eighteenth Amendment

    a. allowed the federal government to collect income taxes.
    b. prohibited the use of the grandfather clause.
    c. outlawed the production and sale of alcoholic beverages in the United States.
    d. gave women the right to vote.


46) The recall measure allows voters to

    a. approve or disapprove legislation already proposed by a state or local government.
    b. remove an elected official from office before the end of his or her term.
    c. choose candidates directly rather than relying on the choices of party leaders.
    d. vote again if they do not like the election's outcome.


47) The first trust that Roosevelt tackled was the

    a. Northern Securities Company.      c. meat-processing industry.
    b. Standard Oil Company.           d. railroads.

48) The purpose of the 1909 National Conference on City Planning was to

a. improve city transportation by paving streets.
b. improve urban housing by approving the construction of settlement houses.
c. eliminate unsafe housing, develop more park land, and improve public transportation.
d. improve city services by hiring sanitation engineers.


49) *The Souls of Black Folk* was written in 1903 by

a. Lincoln Steffens.
b. Upton Sinclair.
c. Booker T. Washington.
d. W.E.B. Du Bois.


50) The boss of New York City's political machine in the late 1800s was

a. Boss Blaine who ran the Mugwumps.
b. Boss Tweed who ran Tammany Hall.
c. Boss McClure who ran the Muckrakers.
d. Boss Haywood who ran the IWW.


51) The public could propose new laws by collecting a certain number of signatures on a petition under a measure known as the

a. initiative.
b. recall.
c. referendum.
d. direct primary.


52) Picketing, hunger strikes, and civil disobedience were methods used by members of the

a. Anti-Saloon League.
b. Niagara Movement.
c. National American Woman Suffrage Association.
d. National Woman's Party.


53) Immigrants, women, African Americans, and migrant workers were unionized by the

a. American Federation of Labor.
b. Industrial Workers of the World.
c. Nineteenth Amendment.
d. Seventeenth Amendment.


54) President Wilson appointed to the Supreme Court a progressive lawyer,

a. Florence Kelley, the first woman to become a Supreme Court justice.
b. Dr. W.E.B. Du Bois, the first African American to become a Supreme Court justice.
c. Louis Brandeis, the first Jewish person to become a Supreme Court justice.
d. Ing Wehteh, the first Chinese American to become a Supreme Court justice.


Call to Freedom
351

55) Reformers opposed to the spoils system wanted a system that used competitive exams to award government jobs based on

a. merit.                                        c. citizenship.
b. civil service.                             d. knowledge of the U.S. Constitution.


56) In his Atlanta Compromise speech of 1895, Booker T. Washington

a. argued that liberal arts education was more important than job training.
b. explained his philosophy that African Americans should focus on improving their own educational and economic well-being.
c. brought attention to cases of racial prejudice that demanded immediate action.
d. drew national attention to the lynching of almost 4,000 black men in the South in 1882.


57) Samuel Gompers and others like him supported the system called capitalism, in which

a. the government could decide how many hours a week a person could work.
b. the government or the workers own and operate a nation's means of production.
c. private businesses run most industries, and competition determines how much goods cost and how much workers are paid.
d. all workers must join a factory's union.


58) The first women to gain the right to vote lived in the

a. Northeast.                                 c. midwestern states.
b. southern states.                        d. western states.


59) The National Consumers' League led efforts to legislate

a. a minimum wage and an eight-hour work day.
b. safety in the workplace and workers' compensation.
c. mine and factory safety laws and new inspection regulations.
d. meat inspection laws and the prohibition of the sale of contaminated food and drugs.


60) America lived by the motto "Get rich; dishonestly if we can, honestly if we must" argued

a. Boss Tweed, in an 1888 speech to his political machine.
b. officials of the Union Pacific Railroad to members of Congress in 1872.
c. participants in The Whiskey Ring to President Grant.
d. Mark Twain, describing the Gilded Age.

## ENHANCED QUESTIONS
**For each of the following, circle the letter of the best choice. Next, expand on the subject by answering the second question in the space provided.**

61) In *Lochner* v. *New York*, the Supreme Court ruled against a 10-hour workday law for bakers, saying that the law

a. deprived businesses of property without due process of law.
b. violated the Fourteenth Amendment's guarantee of liberty.
c. would allow master and employee to contract with each other.
d. prevented the economy from operating without government interference.

Why did the Supreme Court uphold laws limiting women's hours in the 1908 case *Muller* v. *Oregon*? Why was this decision important for progressives?

_____

_____

62) Many people reacted to the widespread corruption of the Gilded Age by demanding

a. elimination of the spoils system of filling government jobs.
b. a socialist system that would reward big business for fair hiring practices.
c. a capitalist system that would place workers' concerns above those of big business.
d. a system of initiative and referendum in national elections.

Why did reformers oppose this system?

_____

_____

63) The party that built its platform around Roosevelt's New Nationalism was the

a. Democratic Party.
b. Republican Party.
c. Bull Moose Party.
d. Socialist Party.

What did this party's program call for, and how did Wilson's program differ?

_____

_____

64) Many reformers of city government wanted to

   a. elect officials in direct primaries.
   b. offer voter initiative to allow citizens to remove an official from office.
   c. allow the referendum to propose laws for adoption by city governments.
   d. replace elected officials with professionals who would run the city like a business.

   How did some city governments change as a result of reformers' efforts?

   _____

   _____


65) A highly effective reform organization with 10,000 local branches was the

   a. Women's Christian Temperance Union.
   b. Anti-Saloon League.
   c. National Woman's Party.
   d. NAACP.

   How did these reformers help influence legislation on the national level?

   _____

   _____

# GRAPHIC IMAGE QUESTIONS
**Examine the image, and then answer the following questions.**

## Women and Suffrage, 1890–1920

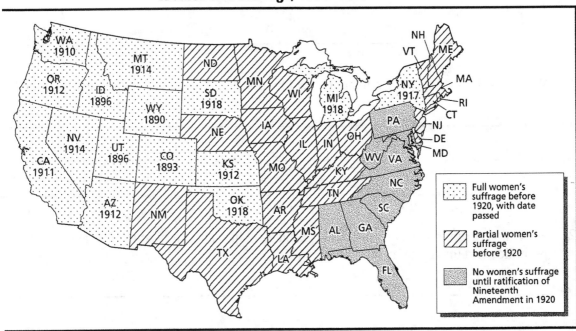

66) Which states had no women's suffrage before the ratification of the Nineteenth Amendment?

_____

67) Which state was the earliest to give women full suffrage?

_____

68) Which New England and Mid-Atlantic states had partial women's suffrage before 1920?

_____

## SHORT ANSWER
**Write a brief answer for each of the following.**

69) What were most progressives' common goals?

_____

_____

_____

70) What reforms did Woodrow Wilson accomplish during his presidency?

_____

_____

_____

71) Why was the suffrage movement opposed by political bosses and many businessmen?

_____

_____

_____

72) How did corrupt bosses and political machines help many immigrants rise above social prejudice and unemployment in the late 1800s?

_____

_____

_____

73) Why did some labor unions favor capitalism while others favored socialism?

_____

_____

_____

**ESSAY**
**On a separate sheet of paper, write an essay on one of the following.**

74) Describe how Lawrence Veiller, Florence Kelley, Susan Blow, John Dewey, and Joseph McCormack applied the scientific method to reform public health and education during the progressive era.

75) Explain why minorities were excluded from reform efforts as the result of what William D. Haywood called "an irreconcilable [incompatible] class struggle." How did Haywood and minority leaders work for reform, and what did they accomplish?

ANSWER KEY

1) referendum

2) Nineteenth Amendment

3) Ida Tarbell

4) Underwood Tariff

5) Federal Trade Commission

6) political machines

7) direct primary

8) Sixteenth Amendment

9) Seventeenth Amendment

10) arbitration

11) T

12) F
Taft transferred more land into government reserves than Roosevelt had.

13) T

14) F
Immigrants could move freely across the borders at this time.

15) F
Although Congress passed federal child labor laws in 1916 and 1919, the Supreme Court declared them unconstitutional.

Call to Freedom
357

16) F

When passed in 1883, the act affected only about 14,000 out of 130,000 federal jobs. The act has been expanded and now affects almost 90 percent of government jobs.

17) T

18) T

19) T

20) F

Roosevelt was the first president to consider conservation an important national issue.

21) d

22) b

23) a

24) c

25) b

26) a

27) c

28) d

29) a

30) d

31) b

# ANSWER KEY

32) b

33) c

34) a

35) c

36) d

37) b

38) a

39) c

40) d

41) a

42) c

43) a

44) d

45) c

46) b

47) a

48) c

ANSWER KEY

49) d

50) b

51) a

52) d

53) b

54) c

55) a

56) b

57) c

58) d

59) a

60) d

61) b
The Court argued that "woman's physical structure and the performance of maternal functions place her at a disadvantage," and therefore their health was a matter of public concern. This was the first case successfully argued from social evidence rather than prior legal principle.

62) a
The spoils system allowed the party in control of government to award jobs to loyal members, whether they were qualified or not. Every time a new party took power, many current government employees were replaced, resulting in ruined careers and inefficient administrations.

Call to Freedom

63) c
New Nationalism called for a strong executive, more active regulation, and the enactment of more social welfare measures. Wilson's New Freedom program called for government action against trusts to ensure free competition in the economy. Wilson also wanted to expand opportunities for small businesses and reduce the tariff rate.

64) d
Several cities changed to a council-manager government, in which a city council appoints a city manager to run the city. This system put power in the hands of professional administrators rather than elected city council members.

65) a
Temperance efforts led to the passage of the Eighteenth Amendment in 1919, which outlawed the production and sale of alcoholic beverages in the United States.

66) PA, MD, WV, VA, NC, SC, GA, AL, FL

67) Wyoming

68) ME, NH, VT, MA, RI, CT, NJ, DE

69) Progressives wanted the government to respond to the needs of its citizens so that people and government working together could solve social problems. Many believed they could accomplish these goals through government regulation of business, health, and safety. They focused their efforts on improving health and education in poor neighborhoods, reforming government, and regulating business.

70) Wilson initiated the Underwood Tariff Act of 1913, the Clayton Antitrust Act of 1914, and pushed for establishment of the Federal Trade Commission in 1914. He accomplished banking reform with the Federal Reserve Act of 1913. He also helped pass the Keating-Owen Child Labor Act, workers' compensation for federal employees, and the Adamson Act which granted railroad workers an 8-hour workday.

71) Political bosses feared women's anticorruption efforts, and many businessmen opposed women's proposals for prohibition and workplace reforms, such as child labor laws and the minimum wage. The vote would give women more power to achieve such reforms.

72) The boss system offered immigrants jobs and social mobility—opportunities often denied to them in larger society. In exchanging their votes for the assurance of a job, Irish immigrants were among those hired to fill 12,000 jobs given to Tammany Hall supporters in 1888.

73) The most powerful labor union, the AFL, favored capitalism in which private businesses run most industries, and competition determines how much goods cost and how much workers are paid. Some workers and union leaders claimed that capitalism was unfair. Instead, they supported socialism, a system in which the government or the workers own and operate a nation's means of production. Socialists such as IWW members hoped that the government would be more sympathetic to workers' concerns than those of big business.

74) Reformers who used the scientific method thought that they could make reforms by studying a problem and then changing the environment. Lawrence Veiller studied the problem of a child living his or her early years in dark rooms, without sunlight or fresh air, and concluded that a child in this environment does not grow up to be a normal healthy person. Veiller successfully campaigned for the 1901 New York State Tenement House Law, which outlawed the construction of dark and airless tenements. The law required new buildings to have better ventilation, toilets, and running water. Florence Kelley's strategy was to "investigate, educate, legislate, and enforce." Beginning her career as a social reformer at Hull House, Kelley traveled throughout the nation lobbying for labor laws to protect women and children. She and her three children had less to investigate, since they themselves found refuge at Hull House in 1891. Kelley took her personal experience and strategy to the national level, serving as a board member of the National Consumers' League. She established around 60 local consumer leagues that lobbied for women's and children's labor issues. Many progressives believed that by improving public education, they could cure social ills and meet the demand from business and industry for better-educated managers. Susan Blow opened the first public kindergarten in St. Louis, Missouri in 1873. Kindergartens taught basic social skills to children between the ages of three and seven, and served the needs of poor city residents, particularly immigrants. John Dewey, an important philosopher and educator, tried to develop teaching methods suited to the interests and needs of students. Dewey wanted to teach children problem-solving skills rather than memorization. The teaching methods that Dewey designed at Chicago's Laboratory School became the model for progressive education throughout the country. Joseph McCormack addressed the need for more well-trained and professionally organized doctors, as well as a medical organization to help spread new medical knowledge. Under McCormack's leadership, the AMA was reorganized in 1901 and joined other progressives in support of laws protecting public health. These reform efforts reflected the progressive belief that society could be improved through the application of scientific method.

75) Haywood, leader of the Industrial Workers of the World, believed that workers and capitalists were engaged in a class struggle that socialism would resolve. Many Americans, particularly those who were rich and powerful, were frightened by the beliefs and actions of the IWW. The IWW unionized many workers who were unwelcome in the AFL and who suffered from prejudice in society: immigrants, women, African Americans, and migrant workers. Migrant workers, American Indians, Chinese Americans, and Mexican Americans did not notably benefit from the general reforms of the progressive movement. Chinese Americans often faced violent discrimination during the late 1800s. Many moved into neighborhoods that became segregated in cities such as San Francisco. Even so, urban reform did little to help Chinese Americans. Mexicans and Mexican Americans who worked in agricultural jobs in Texas and California may have benefited from the IWW's inclusion of migrant workers. However, Mexicans and Mexican Americans struggled to protect their economic and political rights throughout the progressive era. White reformers of the progressive movement also ignored issues involving African Americans. Racial discrimination and segregation increased throughout the nation even while reforms were being initiated for members of other races and classes. Booker T. Washington founded the Tuskegee Institute to provide education and training for African American teachers. He argued that African Americans should not spend their efforts fighting discrimination and segregation but instead should focus on improving their own educational and economic well-being. Other leaders such as Ida B. Wells-Barnett disagreed with Washington. She wrote editorials in her Memphis newspaper *Free Speech* to draw national attention to the lynching of black men in the South. W.E.B. Du Bois also took a direct approach to fighting racial prejudice. Dr. Du Bois brought attention to cases of racial prejudice and wrote dozens of articles and speeches. He and other leaders committed to immediate action met at Niagara Falls, Canada in 1905. Calling themselves the Niagara Movement, the group demanded economic and educational equality, as well as an end to segregation and discrimination. To further the goals of the Niagara movement, Du Bois helped found the NAACP in 1901. He acted as director of publicity and research and editor of the NAACP journal *Crisis*. American Indians—a minority group whose population had declined to about 250,000 in the 1890s—founded the Society of American Indians in 1911. Members believed that adopting the beliefs and practices of the larger society was the best solution to Indians' poverty and unemployment. The organization claimed to speak "for the weak and helpless, for the discouraged and hopeless of our race." Most of its members, however, did not understand the views of Indians who lived on reservations. As for Haywood, who spoke up for the rights of minorities, his union had weakened and practically disappeared by 1920.

# Chapter 21 America As a World Power

**MATCHING**
In the space provided, write the term or the name of the person that best fits the description. Choose your answers from the list below. Not all answers will be used.

imperialism                    subsidy                        Henry Cabot Lodge
dollar diplomacy               Hay-Herrán Treaty              Anti-Imperialist League
General Leonard Wood           spheres of influence          William Seward
Teller Amendment               General John J. Pershing       Hay–Bunau-Varilla Treaty
Captain James Cook             isolationism                  Platt Amendment

1) _____ led 15,000 U.S. soldiers into Mexico to stop Pancho Villa

2) _____ declared that the United States had no intention of taking over Cuba

3) _____ the practice of extending a nation's power by gaining territories for a colonial empire

4) _____ avoiding involvement in the affairs of other nations

5) _____ arranged the purchase of Alaska from Russia for less than two cents per acre

6) _____ treaty that widened the canal zone and enabled the United States to build the Panama Canal

7) _____ areas where foreign nations control trade and natural resources

8) _____ group of Americans who opposed the 1898 peace treaty between the United States and Spain

9) _____ bonus payment

10) _____ policy that emphasized using U.S. economic power and business investment to influence Latin American governments

**TRUE/FALSE**
Write T is a statement is true or F if it is false. If a statement is false, explain why.

11) _____ The Panama Canal was successfully completed under the direction of chief engineer Ferdinand de Lesseps.

## TRUE/FALSE
**Write T is a statement is true or F if it is false.  If a statement is false, explain why.**

11) _____ The Panama Canal was successfully completed under the direction of chief engineer Ferdinand de Lesseps.

_____

12) _____ The nations known as the ABC Powers were America, Britain, and China.

_____

13) _____ In 1900 Dr. Walter Reed proved that yellow fever was transmitted by mosquitoes.

_____

14) _____ In fewer than 50 years, Japan became a world power.

_____

15) _____ President Theodore Roosevelt initiated the policy known as dollar diplomacy by expanding U.S. businesses in Latin America.

_____

16) _____ In 1916 Pancho Villa and his Mexican revolutionaries attacked and burned an American town, killing 17 U.S. citizens.

_____

17) _____ President Grover Cleveland supported the planters' government by annexing Hawaii in 1898.

_____

18) _____ The most colorful group of soldiers in the Spanish American War were the Rough Riders, who were organized by William Randolph Hearst.

_____

19) _____ The McKinley Tariff caused Hawaii's economy to collapse.

_____

20) _____ The Roosevelt Corollary expanded U.S. foreign policy as first set forth in the Monroe Doctrine.

_____

## MULTIPLE CHOICE
**For each of the following, circle the letter of the best choice.**

21) In order to open trade with Japan, President Millard Fillmore

　a. met with leaders of the Tokugawa family in 1854.
　b. organized the Meiji Restoration in 1868.
　c. sent Commodore Matthew Perry there in 1853.
　d. negotiated a commercial treaty with Tokugawa shoguns in 1858.

22) In the late 1800s all that remained of Spain's once-great American empire were

　a. Cuba and Puerto Rico.
　b. Columbia and Mexico.
　c. Venezuela and Mexico.
　d. Cuba, Puerto, and the Dominican Republic.

23) President Woodrow Wilson lifted the arms embargo on Mexico and stationed U.S. warships near Veracruz as a result of conflicts between

　a. Pancho Villa and Venustiano Carranza.
　b. General Victoriano Huerta and Carranza.
　c. Pancho Villa and Emiliano Zapata.
　d. Huerta and Francisco Madero.

24) Phillipe Bunau-Varilla

　a. initiated the Hay–Bunau-Varilla Treaty, which ended the Spanish-American War.
　b. helped put down a revolution that was brewing in Colombia in 1903.
　c. was killed in the Spanish-American War.
　d. organized a revolt in Panama.

25) In 1893 sugar planters in Hawaii revolted because

　a. Chief Kamehameha united Hawaiian resistance.
　b. King Kalakaua signed a new constitution.
　c. the McKinley Tariff had reduced their profits.
　d. Queen Liliuokalani attempted to restore power to the Hawaiian monarchy.

26) The United States first became interested in Hawaii after

　a. British explorer Captain James Cook arrived in the islands in 1778.
　b. miners discovered gold there in 1889.
　c. Queen Liliuokalani took the throne in 1891.
　d. planters established a new government with Sanford B. Dole as president.

27) At the same time that the United States was investing more than $1 billion in Mexico,

    a. John J. Pershing was organizing a revolt against the Mexican government.
    b. most of Mexico's 15 million people were landless and impoverished.
    c. democratic reformer Porfirio Díaz led Mexico's people in a revolt against Madero.
    d. Pancho Villa was planning an attack on border towns in the United States.

28) After Commodore George Dewey destroyed Spain's Pacific fleet in Manilla Bay,

    a. Cubans signed the Platt Amendment that provided protection by U.S. troops.
    b. U.S. troops commanded by Nelson Miles invaded Cuba and met little resistance.
    c. Spain asked for peace and signed a cease-fire in July 1900.
    d. U.S. ships destroyed Spain's Caribbean fleet in the Battle of Santiago Bay.

29) When nations first negotiated for the right to build a canal across Panama,

    a. Panama was controlled by Venezuela.    c. Panama was a province of Colombia.
    b. Spain was still in control of Panama.    d. Panama was a part of the Dominican Republic.

30) In 1887 Hawaii's King Kalakaua signed a new constitution

    a. that returned power to the monarchy.
    b. granting more power to the Hawaiian parliament, which was controlled by planters.
    c. and established a new government headed by Sanford B. Dole.
    d. allowing Hawaiian sugar to be shipped duty-free to the U.S.

31) Of the U.S. soldiers who died during the Spanish-American War,

    a. far more died from food poisoning and disease than from battle wounds.
    b. most were killed by enemy fire.
    c. few caught yellow fever.
    d. most were shot by other U.S. soldiers.

32) Dr. William C. Gorgas contributed to the digging of the Panama Canal by

    a. discovering that mosquitoes cause yellow fever.
    b. discovering that mosquitoes cause malaria and yellow fever.
    c. organizing a vast effort to rid the canal route of the mosquitoes that cause malaria and yellow fever.
    d. providing educational materials about the dangers of yellow fever.

33) Taft wanted to enforce the Monroe Doctrine by

    a. isolating the United States from the countries in Latin America.
    b. allowing U.S. economic power to influence Latin American governments.
    c. turning Latin American countries such as Nicaragua into U.S. territories.
    d. removing U.S. businesses from Latin America.

34) In 1910 the Mexican people found a leader in democratic reformer

a. Victoriano Huerta, who assumed power in February 1913.
b. Porfirio Díaz, who captured Ciudad Juàrez in 1911.
c. Venustiano Carranza, who led a people's revolution against Díaz.
d. Francisco Madero, who began the Mexican Revolution.

35) In 1867 the United States greatly expanded its territory

a. when Secretary of State William Seward annexed Alaska and Samoa.
b. by annexing Samoa and the Midway Islands.
c. with the acquisition of Alaska's 600,000 square miles.
d. with acquisitions gained under the Peace of Paris Treaty with Spain.

36) In 1898 the U.S. Congress issued a resolution that declared Cuba independent,

a. even though Cuba was not a U.S. territory.
b. a move that angered many American citizens who supported Weyler's regime.
c. resulting in the organization of the Anti-Imperialist League.
d. and passed the Philippine Government Act, which granted full independence to the Philippines.

37) America and Mexico stood at the brink of war after U.S. Marines prevented Huerta from receiving arms and weapons supplied by

a. Great Britain.                    c. Russia.
b. Spain.                            d. Germany.

38) The Open Door Policy meant that

a. all European nations should have equal access to trade with Japan.
b. all nations should have equal access to trade with China.
c. Latin American countries were free to trade with all other nations.
d. Japan would allow U.S. ships to enter its harbors after leaders signed the Treaty of Kangawa.

39) Before the Panama Canal opened to traffic on August 15, 1914,

a. Theodore Roosevelt asked Congress to declare war on Colombia.
b. Dr. William C. Gorgas had died of yellow fever.
c. some 6,000 lives were lost building it.
d. workers blasted through 51 miles of solid rock to connect the Atlantic and Pacific oceans.

40) As a result of the McKinley Tariff in 1890,

a. prices for Hawaiian sugar dropped, and the islands' economy collapsed.
b. many Hawaiians worried that foreigners were becoming too powerful.
c. many missionaries and their families moved to Hawaii.
d. thousands of Chinese and Japanese workers arrived in Hawaii in the hopes of growing wealthy in the sugar industry.

Call to Freedom

41) The Roosevelt Corollary was developed in part because of debt problems in

a. Nicaragua and Honduras.
b. Venezuela and the Dominican Republic.
c. Cuba and Puerto Rico.
d. Panama and the Philippines.

42) President Taft's policy of dollar diplomacy led him to establish financial and military agreements with

a. Nicaragua and Honduras.
b. Venezuela and the Dominican Republic.
c. Cuba and Puerto Rico.
d. Panama and the Philippines.

43) Between 1870 and 1914, Europeans built vast colonial empires that seized control of

a. China and Russia.
b. Canada and Mexico.
c. most of Africa and much of Southeast Asia.
d. Hawaii and Alaska.

44) Two major revolutionaries who emerged during the Mexican Revolution were

a. John J. Pershing and Leonard Wood.
b. Cipriano Castro and Valeriano Weyler.
c. Philippe Bunau-Varilla and Thomas Herrán.
d. Pancho Villa and Emiliano Zapata.

45) The purchase that some people called Seward's Folly provided the United States with

a. control of the Samoan Islands.
b. furs, timber, and mineral wealth.
c. a naval refueling station in the Midway Islands.
d. economic control of a thriving sugar industry.

46) "Remember the *Maine*!" became a rallying cry for angry U.S. citizens after

a. Japan sank the U.S. battleship *Maine* during the Russo-Japanese War.
b. Germany sank the *Maine* while it lay in harbor in China's Shandong Province.
c. the *Maine* exploded and sank in Havana Harbor.
d. U.S. soldiers were arrested in Maine.

47) Japan's efforts to modernize and industrialize their nation began in

a. 1868 during the Meiji Restoration.
b. 1856 after Townsend Harris became the first U.S. consul general to Japan.
c. 1895 after Japan invaded and defeated China.
d. 1904 after Japan defeated Russia in the Russo-Japanese War.

48) President Wilson delayed intervening in the Mexican Revolution because he believed that

a. the United States and Latin America should recognize Madero as president of Mexico.
b. the United States should respect the Teller Amendment.
c. Americans' economic interests there did not merit a show of U.S. military force.
d. the U.S. Army was unprepared to train and supply 25,000 soldiers to fight in Mexico.

49) President Wilson's foreign policies differed from Taft's in that he

a. approved of the role of big business in foreign affairs.
b. believed in imperialism and wanted to protect America's economic interests in Latin America.
c. wanted to expand U.S. businesses in Latin America in order to keep Europeans out of the region.
d. believed that the United States had a moral obligation to promote democracy.

50) Spain sent General Valeriano Weyler to Cuba

a. after the Cuban revolt of 1868.
b. to crush the second Cuban rebellion in 1895.
c. to free the several hundred thousand Cubans imprisoned in *reconcentrados*, or reconcenration camps.
d. after the U.S. battleship *Maine* exploded and sank in Havana Harbor.

51) Woodrow Wilson sent more troops into Latin America than any president before him because

a. he wanted to bring democracy to Latin America.
b. he wanted to take over Latin America.
c. he believed that the economic interests of the United States were more important than any other goal.
d. Secretary of State William Jennings Bryan advised him to do so.

52) Wilson demanded an apology from Huerta after U.S. sailors were

a. killed by Villa in Columbus, New Mexico.    c. arrested in Tampico.
b. attacked by Villa's forces in Veracruz.    d. imprisoned for six weeks in Santa Ysabel.

53) In the late 1800s spheres of influence in China were established by

a. Japan and Russia.
b. Germany, Great Britain, and France.
c. Japan, France and Russia.
d. Germany, Russia, Great Britain, France, and Japan.

54) Haiti and the Dominican Republic came under stricter U.S. control during the presidency of

a. William McKinley.    c. William Howard Taft.
b. Theodore Roosevelt.    d. Woodrow Wilson.

55) Secretary of State Seward advised annexing territories

a. to protect the people there from monarchy.
b. to continue the United States's westward expansion.
c. to prevent China from growing even larger.
d. to provide a place for America's growing population.

Call to Freedom

56) In 1946 the United Sates granted full independence to

    a. Cuba.
    b. Puerto Rico.
    c. the Philippines.
    d. Panama.

57) After the 1894 invasion of China, Japan won

    a. trading privileges with Russia.
    b. control of Korea and Port Arthur in China.
    c. control of all Chinese trade.
    d. control of all foreign spheres of influence in China.

58) After the United States recognized Venustiano Carranza as president of Mexico, U.S. troops continued to fight

    a. Huerta's revolutionary forces.
    b. Carranza after his troops invaded New Mexico.
    c. the borderland guerrillas led by Zapata.
    d. troops led by Pancho Villa.

59) When Wilson sent 12,000 soldiers into Mexico in 1916, Mexicans

    a. fought back by burning Columbus, New Mexico and killing 17 U.S. citizens.
    b. welcomed U.S. intervention in the border war that threatened their lives and economy.
    c. greatly resented having U.S. troops in their country.
    d. stopped a train at Santa Ysabel, Mexico, and killed 18 U.S. mining engineers on board.

60) Hawaii became a U.S. territory in 1900 and the 50th state in

    a. 1917.
    b. 1932.
    c. 1945.
    d. 1959.

## ENHANCED QUESTIONS
**For each of the following, circle the letter of the best choice. Next, expand on the subject by answering the second question in the space provided.**

61) The Roosevelt Corollary

    a. gave an economic emphasis to the Monroe Doctrine.
    b. said that the Monroe Doctrine would apply only to European nations.
    c. said that the United States would intervene to enforce the Monroe Doctrine.
    d. added Japan and China to the nations covered by the Monroe Doctrine.

How did Roosevelt change U.S. policy in Latin America?

_____

_____

Call to Freedom
371

62) U.S. ships were able to blockade the Spanish Caribbean fleet in the harbor of Santiago de Cuba because

a. the U.S. fleet was larger and more powerful.
b. Theodore Roosevelt's actions on San Juan Hill inspired the U.S. Navy.
c. the Spanish fleet was unprepared for the U.S. forces.
d. Cuban revolutionaries detained the Spanish fleet.

What happened as a result of this blockade?

_____

_____

63) The peace treaty between Spain and the United States resulted in U.S. control of

a. the Philippines.
b. Cuba and the Philippines.
c. Puerto Rico, Guam, and the Philippines.
d. Puerto Rico, Guam, Cuba, and the Philippines.

How did Filipinos react to U.S. control?

_____

_____

64) In 1900 the Foraker Act established a civil government for the U.S. territory of

a. Guam.                          c. Samoa.
b. Puerto Rico.                   d. the Midway Islands.

How did this territory's government change in 1952?

_____

_____

65) Japanese leaders opened trade with the United States primarily because of

a. Perry's presentation of technological marvels to Japanese leaders.
b. Perry's show of force in Edo Harbor.
c. President Fillmore's letter suggesting a peaceful trade relationship.
d. their victory in the Russo-Japanese War.

How did Japan view the technological benefits of trade?

_____

_____

Call to Freedom

## GRAPHIC IMAGE QUESTIONS
Examine the image, and then answer the following questions.

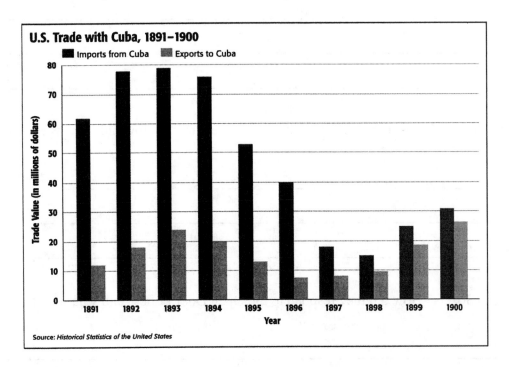

**U.S. Trade with Cuba, 1891–1900**

Source: *Historical Statistics of the United States*

66) About how much was the difference between the imports from Cuba and the exports to Cuba in 1891?

_____

67) In what year was the value of goods exported to Cuba closest to the value of goods imported from Cuba?

_____

68) In what year was the value of imports from Cuba greatest?

_____

## SHORT ANSWER
Write a brief answer for each of the following.

69) Define yellow journalism and describe its impact on U.S. involvement in Cuba.

_____

_____

_____

70) Why did many Americans favor expansion over isolationism?

_____

_____

_____

71) How did the Platt Amendment differ from the Teller Amendment? How did Cubans react to the Platt Amendment?

_____

_____

_____

72) Who were the Boxers? How did they respond to the Open Door Policy, and what was the result?

_____

_____

_____

73) How did the philosophy of Alfred T. Mahan influence Roosevelt's decision to build a stronger navy as well as a canal through Central America?

_____

_____

_____

**ESSAY**
**On a seperate sheet of paper, write an essay on one of the following.**

74) Describe the political and geographical obstacles America overcame in order to build the Panama Canal. Explain the significance of the project and America's motivation for

75) How did the Mexican Revolution affect U.S.-Mexican relations as well as Mexican immigration to the United States in the early 1900s?

Call to Freedom

# ANSWER KEY

1) General John J. Pershing

2) Teller Amendment

3) imperialism

4) isolationism

5) William Seward

6) Hay–Bunau-Varilla Treaty

7) spheres of influence

8) Anti-Imperialist League

9) subsidy

10) dollar diplomacy

11) F
John Stevens and George W. Goethals were the chief engineers of the Panama Canal. De Lesseps engineered the Suez Canal in Egypt, and headed a French company that went bankrupt attempting to canal through Panama in 1881.

12) F
The ABC Powers were Argentina, Brazil, and Chile.

13) T

14) T

15) F
President William Howard Taft initiated dollar diplomacy.

16) T

17) F

Cleveland disapproved of the planters' revolt and refused to annex Hawaii.

18) F

Theodore Roosevelt organized the Rough Riders.

19) T

20) T

21) c

22) a

23) b

24) d

25) d

26) a

27) b

28) d

29) c

30) b

31) a

32) c

33) b

34) d

Call to Freedom

# ANSWER KEY

35) c

36) a

37) d

38) b

39) c

40) a

41) b

42) a

43) c

44) d

45) b

46) c

47) a

48) c

49) d

50) b

51) a

52) c

53) d

54) d

55) b

56) c

57) b

58) d

59) c

60) d

61) c
He gave the United States the role of the Western Hemisphere's "police officer." Under his policies the U.S. military could intervene in Latin American countries guilty of what he called "chronic wrongdoing."

62) a
The United States was able to land troops on Cuba. These troops, with the help of Cuban rebels were able to capture the hills around Santiago and overwhelm the Spanish defenders.

63) d
Filipino rebels had helped U.S. forces capture Manila, and expected to gain their independence after the war. When the United States decided to keep the islands, the rebels began a guerrilla war against U.S. forces that did not end until 1902.

64) b
In 1952 Puerto Rico became a commonwealth, with its own constitution and elected officials.

65) b
Many Japanese leaders beleived that their country needed to industrialize. In 1868 supporters of industrialization came to power and began a period of modernization.

66) imports were valued about $50 million greater than exports, or about six times the value of exports

# ANSWER KEY

67) 1900

68) 1893

69) Yellow journalism is the press's use of sensational, often exaggerated stories to attract readers. Joseph Pulitzer's *New York World* and William Randolph Hearst's *New York Journal* engaged in this practice by writing stories highly critical of Weyler, calling him "pitiless, cold, an exterminator of men." Hearst's paper even created the stories he wanted. To increase support for U.S. action in Cuba and to sell papers, Hearst hired artist Frederick Remington to provide pictures of island conditions. When Remington wrote to Hearst that "there will be no war," Hearst supposedly replied, "You furnish the pictures and I'll furnish the war." Such yellow journalism further increased American support for the Cubans.

70) Many Americans thought that to maintain its economic strength, the United States needed to expand its lands and increase its foreign trade instead of isolating itself from foreign nations. These Americans supported the creation of a strong U.S. military to protect U.S. economic interests around the world.

71) Although the Teller Amendment had stated that the United States had no intention of taking over Cuba, the Platt Amendment limited Cuba's right to make treaties with other nations, required Cuba to sell or lease land to the United States for naval stations, and authorized the United States to intervene in Cuban affairs. The Cubans reluctantly accepted the Platt Amendment.

72) The Boxers were Chinese nationalists who resented foreign involvement in Chinese affairs, such as the foreign trade supported by the Open Door Policy of the United States. The Boxers also opposed mismanagement by the Chinese government. In 1900 they laid siege to a foreign settlement in Beijing during what was called the Boxer Rebellion. They killed more than 200 people. After the Boxers were defeated, Secretary of State Hay sent another Open Door Note to Japan and the European nations, restating the U.S. position on trade with China. The Open Door policy remained in effect long after the Boxer Rebellion.

73) In his book *The Influence of Sea Power upon History*, Mahan argued that the United States needed a strong navy to protect its economic interests. He also explained that a strong navy required overseas bases and coaling stations. After the U.S. battleship *Oregon* failed to arrive in Cuba on time—due to a 67-day voyage around the southern tip of South America—Roosevelt wrote to Mahan, "I believe we should build the canal at once, and, in the meantime we should build a dozen new battleships." Roosevelt believed that naval power was essential to U.S. strength and security, and that the canal would eliminate problems such as the one experienced by the *Oregon*.

74) Since the early 1500s many people had dreamed of building a canal across the Isthmus of Panama in order to cut 8,000 miles off of the voyage between the Caribbean and the Pacific. In 1850 the U.S. and Britain agreed to build and maintain a canal, but the project was never begun. A French effort failed in 1887. The United States became interested once again during the Spanish-American War, when Pacific naval forces needed in the Caribbean were delayed by the long voyage around the southern tip of South America. In 1901 Britain surrendered its interest in the canal in exchange for a U.S. agreement to keep the canal open to all vessels at all times. Next, the United States negotiated with Colombia, the country that owned the proposed canal zone. In 1903 the Colombian government rejected the Hay-Herrán Treaty. That same year Phillipe Bunau-Varilla, the chief engineer of the French canal company, helped organize a revolution in the Colombian province of Panama. The United States then signed the Hay–Bunau-Varilla Treaty with Panama in 1903, paving the way for constructing a canal through 51 miles of dense jungles and swamps. These areas were home to many mosquitoes that carried malaria and yellow fever. Chief engineers John Stevens, George W. Goethals, and their laborers also had to blast and cut a channel through the high mountain range of central Panama. Some 6,000 lives were lost and hundreds of millions of dollars invested in the building of the canal, which finally opened to traffic in 1914. This achievement meant that the world finally had its "highway between the oceans."

75) President Wilson refused to recognize General Huerta, but avoided intervention in the Mexican Revolution until the Tampico incident in 1914. Before this incident could be resolved, Wilson sent U.S. Marines to seize Veracruz to prevent a German ship from delivering arms to Huerta. This assault killed 200 Mexicans and wounded 300, uniting Mexicans against the United States. The two nations stood on the brink of war until the ABC Powers settled the dispute. When Carranza came to power in Mexico, the United States recognized his government and withdrew U.S. troops from Veracruz. However, Mexican rebel Pancho Villa began attacking U.S. civilians in Mexico and New Mexico. Pershing's troops chased Villa more than 300 miles into Mexico, bringing the two countries close to war. Pershing's efforts were unsuccessful, and in 1920 Carranza was overthrown and the revolution ended. The disorder of the revolutionary years led many Mexicans to flee the war's violence and destruction, resulting in large-scale Mexican migration to the United States. Others fled to escape political persecution. The Mexican population of the United States increased dramatically. Over the years, economic and political factors have continued to draw Mexican immigrants to the United States.

# Chapter 22 World War I

## MATCHING
**In the space provided, write the term or the name of the person that best fits the description. Choose your answers from the list below. Not all answers will be used.**

| | | |
|---|---|---|
| U-boats | reparations | Archduke Francis Ferdinand |
| nationalism | mobilize | General John J. Pershing |
| militarism | Bernard Baruch | Selective Service Act |
| stalemate | self-determination | War Industries Board |
| armistice | balance of power | Committee on Public |

1) _____ payments for damages and expenses brought on by war

2) _____ a situation in which neither side can win a decisive victory

3) _____ required men between the ages of 21 and 30 to register to be drafted into the armed forces

4) _____ truce

5) _____ he and his wife Sophie were assassinated during a visit to Sarajevo

6) _____ German submarines

7) _____ prepare military forces for war

8) _____ the right of people to decide their own political status

9) _____ insisted that U.S. troops serve as a "distinct and separate component" of the combined allied forces in Europe

10) _____ the feeling that a specific nation, language, or culture was superior to all others.

## TRUE/FALSE
**Write T is a statement is true or F if it is false.  If a statement is false, explain why.**

11) _____ Liberty bonds provided money for loans to the Allies to allow them to purchase food and war supplies.

_____

12) _____ The Treaty of Brest-Litovsk removed Bulgaria from the war.

_____

13) _____ Fourteen nations around the world fought in World War I.

_____

14) _____ Food Administration leader Bernard Baruch promoted "meatless Mondays" and "wheatless Wednesdays" to decrease domestic consumption.

_____

15) _____ The Treaty of Versailles included all of President Wilson's Fourteen Points.

_____

16) _____ None of the women in the U.S. armed forces received any pay or pension for their service.

_____

17) _____ When World War I began, Austria-Hungary and Germany were known as the Central Powers while Britain, France, and Russia were called the Allied Powers.

_____

18) _____ The fighting at Verdun dragged on for 10 months, making it the longest battle of the war.

_____

19) _____ The American Expeditionary Force included the regular army, the National Guard, and a large force of volunteers and draftees.

_____

20) _____ The nations of Germany, Russia, Britain, and France were known as the Big Four.

_____

**MULTIPLE CHOICE**
**For each of the following, circle the letter of the best choice.**

21) Germany violated the terms of neutrality in the Atlantic when

a. a U-boat sank the British passenger liner *Lusitania*, killing nearly 1,200 people.
b. a U-boat torpedoed the British warship *Sussex*.
c. U-boats broke the *Sussex* pledge by resuming unrestricted submarine warfare.
d. Kaiser Wilhelm I had German merchant ships fitted with guns.

22) The War Industries Board head who had authority over all war industries was

a. Herbert Hoover.
b. George Creel.
c. Bernard Baruch.
d. Jeannette Rankin.

23) Wilson envisioned the League of Nations as an international congress of nations designed to

a. reward the allies and punish enemies.
b. punish Germany for its role in World War I.
c. avoid future wars with Germany.
d. settle disputes and protect democracy.

24) By the late 1800s the world's largest empire was controlled by

a. Germany.
b. Britain.
c. France.
d. Russia.

25) The African American 369th U.S. Infantry, the so-called Harlem Hell Fighters,

a. blew up every temporary bridge that the Germans had built across the Marne.
b. launched the first distinctly American assault at the Second Battle of the Marne.
c. were awarded France's highest military honor for their bravery.
d. were the most decorated combat unit in the war.

26) ". . . the world must be made safe for democracy," said

a. President Wilson.
b. former president Theodore Roosevelt.
c. Henry Cabot Lodge.
d. David Lloyd George.

27) Germany issued the *Sussex* pledge, which included a promise not to

a. violate the terms of neutrality in the Atlantic.
b. sink merchant vessels "without warning and without saving human lives."
c. carry war materials on merchant vessels.
d. "violate the fundamental decencies of civilization."

28) Most of the Fourteen Points dealt with

a. a system to avoid future wars.
b. a vision for postwar Europe.
c. the future of specific nations and regions.
d. the right of people to decide their own political status.

29) The war which later generations would know as World War I was originally called the

a. European War.
b. Austria-Hungarian War.
c. German-Baltic War.
d. Great War.

30) The purpose of the Committee on Public Information was to

a. increase public support for the war effort.
b. recruit movie stars to entertain troops.
c. hold rallies and parades for troops bound for Europe.
d. encourage Americans to rename all things German, such as hamburgers and dachshunds.

31) The "powder keg" of Eastern Europe was lit

a. when Austria-Hungary declared war on Serbia.
b. by the assassination of Archduke Ferdinand.
c. when czar Nicholas II mobilized Russian troops.
d. by Austrian shells launched at the Serbian city of Belgrade.

32) World War I was a conflict unlike any other due to

a. the great number of European nations involved.
b. American involvement in the battles between European nations.
c. new war strategies and new weapons.
d. trench warfare and the use of tanks and machine guns.

33) Two new nations that were formed by the Treaty of Versailles were

a. Estonia and Finland.
b. Latvia and Lithuania.
c. Estonia and Yugoslavia.
d. Czechoslovakia and Yugoslavia.

34) The policy of aggressive military preparedness is

a. militarism.
b. imperialism.
c. mobilization.
d. nationalism.

35) When forced to take a side in the war in Europe, Americans

a. supported the Allies.
b. supported the Central Powers.
c. sympathized with the Allies and with the Central Powers.
d. sympathized with Austria-Hungary while supporting France.

36) The Allied troops' need for American products plus the serious labor shortage created by the war combined to produce

a. more industrial jobs for women.
b. a favorable environment for labor.
c. benefits for women and minorities.
d. fewer strikes and better working conditions.

37) In 1915 the Allied Powers were

    a. Austria-Hungary and Germany.           c. Britain, France, and the United States.
    b. France, Italy, Russia, and the United States.   d. Britain, France, Russia, and Italy.

38) World War I soldiers were the first forces to have to protect themselves against

    a. airplanes that crash-landed in no-man's land.
    b. artillery shells that contained deadly chlorine gas and mustard gas.
    c. food rations poisoned by the enemy.
    d. machine guns that sent out 40-60 rounds of ammunition per minute.

39) "Doughboys" was the nickname given to

    a. U.S. soldiers.           c. German tanks.
    b. German soldiers.      d. hard biscuits.

40) The Paris peace conference was a clash between Wilson's ideals of peace and democracy, and

    a. Clemenceau's desire to punish Germany for invading and crushing France.
    b. David Lloyd George's desire to keep the British Empire together.
    c. the European leaders' desire to reward their allies and punish their enemies.
    d. the Big Four's desire to blame Germany for Europe's economic losses.

41) As a part of the 1918 cease-fire agreement,

    a. Poland became a free nation.
    b. Germany had to surrender its aircraft, tanks, and heavy artillery.
    c. Austria-Hungary surrendered its U-boats.
    d. Germany became a republic.

42) Under the Espionage Act of 1917 and the Sedition Act of 1918,

    a. the army built dozens of training camps.
    b. some 900 American opponents of the war were jailed.
    c. more than one million men between the ages of 21 and 30 were drafted into the armed forces.
    d. German Americans were charged with disloyalty, and some 600 lost their jobs.

43) Germany used its U-boats to

    a. sink Lithuanian merchant ships in the North Sea.
    b. torpedo U.S. ships without warning.
    c. prevent supplies from reaching Britain and the Allies.
    d. stop French supply ships from reaching the port of Verdun.

44) Before large numbers of U.S. troops joined in the fighting, the Germans launched

    a. its first offensive near Flanders, Belgium.
    b. its second offensive along the Somme River in northern France.
    c. two offensives in Belgium.
    d. three major offensives.

45) Wilson's Fourteen Points

    a. outlined a vision for postwar Europe and a system to avoid future wars.
    b. called for a 1917 peace conference near Versailles.
    c. outlined peace terms that were so hard on the Central Powers that they would not cause another war.
    d. was so-called because it dealt with the future of fourteen specific nations.

46) Many Slavic nationalists belonged to a secret group known as the

    a. Baltic Underground, which supported the Allied Powers.
    b. Black Hand, which used violence to achieve its goals.
    c. Knights of Latvia, led by Gavrilo Princip.
    d. Lithuanian League, led by Serbs who wanted Lithuania to become a free nation.

47) Due to congressional opposition and President Wilson's refusal to negotiate, the United States

    a. did not send representatives to the peace conference at Versailles.
    b. was not represented on the council of the League of Nations.
    c. did not ratify the Treaty of Versailles, and never joined the League of Nations.
    d. refused to allow the former Central Powers to join the League of Nations.

48) President Wilson created the War Industries Board to

    a. give Herbert Hoover greater control over the war effort.
    b. oversee the production and distribution of goods manufactured by the nation's war industries.
    c. provide money for loans to the Allies to allow them to purchase war materials manufactured in the United States.
    d. establish price and production controls over farm machinery, fertilizer, food, and fuel.

49) Most of the supplies and war materials used by the Allies were carried by

    a. U.S. ships.               c. the British merchant ship *Lusitania*.
    b. British U-boats.         d. the French merchant ship *Sussex*.

50) Russia mobilized for war to support

    a. Germany.               c. Serbia.
    b. Austria-Hungary.       d. Belgium.

51) The CPI head who launched a nationwide campaign of publicity and propaganda was

a. Henry Cabot Lodge.
b. Bernard Baruch.
c. Herbert Hoover.
d. George Creel.

52) Two massive systems of opposing trenches stretched

a. for 40 miles along France's eastern boundary.
b. for 400 miles across the western front.
c. from Berlin to Verdun.
d. from Belgrade to the Somme River, in northeastern France.

53) For President Wilson, the most important part of the peace settlement was

a. the creation of the League of Nations.
b. persuading the U.S. Senate to ratify separate treaties with Germany and Austria.
c. ensuring that Italy received the territory it had been promised when it agreed to support the Allies.
d. punishing Germany so severely that it could never again threaten Europe.

54) The first country to declare war in 1914 was

a. Germany, which declared war on France.
b. Germany, which declared war on Russia.
c. Austria-Hungry, which declared war on Serbia.
d. Austria-Hungary, which declared war on German

55) Almost 3 million American men who fought in World War I were

a. veterans of the Spanish-American War.
b. members of the National Guard.
c. required to serve in segregated units.
d. draftees.

56) The peace conference at Versailles was attended by the leaders of

a. the Big Four nations.
b. 55 nations.
c. 13 European nations, the United States and Britain.
d. the United States, Britain, and all European nations other than Germany.

57) By 1918 an average of 802 German civilians were dying daily from

a. starvation.
b. disease.
c. the effects of poison gas.
d. wounds received from exploding artillery shells.

58) President Wilson's opponent in the election of 1916 was

a. Herbert Hoover.
b. Henry Cabot Lodge.
c. Charles Evans Hughes.
d. Arthur Zimmerman.

59) The Food Administration was created to

a. provide rations for the more than 3 million Allied troops serving in Europe.
b. motivate farmers to produce high levels of food.
c. guarantee farmers high prices for their crops.
d. increase agricultural production and decrease domestic consumption.

60) World War I ended when the

a. armistice went into effect.
b. the Allies reached a peace agreement with Austria-Hungary.
c. Kaiser Wilhelm II abandoned the throne and fled to the Netherlands.
d. the Ottoman Empire quit the war.

## ENHANCED QUESTIONS
**For each of the following, circle the letter of the best choice. Next, expand on the subject by answering the second question in the space provided.**

61) Trench warfare was the strategy of

a. driving enemy troops into 40-foot-long ditches that prevented soldiers from advancing forward.
b. fighting from deep ditches to defend a position.
c. using airplanes to fire on soldiers who dug long, deep ditches to protect themselves from enemy bullets and shells.
d. launching artillery shells into deep ditches where soldiers lived for weeks while defending their positions.

Describe no-man's-land and its impact on trench warfare.

_____

_____

62) In the First Battle of the Marne,

a. French troops launched a daring counterattack against Germany, rushing to stop the enemy along the Marne River east of Paris.
b. the Russians attacked the Central Powers along the Marne River in East Prussia.
c. the Belgians fiercely resisted the Germany army, upsetting the Schlieffen Plan.
d. the Allies launched a two-pronged attack on Germany—one in the north through Belgium and one in the south along the Marne River.

What role did U.S. troops and military personnel play in the Second Battle of the Marne?

_____

_____

Call to Freedom

63) The Triple Entente united Britain, France, and Russia in

a. 1893, 15 years before the Triple Alliance united Germany and Italy.
b. 1917, 25 years after the Triple Alliance united Germany and Austria-Hungary.
c. 1907, 15 years after the Triple Alliance united Austria-Hungary, Germany, and Italy.
d. 1879, 18 years before the Triple Alliance united Austria-Hungary, Bosnia, and Herzegovina.

Define balance of power, and explain how the Triple Entente and the Triple Alliance affected Europe's balance of power.

_____

_____

64) Americans were outraged when the Zimmerman Note revealed a proposed alliance between

a. Germany and Belgium against the United States.
b. Austria-Hungary and Germany against the United States.
c. Russia and Germany against the United States.
d. Germany and Mexico against the United States.

How did President Wilson and Congress respond to the Zimmerman Note?

_____

_____

65) In April 1918 President Wilson created the National War Labor Board to

a. settle disputes between workers and management.
b. replace more than 4 million striking workers in the railroad and automobile industries.
c. encourage women to work in factory positions left vacant by departing soldiers.
d. oversee the production of steel, copper, cement, rubber, and other basic materials.

How did workers benefit from the creation of this board?

_____

_____

## GRAPHIC IMAGE QUESTIONS
**Examine the image, and then answer the following questions.**

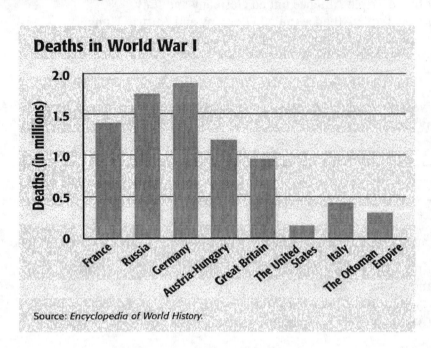

**Deaths in World War I**

Source: *Encyclopedia of World History.*

66) Of the major powers, which country suffered the most deaths?

_____

67) Which country suffered the fewest deaths?

_____

68) How many Russians were killed during World War I?

_____

## SHORT ANSWER
**Write a brief answer for each of the following.**

69) Describe the human and economic costs of World War I.

_____

_____

_____

Call to Freedom

70) What effect did the war have on women and African Americans?

_____

_____

_____

71) What was trench warfare like?

_____

_____

_____

72) What were the main causes of World War I?

_____

_____

_____

73) How was propaganda used to influence public opinion in the United States?

_____

_____

_____

**ESSAY**
**On a seperate sheet of paper, write an essay on one of the following.**

74) Describe the League of Nations that President Wilson envisioned.

75) Explain how President Wilson's Fourteen Points outlined his vision for postwar Europe and a system to avoid future wars.

1) reparations

2) stalemate

3) Selective Service Act

4) armistice

5) Archduke Francis Ferdinand

6) U-boats

7) mobilize

8) self-determination

9) General John J. Pershing

10) nationalism

11) T

12) F
The Treaty of Brest-Litovsk removed Russia from the war.

13) F
Thirty nations around the world fought in World War I.

14) F
Herbert Hoover led the Food Administration.

15) F
The Treaty of Versailles included some, but not all, of the Fourteen Points.

16) T

Call to Freedom

17) T

18) T

19) T

20) F
The Big Four were President Wilson of the United States, British Prime Minister David Lloyd George, French Premier Georges Clemenceau, and Italian prime minister Vittorio Orlando.

21) a

22) c

23) d

24) b

25) c

26) a

27) b

28) c

29) d

30) a

31) b

32) c

33) d

34) a

35)  c

36)  b

37)  d

38)  b

39)  a

40)  c

41)  d

42)  b

43)  c

44)  d

45)  a

46)  b

47)  c

48)  b

49)  a

50)  c

51)  d

52)  b

Call to Freedom

# ANSWER KEY

53) a

54) c

55) d

56) b

57) a

58) c

59) d

60) a

61) b
The area between opposing trenches was called no-man's-land. It varied in width from about 200 to 1,000 yards. The soldiers often left their trenches to fight in no-man's-land. The area was littered with the bodies of men.

62) a
During this battle, the U.S. 3rd Division blew up every temporary bridge that the Germans had built across the Marne River. Both sides suffered heavy casualties, but the Germans' losses crippled their ability to launch an offensive. This marked the turning point of the war.

63) c
Balance of power was a situation in which the strength of rival nations is nearly equal. The Triple Alliance and the Triple Entente created a balance of power in Europe that was complicated and fragile.

64) d
As a result of the Zimmerman Note, President Wilson asked Congress to declare war on Germany. The Senate and the House approved, and on April 6, 1917, the United States declared war on Germany.

65) a
The board was sympathetic to workers and supported their right to collective bargaining. It also outlined minimum-wage and maximum-hour standards, and required that female workers be paid the same as males.

66) Germany

67) the United States

68) about 1.8 million

69) The Allies lost 5.1 million soldiers on the battlefield. The Central Powers lost 3.5 million. More than 20 million soldiers on both sides had been wounded. Thousands of civilians were also killed in the fighting. The economies of the nations involved in the war were ruined. The war cost the Allies $145 billion, and the Central Powers $63 billion. More than $30 billion in property was destroyed. Industry and agriculture were nearly wiped out in belgium, France, and other parts of Europe.

70) Initially the government trained African American soldiers to fill noncombat roles. The majority of the 400,000 who eventually served in the armed forces did so in segregated units commanded by white officers. African American soldiers were awarded for their bravery in France. Most of the 25,000 female volunteers who served in France worked as nurses. Others served as signalers, typists, and interpreters. Many female nurses and ambulance drivers worked at the front lines. Many other women volunteered for the Red Cross and worked at home and abroad. More than 1.5 million worked in factory positions left vacant by departing soldiers.

71) Trenches ranged from simple holes to complex networks that were six to eight feet deep and had several levels with rooms for sleeping and eating. The trenches were cold, wet, and dirty, and were filled with trash, rats, and the remnants of long-dead soldiers. Trench warfare brought many health problems. The troops battled boredom and lice. Their diet consisted of hard biscuits, bacon, dried beef, and canned emergency rations.

72) The war was caused by long-simmering tensions in Europe after nationalism became a force for unification. The Pan-German movement and the Pan-Slavic movement had opposing goals. As nations competed to gain territory and build international empires, tensions and jealousies flared. As tensions grew, nations turned to militarism. Then the Triple Alliance united against the Triple Entente and created a fragile balance of power in Europe. When austria-Hungary annexed Bosnia and Herzegovina, nationalists reacted by assasssinating the heir to the throne of Austria-Hungary. This act was the spark that lit the "powder keg" of Eastern Europe. Five separate declarations of war initiated the Great War.

73) Britain, France, and Germany used propaganda to influence public opinion in the United States. British propaganda represented Germany as cruel and inhumane. German propaganda showed Wilson as a hypocrite. Two weeks after Congress declared war on Germany, the CPI was formed to lauch a nationwide campaign of publicity and propaganda. Hollywood produced movies lilke *The Kaiser: The Beast of Berlin* that showed enemy leaders as evil monsters.

Call to Freedom

74) In Wilson's vision, the League would consist of a council, an assembly, and a permanent administrative staff. Each member nation would be represented in the assembly and have one vote. The council would have four rotating members elected by the assembly, and five permanent members—Britain, France, Italy, Japan, and the United States. Eventually, all independent nations would be allowed to join, but the former Central Powers would not be allowed to join at first. Member nations would present disagreements to the Permanent court of International Justice, or World Court. If a member nation did not obey its judgement, the League could impose penalties on that nation. Penalties would include a ban on trade, or in the most extreme cases, the use of military force.

75) Wilson's vision for postwar Europe and a system to avoid future wars was a plan called the Fourteen Points. Most of the Fourteen Points dealt with the future of specific nations and regions. Other points called for freedom of ships on the seas, smaller armies and navies, lower trade tariffs, fair settlement of colonial claims of independence, and an end to secret agreements between nations. Wilson also emphasized the right of self-determination—the right of people to decide their own political status. The last point, the most important one to Wilson, called for the creation of the League of Nations—an international congress of nations designed to settle disputes and protect democracy.

## Chapter 23 The Roaring Twenties

**MATCHING**
**In the space provided, write the term or the name of the person that best fits the description. Choose your answers from the list below. Not all answers will be used.**

| | | |
|---|---|---|
| disarmament | W. C. Handy | talkie |
| speakeasies | flappers | Billy Sunday |
| nickelodeons | John T. Scopes | demobilization |
| communists | expatriates | anarchists |
| assembly line | W. E. B. Du Bois | bootleggers |

1) _____ called for "a renaissance of American Negro literature"

2) _____ limits on military weapons

3) _____ people who leave their native country to live elsewhere

4) _____ secret, illegal clubs that served alcohol

5) _____ people who favor government ownership of all property

6) _____ movie with sound

7) _____ broke Tennessee law by teaching evolution

8) _____ young women who used their freedom to challenge traditional dress and behavior

9) _____ system of chains, slides, and conveyor belts that moves parts between workers

10) _____ return to a peacetime economy

**TRUE/FALSE**
**Write T is a statement is true or F if it is false. If a statement is false, explain why.**

11) _____ The Natural Origins Act restricted the number of Japanese immigrants to 3 percent of that nationality's population in the 1910 U.S. census.

_____

12) _____ Secretary of the Interior Albert Fall was jailed for his involvement in the Teapot Dome scandal.

_____

13) _____ Henry Ford's "universal car," the Model T, was commonly called the Tin Lizzie.

_____

14) _____ By the mid-1920s, the influence of the Ku Klux Klan was felt only in Georgia and Alabama, where members controlled local and state politics.

_____

15) _____ Early theaters were called nickelodeons because admission was usually a nickel.

_____

16) _____ Attorney General A. Mitchell Palmer ordered raids on suspected radicals, who often were arrested without search warrants or evidence.

_____

17) _____ The Kellogg-Briand Pact was effective in preventing war.

_____

18) _____ Between 1921 and 1929, U.S. manufacturing nearly doubled.

_____

19) _____ The American Civil Liberties Union worked to ensure that anarchists Sacco and Vanzetti were executed.

_____

20) _____ The Emergency Quota Act set strict immigration limits on all nations in the Western Hemisphere.

_____

## MULTIPLE CHOICE
**For each of the following, circle the letter of the best choice.**

21) Interests followed for a short time with great enthusiasm are called

    a. fads.
    b. flappers.
    c. xenophobias.
    d. talkies.

22) During the 1920s, most magazine, newspaper and radio ads used psychology to pressure

    a. young men and women into believing that life was more fun at the movies.
    b. men into believing that they could easily repair and maintain a Model T.
    c. women into believing that they needed more, newer, and better versions of products.
    d. apartment dwellers into believing that they could afford to buy a home on the installment plan.

23) People who smuggled illegal alcoholic drinks into the United States were known as

    a. speakeasies.
    b. bootleggers.
    c. agents.
    d. actors.

24) *The Jazz Singer* was the

    a. first full-length feature talkie, released in 1927.
    b. first plane to cross the Atlantic Ocean.
    c. honorary title given to Bessie Smith, who was also known as the "Empress of the Blues."
    d. title of the autobiography of W. C. Handy, who was also known as the Father of the Blues.

25) Some members of the press placed the blame for postwar labor strikes on

    a. nativists and communists.
    b. the Ku Klux Klan.
    c. immigrants from Mexico, Japan, and southern Europe.
    d. communists and foreign radicals.

26) In an effort to strengthen America's postwar economy, President Harding

    a. named Herbert Hoover as director of the Bureau of the Budget.
    b. appointed Calvin Coolidge as Secretary of Commerce.
    c. assembled a talented and experienced cabinet.
    d. rejected the trickle-down economic theory endorsed by President McKinley.

27) Young writers who criticized American culture during the 1920s were known as

    a. ragtimers.
    b. the Lost Generation.
    c. flappers.
    d. radicals.

28) The purpose of the Universal Negro Improvement Association was to

a. campaign against the National Origins Act, which banned African immigrants from the United States.
b. protect African American citizens from racial hostility and violence.
c. support the NAACP on the state and local level.
d. end imperialism in Africa and discrimination in the United States.


29) The production of synthetic fabrics hurt the textile industry because synthetics

a. required more labor than did traditional material.
b. required less labor than did traditional material.
c. could be manufactured by unskilled workers, who received less pay than skilled workers.
d. were favored by the more than 2 million women who joined the workforce after World War I.


30) Alfred Steiglitz and Ansel Adams were well-known

a. photographers.
b. journalists.
c. expatriates.
d. aviators.


31) After World War I, most Mexican immigrants

a. settled in the Northeast, where they found industrial work.
b. earned higher wages than many African Americans and southern Europeans.
c. received low wages and faced discrimination in employment and housing.
d. settled in the Midwest, where farm production remained high and jobs were plentiful.


32) Joplin, a classically trained African American composer.

a. African American musicians who moved from Harlem to Chicago during the 1920s.
b. Scott Joplin, a classically trained African American composer.
c. Louis Armstrong and his band, the Hot Five.
d. Edward "Duke" Ellington in his composition, "Take the A Train."


33) Harding's administration supported the American Plan, in which

a. the courts upheld workers' rights to join unions.
b. immigrants were denied union membership.
c. union membership was required.
d. union membership was not required and was sometimes forbidden.


34) The Red Scare refers to many Americans' fear of

a. a Russian invasion of western Europe and North America.
b. postal workers.
c. radicals and communists.
d. anarchists.

35) African American spirituals, European harmonies, and West African rhythms influenced the musical style that came to be known as

a. jazz.
b. ragtime.

c. the blues.
d. realism.

36) Crime became big business as a result of

a. fundamentalism.
b. prohibition.

c. the Twenty-first Amendment.
d. the Palmer raids.

37) Demobilization resulted in a dramatic rise in

a. manufacturing, especially in the electrical appliances industry.
b. contracts for war materials.
c. immigration.
d. prices and unemployment.

38) The first pilot to complete a solo flight across the Atlantic Ocean was

a. Amelia Earhart.
b. Douglas Fairbanks.

c. Charles Lindbergh.
d. Isadore Einstein.

39) A proposal to limit the naval strength of the world's most powerful nations was presented in 1921 by

a. Secretary of State Charles Evans Hughes.
b. former ambassador John W. Davis.

c. Senator Robert La Follette.
d. Socialist political candidate Eugene V. Debs.

40) After the Eighteenth Amendment went into effect, many usually law-abiding Americans

a. smuggled alcohol out of the United States.
b. manufactured home-made alcohol, which poisoned more than 3,400 citizens in 1928 alone.
c. disregarded the law by entering speakeasies and purchasing bootleg alcohol.
d. opened speakeasies and supported the criminal activities of gangsters such as Al Capone.

41) Many members of the Ohio Gang were

a. cabinet members whose illegal actions tainted Coolidge's presidency.
b. President Harding's friends whose illegal actions resulted in scandal.
c. undercover government agents who worked to end organized crime in Chicago.
d. arrested and charged with the murder of Al Capone in Cincinnati, Ohio.

42) Sherwood Anderson, Ernest Hemingway, e.e. cummings, and John Dos Passos were

a. federal agents who participated in the Palmer raids.
b. gold medal winners at the 1924 Olympics.
c. among the most creative composers and musicians of the Jazz Age.
d. writers and poets of the Lost Generation.

43) When a city experienced a general strike,

 a. all workers in all the city's industries refused to report to their jobs.
 b. police officers who went on strike were fired.
 c. steelworkers and police officers refused to report to their jobs while members of other labor unions continued to work.
 d. women gave up their wartime jobs to returning veterans.

44) The re-created Ku Klux Klan targeted and terrorized

 a. Native Americans.                 c. communists.
 b. Protestants.                      d. foreigners, Jews, Catholics, and African Americans.

45) Perhaps the greatest athlete of the 1920s was American Indian

 a. Helen Wills.                      c. Gertrude Ederle.
 b. Jim Thorpe.                       d. Red Grange.

46) Warren G. Harding won a landslide victory after promising

 a. an end to scandals that had rocked the previous administration.
 b. immediate reduction in government spending.
 c. a return to normalcy.
 d. a chicken for every pot and a car in every garage.

47) In 1919 the Metal Workers Union in Seattle went on strike for higher wages and

 a. a safe work environment.          c. medical care.
 b. shorter hours.                    d. a better retirement plan.

48) George Bellows, Georgia O'Keeffe, and Charles Sheeler were

 a. notable American artists of the 1920s.
 b. popular movie stars.
 c. encouraged by W. E. B. Du Bois to present a realistic description of African American life.
 d. writers whom Gertrude Stein described as "a lost generation."

49) The Twenty-first Amendment

 a. gave American Indians citizenship.    c. ended national prohibition.
 b. established national prohibition.     d. gave women the right to vote in all elections.

50) The 1920s are often called the

 a. Red Scare.                         c. Lost Generation.
 b. Jazz Age.                          d. Great Migration.

51) Fundamentalism was strongest in

    a. Canada.
    b. New York City, Chicago, and Kansas City.
    c. cities facing problems with organized crime and gang violence.
    d. rural areas and small towns.

52) During the late 1920s, NBC and CBS went on the air and provided

    a. coast-to-coast radio coverage to 70 percent of the nation's homes.
    b. the nation with its first talkies.
    c. free books for schools.
    d. elaborate theaters where Americans gathered to watch variety shows that were broadcast on radio.

53) The summer of 1919 is known as "Red Summer" for its

    a. gang warfare that resulted in some 700 gang murders in Chicago.
    b. racial violence and bloodshed.
    c. labor strikes that many people blamed on communists.
    d. raids on suspected radical and communist organizations.

54) After Coolidge became president he

    a. complained that "my . . . friends . . . keep me walking the floor nights."
    b. accepted bribes in exchange for awarding government contracts for the construction of hospitals.
    c. fired the people involved in the Harding scandals.
    d. dismissed the striking Boston police force.

55) Blues and jazz developed in

    a. the western United States.
    b. the Mississippi Delta region and New Orleans.
    c. New York.
    d. West Africa.

56) "The business of America is business," said

    a. Warren G. Harding.
    b. Calvin Coolidge.
    c. Charles Evans Hughes.
    d. Andrew Mellon.

57) Art deco describes the 1920s style of

    a. music.
    b. photography.
    c. literature.
    d. architecture.

58) The significance of the Teapot Dome scandal was that

a. herds of cattle needed to feed the army were given as bribes to government officials.
b. injured World War I veterans went without medical supplies.
c. the illegal acts committed could have deprived the United States of oil reserves during an international conflict.

59) John T. Scopes was defended by

a. William Jennings Bryan.
b. Billy Sunday and Aimee Semple McPherson.

c. Clarence Darrow and the ACLU.
d. James Thomas Heflin.

60) The "Empress of the Blues" was

a. Bessie Smith.
b. Memphis Minnie.

c. Gertrude "Ma" Rainey.
d. Mamie Smith.

## ENHANCED QUESTIONS
**For each of the following, circle the letter of the best choice. Next, expand on the subject by answering the second question in the space provided.**

61) Fundamentalism taught that

a. architecture was very important.
b. all people had the same basic needs and values.

c. education should focus on "back to basics."
d. the Bible was inerrant, or literally true.

What impact did fundamentalism have on the teaching career of John T. Scopes?

_____

_____

62) To help Americans afford his cars, Henry Ford

a. abolished the assembly line that lowered production costs.
b. gave away a free car to every rural family.
c. sold them on an installment plan.
d. reduced his own salary.

How did this business tactic make cars affordable for many buyers?

_____

_____

63) The remarkable period of African American artistic accomplishment in the 1920s became known as the

a. Harlem Renaissance.
b. era of black imperialism.
c. black national period.
d. Jazz Age.

How did the Great Migration contribute to this development?

_____

_____

64) Fear and hatred of foreigners is known as

a. the Red Scare.
b. xenophobia.
c. nativism.
d. fundamentalism.

How did this outlook affect Nicola Sacco and Bartolomeo Vanzetti?

_____

_____

65) In 1921 the world's major nations discussed disarmament

a. at the Washington Conference.
b. and the effects of the Kellogg-Briand Pact.
c. and a proposal to outlaw war.
d. as a means of reopening trade with Germany.

What decisions resulted from these discussions?

_____

_____

Call to Freedom

## GRAPHIC IMAGE QUESTIONS
**Examine the image, and then answer the following questions.**

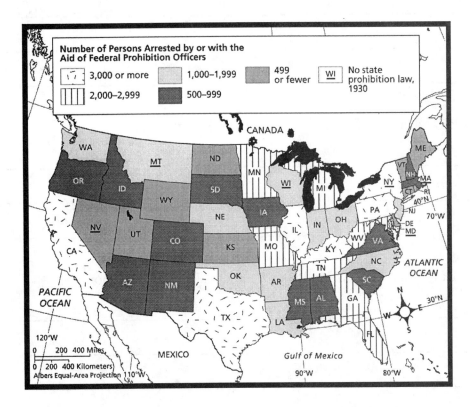

66) Which states had 3,000 or more alcohol-related arrests in 1929?

_____

67) Where were there no state prohibition laws in 1930?

_____

68) How many states had fewer than 500 arrests in 1929?

_____

## SHORT ANSWER
**Write a brief answer for each of the following.**

69) How did the growth of the auto industry affect other industries and change Americans' lives?

_____

_____

_____

70) What were Marcus Garvey's contributions to the struggle for rights for African Americans?

_____

_____

_____

71) How did advertising influence U.S. economic growth during the 1920s?

_____

_____

_____

72) How did Charles Dawes and Andrew Mellon help strengthen the U.S. economy?

_____

_____

_____

73) How did demobilization affect organized labor?

_____

_____

_____

**ESSAY**
**On a seperate sheet of paper, write an essay on one of the following.**

74) Discuss whether Hoover's campaign promise of "a chicken for every pot and a car in every garage" was extended to these groups: African Americans, Mexican Americans, American Indians, farmers, unmarried women, and members of labor unions. Do you believe Hoover was able to fulfill his promise to these people? Explain your answer.

75) Discuss the positive and negative effects of the Great Migration on the life and culture of African Americans during the Jazz Age.

Call to Freedom

# ANSWER KEY

1) W. E. B. Du Bois

2) disarmament

3) expatriates

4) speakeasies

5) Communists

6) talkie

7) John T. Scopes

8) flappers

9) assembly line

10) demobilization

11) F
The National Origins Act completely banned Japanese immigrants from the United States.

12) T

13) T

14) F
By the mid-1920s, more than 5 million Klan members influenced elections in states from Oregon to Maine.

15) T

16) T

17) F

The Kellogg-Briand Pact outlawed war, but the treaty lacked a means of enforcement and therefore was not effective.

18) T

19) F

Although the ACLU worked to have the conviction overturned, Sacco and Vanzetti were executed.

20) F

The act set no immigration limit on nations in the Western Hemisphere. However, the law limited total immigration and restricted European immigration.

21) a

22) c

23) b

24) a

25) d

26) c

27) b

28) d

29) b

30) a

31) c

32) b

Call to Freedom

ANSWER KEY

33)  d

34)  c

35)  a

36)  b

37)  d

38)  c

39)  a

40)  c

41)  b

42)  d

43)  a

44)  d

45)  b

46)  c

47)  b

48)  a

49)  c

50)  b

# ANSWER KEY

51) d

52) a

53) b

54) c

55) b

56) b

57) d

58) c

59) c

60) a

61) d
Fundamentalists strongly opposed Darwin's theory of natural selection, which argued that species evolved over time by adapting to their environments. When applied to humans, this theory contradicted the biblical account of creation. Tennessee law made it illegal to teach any theory contrary to creation. When Scopes, a high school science teacher, taught the theory of evolution in Tennessee, he was arrested, brought to trial, and convicted.

62) c
Buyers made a small initial payment and then paid monthly until the balance was cleared.

63) a
The Great Migration made Harlem, New York, the nation's largest African American community. The Harlem Renaissance took its name from the area, though many Harlem Renaissance artists did not live there.

64) b
Sacco and Vanzetti, two Italian immigrants and anarchists, were arrested and charged with robbery and murder. Despite a lack of solid evidence and a trial that many people considered unfair, the two were convicted, sentenced to death, and executed.

65) a

The conference produced a number of treaties that limited naval size and reinforced an open trading policy in Asia.

66) California, Texas, Illinois, Kentucky, Pennsylvania, New York

67) Nevada, Montana, Wisconsin, New York, Maryland, Massachusetts

68) nine

69) The auto industry employed some 375,000 workers. Millions more held jobs that supported the automobile business. The massive growth in the automobile industry stimulated growth in related industries, such as steel, rubber, glass, paint, machine tools, gasoline, lubricants, petroleum, and construction. Service stations, roadside restaurants, insurance companies and body shops also flourished. Americans who owned cars began traveling widely and taking driving vacations.

70) Garvey founded the Universal Negro Improvement Association to end imperialism in Africa and discrimination in the United States. He encouraged blacks to be proud of their heritage and to work to become self-sufficient. He founded a steamship line to promote black businesses. His organization, the UNIA, helped establish a number of black businesses.

71) Magazines and newspapers carried ads encouraging people to buy, and radios aired commercials for thousands of products. Most ads targeted women and used psychology to pressure them into believing that they needed more, newer, and better versions of various products. Ads propelled the consumer purchasing spree of the decade.

72) Dawes, director of the Bureau of the Budget, was an experienced business leader who successfully cut government spending and balanced the federal budget. Treasury Secretary Mellon proposed numerous tax cuts, many of which benefited wealthy Americans. He argued that if the wealthy kept more of the money they earned, they would invest it, and that this new investment would create more jobs. The nation soon entered a period of rapid economic growth. During Coolidge's presidency, Mellon continued his tax-cutting program and the economy boomed.

73) During the war, union membership had increased as the government supported union demands for higher wages, fearing work stoppages in war industries. As a result of demobilization, however, the government no longer supported labor. Union membership declined. The courts often struck down proworker legislation. Business leaders launched open-shop campaigns that unions fought with little success.

74) In 1928, during an economic boom, Hoover told the nation that the end of poverty was in sight. However, in many cases, the rich got richer while the poor stayed poor. New cars and ample food eluded many Americans who would have heard Hoover's promise on the radio or read it in a newspaper—if they had a radio and if they were able to read or buy a newspaper. African Americans did not have equal opportunities to share in the boom times. Instead, they still sought basic civil rights, and freedom from fear of lynchings and racial violence. They and Mexican Americans received lower wages than white people, and faced discrimination in employment and housing. Most American Indians lived in poverty. Farmers faced such economic difficulty that nearly half a million of them lost their land. Farm laborers were poorly paid, and working conditions were often difficult. Some lived in crude shelters made of burlap, canvas, and palm branches. Although the number of employed women rose by 2 million during the 1920s, their jobs were mostly low-paying. Organized labor also struggled to share in the boom times of the 1920s, but the government no longer supported labor as it had during World War I. Strikers' demands were rarely met as the courts struck down proworker legislation and management hired strikebreakers instead. Unless Hoover could convince Congress to enact legislation that would help bridge the gap between rich and poor, he would be unable to fulfill his promise to these groups of voters.

75) During World War I, hundreds of thousands of African Americans had moved north in the event known as the Great Migration. As African Americans became a greater presence in the North, many whites feared competition for housing and jobs. Racial tension spread throughout the country. Race riots—violent attacks by whites against blacks—occurred in Chicago, Tulsa, and Knoxville. The Ku Klux Klan gained members, and terrorized black citizens. Many black citizens were lynched. However, the Great Migration also made Harlem, New York, the nation's largest African American community, and launched a remarkable period of African American artistic accomplishment known as the Harlem Renaissance. In 1920, W. E. B. Du Bois called for "a renaissance of American Negro literature." As editor of the *Crisis*, Du Bois published the works of many young African American writers, such as Langston Hughes and Claude McKay. Much of this literature tried to present a realistic description of African American life. For example, Langston Hughes's poem, "I, Too," expressed both pride in being an African American and faith in the American dream. Black writers expressed black Americans' hopes for the future in a nation where civil rights and freedom from prejudice and fear were only visions during the 1920s, regardless of the work of leaders such as Marcus Garvey and the efforts of the NAACP.

## Chapter 24 The Great Depression

**MATCHING**

**In the space provided, write the term or the name of the person that best fits the description. Choose your answers from the list below. Not all answers will be used.**

| | | |
|---|---|---|
| fascism | Huey Long | Marian Anderson |
| Frances Perkins | Tennessee Valley Authority | Great Depression |
| Second New Deal | Mary McLeod Bethune | Duke Ellington |
| Mahalia Jackson | totalitarianism | Public Works Administration |
| Federal Project One | Harry Hopkins | Federal Emergency Relief Administration |

1) _____ economic downturn that lasted for more than a decade

2) _____ FERA head who in four months gave more than 4.2 million workers jobs building public projects

3) _____ political system in which the government controls every aspect of citizens' lives

4) _____ program that employed some 40,000 artists and writers

5) _____ provided grants to states for direct relief payments to the poor and the unemployed

6) _____ recorded "It Don't Mean a Thing (If It Ain't Got The Swing)"

7) _____ political theory which calls for a strong government headed by one individual

8) _____ secretary of labor who was the first female cabinet member in American history

9) _____ described by President Roosevelt as seeking "not only cure of the symptoms but also removal of their cause"

10) _____ New Deal program designed to help one of the poorest and least-developed parts of the United States

**TRUE/FALSE**
**Write T is a statement is true or F if it is false.  If a statement is false, explain why.**

11) _____ During sit-down strikes, workers remained in factories but refused to work.

_____

12) _____ During the 1930s the United States ended its economic and political influence over Latin American nations.

_____

13) _____ Federal Writers' Project writer John Steinbeck wrote the most famous novel set in the depression—*Gone With the Wind*—in April 1939.

_____

14) _____ Between October and December 1929, U.S. unemployment rose from less than 500,000 to more than 4 million.

_____

15) _____ The National Labor Relations Act made unions and collective bargaining legal.

_____

16) _____ In 1936 Italy, Germany, and Japan formed a military alliance, calling themselves the Axis Powers.

_____

17) _____ Many African Americans were included in New Deal programs and generally supported President Roosevelt.

_____

18) _____ During the Great Depression, Herbert Hoover gave many fireside chats—radio addresses in which he spoke directly to the American people.

_____

19) _____ Benito Mussolini and his followers were called Blackshirts because of the secret meetings they conducted after dark.

_____

20) _____ The Agricultural Adjustment Act and the National Industrial Recovery Act were declared unconstitutional by the Supreme Court.

_____

## MULTIPLE CHOICE
**For each of the following, circle the letter of the best choice.**

21) The Congress of Industrial Organizations differed from the AFL in that the CIO

    a. refused to admit African Americans, immigrants, and women.
    b. organized all workers in a particular industry—skilled and unskilled—into one union.
    c. was made up of craft-based unions.
    d. turned away unions that admitted unskilled laborers.

22) On *Kristallnacht*, or the "Night of Broken Glass,"

    a. Mussolini started his campaign against Jews.
    b. Mussolini attacked the African nation of Ethiopia.
    c. Nazis destroyed many Jewish businesses and synagogues.
    d. Nazis won 38 percent of the vote in German elections.

23) Under the Emergency Banking Act, the government planned to

    a. inspect each bank's finances and then allow healthy banks to reopen.
    b. initiate New Deal programs with money borrowed from the nation's healthiest banks.
    c. order failing banks to stay open until depositors retrieved their savings.
    d. order banks to close their doors to uninsured depositors.

24) On October 29, 1929—a date many people still remember with horror as Black Tuesday—the stock market

    a. began a gradual downturn.        c. closed its doors.
    b. collapsed and lost much of its stock value.    d. canceled all stock sales.

25) The Black Cabinet referred to the many

    a. stock brokers who warned President Hoover that "sooner or later a crash is coming."
    b. political and business leaders who attempted to revive the stock market after Black Tuesday.
    c. Italian officials who secretly supported Mussolini's Blackshirts.
    d. African American leaders that Roosevelt appointed to his administration.

26) Mussolini's government was

    a. called the Third Reich.           c. based on fascism.
    b. ruled by the National Socialist Party.    d. based on Nazism.


27) The Hundred Days was a

    a. special session of Congress during which the New Deal was launched.
    b. name given to the first Nazi wave of terror that swept through Germany and Austria.
    c. period of time during which failed banks were allowed to remained closed.
    d. severe drought that struck the Great Plains during the early 1930s.


28) Members of the National Socialist Party were also known as

    a. Blackshirts.           c. Okies.
    b. Nazis.              d. socialists.


29) During the depression, many state travel guides, oral histories, and collections of American folklore were created by

    a. a group of artists known as the regionalists.
    b. Woody Guthrie, Will Rogers, and gospel artists such as Mahalia Jackson and Sister Rosetta Tharpe.
    c. artists hired by the Federal Arts Project and the Federal Music Project.
    d. writers hired by the Federal Writers' Project.


30) Roosevelt planned his policies with the help of a group of expert policy advisers known as the

    a. Brain Trust.          c. New Deal Cabinet.
    b. Bulls and Bears.       d. National Recovery Congress.


31) Congress rejected Roosevelt's Judicial Procedures Reform Act because

    a. bank foreclosures on farmers' loans were tarnishing the administration's reputation.
    b. Republican members wanted to strengthen their control of Congress.
    c. they feared it would destroy the independence of the Supreme Court.
    d. the Supreme Court advised that the bill would be unconstitutional.


32) Adolf Hitler called his aggressive new German empire

    a. *Kristallnacht.*        c. the Republic of Rhineland.
    b. *Mein Kampf.*        d. the Third Reich.


33) Hospitals, schools, parks, airports, and rural roads were built by millions of workers hired by the

    a. National Labor Relations Board.    c. Tennessee Valley Authority.
    b. Works Progress Administration.    d. National Recovery Administration.

34) During the 1930s, much of northern China was invaded and occupied by the aggressive military forces of

a. Japan.
b. Italy.
c. Germany.
d. the Axis Powers.

35) When a bank auctioned a farmer's land and belongings during foreclosure proceedings, the farmer's friends and neighbors often

a. staged protest marches at the bank.
b. bid higher-than-market prices for the items, then refused to pay the bank.
c. expanded their own holdings by purchasing items at very low prices.
d. bid low amounts, then returned the sold items to the original farmer.

36) Millions of Americans lost their savings during the depression because

a. they had not taken advantage of the bull market.
b. they had not purchased deposit insurance on their savings.
c. banks did not have enough money to pay all withdrawing depositors.
d. banks turned away all depositors who had bought on margin.

37) The Roosevelt administration responded to military aggression by the Axis Powers by

a. refusing to acknowledge Mussolini and Hitler as political leaders.
b. passing neutrality laws to prohibit the sale of weapons to any nation at war.
c. sending financial aid to countries that were under attack by aggressors.
d. warning the Axis Powers that the United States would declare war on any European nation that violated the Treaty of Versailles.

38) Young men between 17 and 24 from families on relief helped their families by working for the

a. Civilian Conservation Corps.
b. Civil Works Administration.
c. Public Works Administration.
d. Works Progress Administration.

39) Among the best-known gospel artists of the 1930s were singers

a. Benny Goodman and Count Basie.
b. Anna "Grandma" Moses and Sister Rosetta Tharpe.
c. Marian Anderson and Mahalia Jackson.
d. Mahalia Jackson and Sister Rosetta Tharpe.

40) The role of Government should not "be extended to the relief of individual suffering," said

a. Hoover.
b. Roosevelt.
c. Huey Long.
d. Harry Hopkins.

Call to Freedom
419

41) The Louisiana senator who proposed higher taxes on the wealthy was

a. Harry Hopkins.  c. Huey Long.
b. Robert C. Weaver.  d. Charles E. Coughlin.

42) Governments founded on fascism and Nazism are still remembered for their

a. individual freedoms.
b. strong economies.
c. regulations on big business.
d. violence against opposition and military aggression.

43) Many businesses slowed production, reduced their workforce, or closed down entirely as a result of

a. the bear market.  c. sit-down strikes by non-union workers.
b. the banking crisis.  d. major strikes organized by the AFL and the CIO.

44) *Little Orphan Annie, The Lone Ranger*, and *The Shadow* were

a. popular plays sponsored by the Federal Theater Project.
b. written by novelists employed by Federal Project One.
c. radio shows that provided inexpensive entertainment during the Great Depression.
d. light, escapist movies that helped people endure the Great Depression.

45) During the depression, black workers

a. were often the last to be hired and the first to be fired.
b. received higher wages than white workers due to anti-discrimination codes established by the National Industrial Relations Act.
c. often abandoned their Dust Bowl farms and headed west, often to California.
d. voted overwhelmingly against Roosevelt, whose New Deal had not been extended to African American citizens.

46) The National Youth Administration

a. aided children whose unemployed parents received Social Security payments.
b. provided part-time jobs that allowed many students to stay in school instead of dropping out to search for work.
c. provided payments to parents whose children had visual impairments and other disabilities.
d. hired young men who lived and worked in camps run by the U.S. Army.

47) In 1922 the Italian king gave Mussolini "temporary" dictatorial powers that lasted

a. 12 years.  c. a decade.
b. until 1930.  d. for over two decades.

48) "All along your green valley I'll work till I die," sang folk musician and songwriter

    a. Duke Ellington.            c. Woody Guthrie.
    b. Will Rogers.               d. Mahalia Jackson.

49) Critics who thought the New Deal went too far tended to

    a. see the New Deal as Socialist-leaning, and Roosevelt as a potential dictator.
    b. favor Hoover's "Share the Wealth" plan over expensive New Deal programs.
    c. support Hoover for reelection in 1936.
    d. be members of the conservative Freedom Party.

50) During the 1930s, Nicaragua, Cuba, El Salvador, and Guatemala

    a. put their industries under national control.    c. fought regional wars.
    b. fell under the rule of dictators.           d. began holding free elections.

51) While most Americans supported Roosevelt in 1936, his opponent had strong support from

    a. Dust Bowl farmers who were disenchanted with the New Deal.
    b. African Americans, Mexican Americans, and other minorities.
    c. the business community.
    d. union leaders in the AFL and the CIO.

52) The Securities and Exchange Commission, created during the depression, continues to

    a. regulate companies that sell stocks or bonds.
    b. insure bank accounts up to $100,000 per account.
    c. inspect banks, insure bank deposits, and guard against stock fraud.
    d. oversee the Federal Deposit Insurance Corporation.

53) Thomas Hart Benton, John Steuart Curry, and Grant Wood

    a. were Federal Arts Project photographers who recorded rural life during the depression.
    b. hosted popular radio shows during the early days of the depression.
    c. helped a new style of jazz, called swing, to sweep the nation.
    d. were artists who became known as the regionalists.

54) Congress created the Federal Deposit Insurance Corporation to

    a. inspect banks.             c. restore the nation's banks.
    b. protect bank accounts.       d. regulate the sale of bank stocks.

55) A major cause of business failures and unemployment in Latin America was

    a. civil war.
    b. totalitarianism.
    c. low consumer demand due to a small middle class.
    d. the abrupt withdrawal of U.S. troops during Hoover's administration.

56) Haile Selassie

    a. led his fascist followers in a march on Rome in 1922.
    b. blamed Communists and Jews for Germany's defeat in World War I.
    c. violated the Treaty of Versailles when he conquered the Rhineland.
    d. fought bravely against Mussolini, but could not defend Ethiopia from conquest.

57) Eleanor Roosevelt strongly supported

    a. minority rights.
    b. the Liberty League.
    c. the Civil Works Administration, launched in 1934.
    d. segregation in government work programs.

58) The New Deal's first goal was to

    a. raise taxes to pay for programs to battle the depression.
    b. restore the nation's confidence in the banks.
    c. provide direct relief payments to the poor and the unemployed.
    d. regulate the stock market and protect investors' money.

59) As the presidential election of 1932 approached, most Americans

    a. blamed big business for the depression.
    b. believed that Hoover could not end the depression.
    c. hoped to re-elect Roosevelt.
    d. wanted the federal government to lower taxes to stimulate the economy.

60) The National Recovery Administration and the Public Works Administration were

    a. new programs in the Second New Deal.
    b. primarily responsible for providing direct relief to the poor.
    c. agencies of the National Industrial Recovery Act.
    d. declared unconstitutional by the Supreme Court.

## ENHANCED QUESTIONS
**For each of the following, circle the letter of the best choice. Next, expand on the subject by answering the second question in the space provided.**

61) When people bought on margin, they purchased stocks

    a. on credit with a loan from their bank.
    b. on credit with a loan from their broker.
    c. with cash when prices were high, and traded stocks when prices fell.
    d. with cash when prices were low, and purchased stocks on credit when prices increased.

Explain how these buyers profited during a bull market and during a bear market.

_____

_____

Call to Freedom

62) The so-called Dust Bowl was created when

    a. North Dakota farmers overworked their land.
    b. North Texas farmers failed to take precautions against soil erosion.
    c. a severe drought struck the Great Plains.
    d. heavy winds swept away dried-out topsoil during a severe drought on the Great Plains.

How did the Dust Bowl affect farm life in this area?

_____

_____


63) To help the elderly, people with disabilities, children, and job searchers, Congress passed the

    a. Social Security Act.               c. Emergency Banking Act.
    b. National Labor Relations Act.      d. National Industrial Recovery Act.

Describe the three main parts of the program that this act created.

_____

_____


64) *Mein Kampf* was written by

    a. Benito Mussolini.               c. Haile Selassie.
    b. Adolf Hitler.                 d. Anastasio Somoza.

Explain the global significance of *Mein Kampf*.

_____

_____


65) The Bonus Army was made up of a small "army" of

    a. Dust Bowl farmers.
    b. skilled workers who belonged to craft-based unions.
    c. unemployed World War I veterans.
    d. striking workers at the Goodyear Tire Factory and at General Motors plants.

Why did the Bonus Army travel to Washington, D.C. in 1932? How did Hoover respond to the Bonus Army, and how did Americans view Hoover's response?

_____

_____

## GRAPHIC IMAGE QUESTIONS
**Examine the image, and then answer the following questions.**

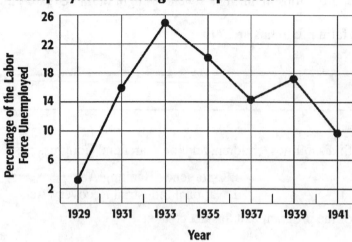

**Unemployment During the Depression**

Source: *Historical Statistics of the United States*

66) In what year were the most people unemployed?

_____

67) What percentage of people were unemployed in 1937?

_____

68) When did unemployment decrease most dramatically?

_____


## SHORT ANSWER
**Write a brief answer for each of the following.**

69) What were the major causes of the Great Depression?

_____

_____

_____

Call to Freedom

70) Define and evaluate the New Deal.

_____

_____

_____

71) Describe the economic pattern known as the business cycle.

_____

_____

_____

72) What effect did the Great Depression have on families?

_____

_____

_____

73) What was the Good Neighbor policy?

_____

_____

_____

**ESSAY**
**On a seperate sheet of paper, write an essay on one of the following.**

74) Describe the political and economic problems of nations that have an unequal distribution of wealth and practically no middle class. How did the Great Depression affect such nations?

75) How did the experiences of Italy and Germany differ from that of the United States during the depression of the 1930s?

# ANSWER KEY

1) Great Depression

2) Harry Hopkins

3) totalitarianism

4) Federal Project One

5) Federal Emergency Relief Administration

6) Duke Ellington

7) fascism

8) Frances Perkins

9) Second New Deal

10) Tennessee Valley Authority

11) T

12) F
Even after Roosevelt initiated his Good Neighbor Policy, the United States still had tremendous economic and political influence over Latin American nations.

13) F
The most famous novel set during the depression was *The Grapes of Wrath* by John Steinbeck.

14) T

15) T

16) F
The Axis Powers in 1936 were Italy and Germany.

17)  T

18)  F
Roosevelt, not Hoover, initiated fireside chats—radio addresses in which he spoke directly to the American people.

19)  F
Mussolini and his followers were called Blackshirts after the color of their uniforms.

20)  T

21)  b

22)  c

23)  a

24)  b

25)  d

26)  c

27)  a

28)  b

29)  d

30)  a

31)  c

32)  d

33)  b

34) a

35) d

36) c

37) b

38) a

39) d

40) a

41) c

42) d

43) b

44) c

45) a

46) b

47) d

48) c

49) a

50) b

51) c

# ANSWER KEY

52)  a

53)  d

54)  b

55)  c

56)  d

57)  a

58)  b

59)  b

60)  c

61)  b
   When the stock market was a bull market, or one with rising stock prices, buyers bought on margin, then sold the stocks at a higher price, repaid the loan, and kept the profits. During a bull market, buyers who bought on margin could make large profits from a small cash investment. This practice was only profitable, however, if stock prices rose. The danger of a bear market, or one with declining stock prices, always threatened to wipe out the newfound wealth.

62)  d
   The Dust Bowl destroyed farm life in the area. Many farmers and their families, often called Okies because many were from Oklahoma, simply abandoned their farms. Most of them headed west, often to California, to look for work.

63)  a
   First, the Social Security program created a pension system for retired workers over age 65. Second, it offered unemployed people short-term cash benefits while they looked for work. Third, it provided payments to women with dependent children as well as people with disabilities.

64) b

At a time when many Germans felt bitter about the terms of the Treaty of Versailles, Hitler offered Germans a scapegoat for their troubles. In *Mein Kampf,* he outlined his theories. He blamed intellectuals, Communists, and particularly Jews for Germany's defeat in World War I and for its later problems. *Mein Kampf* also presented Hitler's plan for Germany's rise to regional and global power.

65) c

The Bonus Army, many with families in tow, traveled to Washington, D.C. and demanded payment of their government war bonuses. They regarded themselves as heroes trying to collect a debt long overdue. Hoover, however, saw the Bonus Army as a dangerous mob and ordered federal troops to restore order. They drove the veterans from their camps with bayonets and tear gas. Most Americans were outraged that the government had turned its guns on veterans who had once risked their lives for their country.

66) 1933

67) 14 percent

68) between 1939 and 1941

69) Though historians and economists remain somewhat uncertain about its exact causes, most agree that two factors—overproduction and declining markets, and global trade problems—helped create the Great Depression.

70) During a special session of Congress, which became known as the Hundred Days, Congress approved numerous programs to battle the depression by providing jobs and stimulating the economy. Together these programs became known as the New Deal. The New Deal greatly expanded the role of the federal government and the president. It also transformed Americans' expectations of the government. Some people argue that the New Deal did not really end the depression, while others claim it prevented the nation's economic and political collapse.

71) When production exceeds consumption and surpluses pile up, manufacturers decrease production and lay off workers. This causes a depression and some businesses fail, but eventually consumers buy up surpluses and companies increase production and re-hire workers, leading to increased demand and prosperity. This economic pattern is known as the business cycle.

Call to Freedom

72) The Great Depression took a heavy toll on families. Many did not have enough money to provide basic life essentials—food, clothing, and shelter. During the depression years struggle to survive, divorce rates went up while marriage and birth rates went down. Some men left their families and crisscrossed the country in search of jobs. Some never returned. Women often worked long hours at low-paying, unpleasant jobs. Children often had to drop out of school and go to work. Some ran away from home. However, in many cases, the struggle brought out the strength of family and community as people helped each other to survive.

73) Roosevelt tried to improve U.S. relations with Latin America by not using military force there. He explained his Latin American policy by using the symbol of the good neighbor. He promised to make the United States a "good neighbor—the neighbor who . . . respects the rights of others— the neighbor who respects his obligations and . . . his agreements." As part of his Good Neighbor policy, Roosevelt canceled the Platt Amendment which gave the United States the right to intervene in Cuba, and withdrew the marines who had been stationed in Haiti since 1915.

74) The Great Depression had global significance in nations that had an unequal distribution of wealth, or in nations that had practically no middle class. Speaking of El Salvador, a U.S. diplomat pinpointed a major cause of tension in Latin America when he said: "There is practically no middle class between the very rich and the poor. Roughly 90 percent of the wealth of the country is held by about one-half of one percent of the population. . . . The [rest of the] population has practically nothing." With such a small middle class, few people earned enough money to purchase many goods, which led to business failures and unemployment. In the 1920s these conditions led to a civil war in Nicaragua. In 1937 Nicaragua fell under the rule of a dictator, as did Cuba, El Salvador, and Guatemala. In the United States in 1929, the top 5 percent of Americans earned one third of all income, while the bottom 40 percent earned only one eighth. Most Americans did not earn much money, and so could not afford to buy many products. Yet during the 1920s many Americans did buy many products on the installment plan. Production increased as a result. Then gradually the buying stopped and even decreased. Production kept going, however, and these flat or declining markets left business owners with huge surpluses, much larger than usual in the normal business cycle of depression and recovery. Producers began to lay off workers. The Great Depression hit Americans very hard. Unemployment skyrocketed, affecting as much as 25 percent of the American work force at certain times. People struggled to feed and house themselves and their families. Many people became angry with the lack of help from the federal government. As the depression deepened, many people, who had previously believed in keeping government out of business, became convinced that the federal government should play a greater role in fixing the economy. The result in the United States was the election of President Roosevelt and the implementation of New Deal programs designed to provide employment, relief, and economic stimulation. Some of the long-term results of the New Deal included a growth in the size and power of government and its role in government. Some New Deal programs like FDIC and social security are still active today.

75) One experience all three countries had in common during the period was that they suffered high unemployment and extreme hardship from the worldwide Great Depression. Italy already had a totalitarian government headed by Benito Mussolini by 1930. Mussolini's government was based on the political theory of fascism, which called for a strong government headed by one person. Mussolini's government and fascist governments in general did not allow opposition or opposing opinions. Fascists governments were strong and individual freedoms small. Mussolini looked to military conquest and the formation of foreign colonies as a way to improve his country's economy. In 1935, Italy attacked and gradually conquered the African nation of Ethiopia. Similarly, Germany was suffering greatly in the 1930s from the payment of World War I reparations and the effects of the depression. Germany also turned to a strong single leader and in 1933 elected Nazi leader Adolf Hitler as chancelor of Germany. Hitler took the German people's anger at their economic suffering and turned it toward other groups and nations that he blamed for Germany's hardships. Hitler blamed intellectuals, Communists, and particularly Jews for Germany's defeat in World War I and its economic problems. Once in charge of government, Hitler gradually turned himself into a dictator and began a campaign of violence and persecution against his opponents, particularly Jews. In violation of the terms of the Treaty of Versailles he also began a military buildup and sent troops back into the Rhineland. The United States also suffered greatly during the depression of the 1930s. At the depression's peak, some 25 percent of the workforce was unemployed and many others worked for reduced wages or on reduced hours. Many farmers lost their land. People had trouble feeding and housing their families. Some families broke up—the men going off to look for work or children running away to try and manage on their own. The suffering made many Americans angry and many blamed the government for their problems, particularly President Hoover. Instead of turning to totalitarian government, however, they turned to a democratic election and chose a new president, Franklin D. Roosevelt, along with many new members of Congress. Congress gave the new president a great deal of power and passed most of his legislation in an attempt to try to help the nation cope with the depression. The government grew larger and exercised economic power and regulation to a greater degree than ever before. Yet, neither Congress or the American people wanted a dictator. Most people rejected leaders who suggested more extreme or radical solutions. When it was perceived that some of Roosevelt's proposed legislation threatened the independence of the Supreme Court, Congress and the people rejected it. The strength of people's faith in America's democratic institutions and traditions maintained the U.S. government through the turmoil of the Great Depression. Yet during the same period the governments of Italy and Germany were transformed into antidemocratic dictatorships determined on military aggression.

# Chapter 25 World War II

**MATCHING**
**In the space provided, write the term or the name of the person that best fits the description. Choose your answers from the list below. Not all answers will be used.**

genocide          Blitzkrieg           Holocaust
braceros          V-E Day              *Luftwaffe*
kamikaze          War Production Board  nonaggression pact
D-Day             internment           Dwight D. Eisenhower
Omar Bradley      Erwin Rommel         Fair Employment

1) _____ forced relocation and imprisonment

2) _____ Hitler's and Stalin's agreement not to attack one another and to divide Poland between their countries

3) _____ created to prevent racial discrimination in war industries and government jobs

4) _____ deliberate murder of an entire people

5) _____ tactic of crashing piloted planes into the enemy's ships

6) _____ method of warfare that combined dive-bombers in the air and fast-moving tanks on the ground

7) _____ commanded British-American force in North Africa

8) _____ helped meet a labor shortage in the West and Southwest

9) _____ June 6, 1944—the day when thousands of Allied soldiers landed on the beaches of Normandy, France

10) _____ Nazi Germany's attempt to exterminate the Jews of Europe

**TRUE/FALSE**
**Write T is a statement is true or F if it is false.  If a statement is false, explain why.**

11) _____ The atomic bomb was developed by 18 top U.S. scientists working in secret on a program known as the Manhattan Project.

_____

12) _____ The Battle of Stalingrad marked the turning point in the war between Germany and the Soviet Union.

_____

13) _____ Mobilizing for war was a costly task for the millions of U.S. workers who experienced decreased earnings and rising unemployment.

_____

14) _____ The Battle of the Bulge resulted in the heaviest losses ever sustained by the U.S. Army in a single action.

_____

15) _____ Of the approximately 50 million people who died during World War II, more than half were civilians.

_____

16) _____ The Battle of Midway was the largest naval engagement in history.

_____

17) _____ Germany declared war on the United States in 1941 because Roosevelt extended Lend-Lease aid to the Soviet Union.

_____

18) _____ Roosevelt called June 6, 1944, "a date which will live in infamy."

_____

19) _____ More than 600 American prisoners and 10,000 Filipino prisoners died at the hands of the Japanese on the 65-mile-long Bataan Death March.

_____

20) _____ The Selective Training and Service Act—requiring all men between the ages of 21 and 35 to register—was the first peacetime draft in U.S. history.

_____

Call to Freedom

## MULTIPLE CHOICE
**For each of the following, circle the letter of the best choice.**

21) The nuclear weapon that offered an alternative to invasion was

a. sonar technology.
b. radar.
c. the long-range patrol bomber.
d. the atomic bomb.

22) The Maginot Line was

a. a fortified wall that France had built along its border with Germany.
b. the political boundary that separated Germany from Poland.
c. the most decorated U.S. infantry unit at Iwo Jima.
d. contested when Congress debated whether to fight Hitler or remain neutral.

23) The U.S. Navy won the Battle of the Coral Sea and the Battle of Midway after

a. successfully cutting the flow of Japan's raw materials from Southeast Asia.
b. U.S. marines on Guadalcanal prevented Japanese ships from refueling there.
c. the navy's code breakers read intercepted Japanese battle plans.
d. several months of bloody jungle warfare ashore.

24) In Poland the Nazis uprooted Jews from their homes in the countryside and forced them

a. into cattle cars that transported them to concentration camps in Berlin.
b. into isolated urban areas known as ghettos.
c. to work in ammunition plants in Warsaw.
d. to dig military trenches for German soldiers fighting the Battle of the Bulge.

25) The so-called zoot-suit riots in Los Angeles began when

a. more than 200,000 braceros surged across the Mexican border and demanded jobs in California.
b. U.S. sailors attacked young Mexican Americans dressed in outfits called zoot-suits.
c. young Mexican Americans wearing zoot-suits hurled taunts at Japanese Americans.
d. unemployed braceros set fire to clothing stores owned by affluent Mexican Americans.

26) Two weeks after the invasion of Pearl Harbor, Roosevelt and Churchill agreed to focus on

a. turning back the Japanese assault against the United States.
b. defeating the Japanese in the South Pacific.
c. protecting the Soviet Union from a German invasion.
d. the war in Europe, rather than Japan.

27) Immediately after bombing Pearl Harbor, the Japanese went after

a. U.S. holdings in the Pacific and British and Dutch possessions in Southeast Asia.
b. German submarines in the Java Sea.
c. the Chinese colonies of Hong Kong and Singapore.
d. India, Australia, and the West Coast of the United States.

28) In 1939 the nations known as the Allied Powers were

a. Germany and Poland.

b. Germany and Italy.

c. Britain and France.

d. Britain, France, and the Soviet Union.

29) As men left the workforce to join the armed forces,

a. women replaced them in factories and business offices.

b. resulting unemployment led to decreased income taxes for middle and lower income Americans.

c. higher-paying jobs opened for African American civilians.

d. civilians flocked to see movies that depicted the horrors of war.

30) World War II began on September 1, 1939 when

a. Hitler became chancellor of Germany.

b. German forces invaded Poland.

c. Germany seized Czechoslovakia.

d. German and Italian forces invaded Albania.

31) After defeating the German Afrika Korps, the Allies launched an offensive campaign in

a. Germany.

b. Belgium.

c. France.

d. Italy.

32) The Battle of Britain describes

a. the fight for ocean trade routes that broke out between Germany and Britain.

b. the 12-day attack on British ships by German submarines in the English Channel.

c. the battles between the British and German air forces for air supremacy over Britain.

d. aerial combat between the *Luftwaffe* and the Royal Air Force in the skies over France.

33) The Japanese took defensive actions, rather than the offensive, after the Battle of

a. Leyte Gulf.

b. Midway.

c. the Coral Sea.

d. the Bulge.

34) To pay for the war effort, the U.S. government

a. asked civilians to limit purchases of canned foods and gasoline needed to supply U.S. troops overseas.

b. increased the production of war materials sold to Britain and France.

c. raised taxes and sold war bonds.

d. earned interest on funds allocated to the Lend-Lease Act.

35) The general who kept his promise to return to the Philippines was

a. Douglas MacArthur.

b. Dwight D. Eisenhower.

c. George C. Marshall.

d. George Patton.

Call to Freedom

36) The War Production Board was in charge of

    a. preventing discrimination in war industries.
    b. overseeing the production of war supplies loaned to the Allied Powers.
    c. approving deferment applications from people who held jobs that were vital to the war effort.
    d. converting factories to war production.

37) Japan formally surrendered on September 2, 1945,

    a. fearing that Truman intended to use atomic bombs to end the war.
    b. the day after the *Enola Gay* dropped an atomic bomb on Hiroshima.
    c. less than a month after U.S. forces dropped a second atomic bomb, this time on the city of Nagasaki.
    d. only days after Hitler committed suicide in his underground bunker in Berlin.

38) Guadalcanal was important to Japan because

    a. more than half the battleships in the U.S. Pacific Fleet were anchored there.
    b. it offered Japan a base from which its air force could threaten the vital sea link between Australia and the United States.
    c. the loss of this oil-rich island would deprive Japan of fuel for its fighter planes and battleships.
    d. of its strategic position between Iwo Jima and the Philippines.

39) During the two years of fighting between the Allies and the Afrika Korps, General

    a. Eisenhower helped boost Allied morale by bombing enemy tanks along the Suez Canal.
    b. Patton proved to be a bold and aggressive leader.
    c. Bradley became known as the GI's General.
    d. Rommel became known as "the Desert Fox."

40) Italy joined Germany and declared war on the Allied Powers

    a. after the Japanese bombed Pearl Harbor.
    b. when French general Charles de Gaulle formed a "Free French" force to fight Mussolini.
    c. as Hitler's forces advanced on the French capital of Paris.
    d. after Hitler negotiated a nonaggression pact with Mussolini.

41) In 1945, Allied forces suffered high casualties as they fought to take Japan's last island strongholds,

    a. Iwo Jima and Okinawa.          c. Kiska and Attu.
    b. Guam and Wake Island.        d. Corregidor and Guadalcanal.

42) During the liberation of their country, French citizens surged out into the streets

    a. to celebrate the news that Allied forces had swarmed ashore in Normandy.
    b. as U.S. General Omar Bradley led Allied soldiers into Paris.
    c. to welcome U.S. General Douglas MacArthur on his promised return to Paris.
    d. to aid Soviet and French soldiers returning from the grueling struggle at Stalingrad.

43) Under internment, the U.S. government removed most Japanese people from the West Coast and

   a. deported them to either Hawaii or the Solomon Islands.
   b. housed them at the Fort Leavenworth reservation in Kansas.
   c. transported them to remote camps throughout the western United States.
   d. imprisoned them in military barracks near Alamogordo, New Mexico.

44) The Allies took the offensive in the Pacific after winning victories in the

   a. Java Sea.                                      c. Java Sea, and at Midway.
   b. Coral Sea, at Midway, and on Guadalcanal.     d. Coral Sea and on Guadalcanal.

45) Jews arriving at Nazi death camps across Europe were sent to

   a. the front to build war fortifications.
   b. gas chambers for immediate execution.
   c. facilities where they would be used in cruel medical experiments.
   d. work as slave labor in camp factories or go to gas chambers for immediate execution.

46) Between April and June 1940, Hitler invaded the western European nations of

   a. Denmark, Norway, and Belgium.
   b. Finland, Luxembourg, and the Netherlands.
   c. Belgium, France, and the Netherlands.
   d. Denmark, Norway, Belgium, Luxembourg, the Netherlands, and France.

47) The Soviets saved their nation by defeating the Germans

   a. in the Battle of Stalingrad.
   b. in a huge tank battle near the city of Kursk.
   c. at Stalingrad and Kursk.
   d. in fierce, hand to hand combat in the streets of Stalingrad.

48) As U.S. farmers attempted to feed Americans as well as the European Allies,

   a. agricultural production remained high throughout the war.
   b. agricultural production dipped drastically as factories stopped manufacturing farm machinery in order to produce war materials.
   c. citizens protested high food prices and government limits on canned goods.
   d. food shortages led to government limitations on canned goods and grains.

49) By the end of 1941 the *Einsatzgruppen* had

   a. initiated its "lightning war" in a deadly sweep across Poland.
   b. rounded up and killed some 600,000 Jews.
   c. dropped bombs on more than a dozen British cities.
   d. caused enormous damage to Allied ships and killed more than 4,000 Allied sailors.

Call to Freedom

50) The Japanese needed to knock out the U.S. fleet at Pearl Harbor in order to

a. pave the way for their conquest of the United States.
b. force Roosevelt to reopen the sale of products critical to Japanese industry.
c. gave them time to complete their conquest of Southeast Asia.
d. force Roosevelt to unlock Japanese funds in the United States.

51) By mid-1942 the Nazis began to ship Jews from

a. all areas of German-occupied Europe to death camps across Europe.
b. Germany to concentration camps in Munich.
c. Germany and France to a death camp in Auschwitz.
d. Germany and Belgium to death camps across Europe.

52) Hitler broke the nonaggression pact when he invaded

a. Italy.
b. France.
c. Britain.
d. the Soviet Union.

53) The purpose of Operation Overlord was to

a. break through the Allied lines in the Ardennes.
b. launch an Allied invasion of German-occupied France.
c. capture the Suez Canal, a vital Axis supply route.
d. launch an Allied attack in North Africa.

54) During World War II, over 300,000 women

a. served as Army and Navy nurses in combat areas.
b. invested in war bonds to help fund the war.
c. worked in the armed forces.
d. ran spy missions and flew planes from factories to combat units.

55) The Holocaust stemmed from

a. Jewish revolts against the German soldiers in the Netherlands.
b. Jewish uprisings against the Nazis in Poland.
c. the political opposition of Jews to Hitler.
d. Nazi agression and persecution.

56) The U.S. general who was President Roosevelt's top military adviser

a. George C. Marshall.
b. Dwight D. Eisenhower.
c. Omar Bradley.
d. George Patton.

57) Allied troops advanced toward Japan using the strategy of

a. daylight bombing.
b. island hopping.
c. invading the Philippines first.
d. dropping the atomic bomb on Okinawa.

58) Germany and the Soviet Union both invaded

    a. Finland.                                c. Poland and Finland.
    b. Poland.                                d. Finland, Estonia, Latvia, and Lithuania.

59) Of nearly 16 million Americans who served in the military during World War II, about

    a. 1 million were African Americans.        c. 300,000 were Japanese Americans.
    b. 100,000 were Mexican Americans.     d. 100,000 were women.

60) Killed by the Nazis during the Holocaust were some

    a. 1 million Jews.
    b. 3 million Jews, gypsies, Slavs, political and religious radicals, and other people.
    c. 4 million Jews and thousands of other people.
    d. 6 million Jews—about two thirds of all Jews living in Europe before the war—and thousands of other people.

## ENHANCED QUESTIONS
**For each of the following, circle the letter of the best choice. Next, expand on the subject by answering the second question in the space provided.**

61) The commander of the U.S. Pacific fleet was Admiral

    a. James Doolittle.                    c. James Byrnes.
    b. Chester Nimitz.                 d. Daniel Inouye.

How did he stop Japan's 1942 advance in the Pacific?

_____

_____

62) Fighting broke out in North Africa because the Axis powers hoped to capture the

    a. Suez Canal, a vital Allied supply route.    c. Mediterranean Sea.
    b. soil-rich Nile River region.            d. Strait of Gibraltar, Morocco, and Libya.

What obstacles did generals Montgomery and Eisenhower face during this campaign? Why did the Axis powers surrender?

_____

_____

63) When Hitler threatened Czechoslovakia with war in 1938, French and British leaders

   a. formed a military alliance that came to be called the Allied Powers.
   b. sent troops to defend Czechoslovakia.
   c. met with Hitler at the Munich Conference.
   d. demanded that Hitler return the Sudentenland to Czechoslovakia.

   How did this step affect the future of Czechoslovakia, France, and Britain?

   _____

   _____


64) To retain the "purity" of the German nation, Hitler and the Nazis decided in 1933 to

   a. encourage German Jews to emigrate, and imprison those who didn't.
   b. uproot Jews from their German homes, and force them to live in Poland.
   c. kill all newborn infants of German Jewish parents.
   d. kill all German Jewish women of child-bearing age.

   How did this "solution" change after German expansion brought more and more Jews under Hitler's control?

   _____


65) The Battle of the Atlantic

   a. tarnished the spirit of cooperation that had existed between Roosevelt and Churchill.
   b. began when German submarines attacked British cargo ships bound for the Soviet Union.
   c. raged as the U.S. Navy sank dozens of German submarines between 1941 and 1943.
   d. was the naval fight between Germany and the Allied Powers to control ocean trade routes.

   How did the Atlantic Charter state America's and Britain's positions in the Battle of the Atlantic?

   _____

   _____

## GRAPHIC IMAGE QUESTIONS
**Examine the image, and then answer the following questions.**

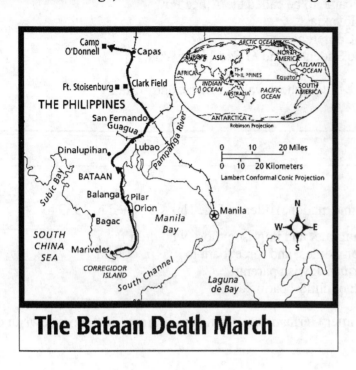

**The Bataan Death March**

66) About how far did prisoners have to march to reach San Fernando from Mariveles?

_____

67) In what general direction did they travel?

_____

68) What was the final destination of the Bataan Death March?

_____

## SHORT ANSWER
**Write a brief answer for each of the following.**

69) Why did Roosevelt argue that the United States "must be the great arsenal of democracy"?
How did the Lend-Lease Act address Roosevelt's argument?

_____

_____

_____

Call to Freedom

70) How did Roosevelt increase American preparedness for war while retaining respect for U.S. neutrality laws?

_____

_____

_____

71) Why did the Allies adopt the strategy of island-hopping? How successful was this strategy?

_____

_____

_____

72) How did convoys and the atomic bomb help the Allies win World War II?

_____

_____

_____

73) How did the United States mobilize for World War II?

_____

_____

_____

**ESSAY**
**On a seperate sheet of paper, write an essay on one of the following.**

74) Describe Nazi actions toward Jews. Also describe U.S. discrimination against African Americans, Japanese Americans, and Mexican Americans during World War II.

75) Explain what motivated Germany and Japan to launch independent acts of aggression against other people and nations during the 1930s and 1940s, and why the United States was drawn into war with both Germany and Japan.

ANSWER KEY

1) internment

2) nonaggression pact

3) Fair Employment Practices Committee

4) genocide

5) kamikaze

6) Blitzkrieg

7) Dwight D. Eisenhower

8) braceros

9) D-Day

10) Holocaust

11) F
Hundreds of Allied scientists worked on the Manhattan Project.

12) T

13) F
As America mobilized for war, production boomed, causing earnings to rise and unemployment to nearly vanish.

14) T

15) T

16) F
The largest naval engagement in history was the Battle of Leyte Gulf.

Call to Freedom

17) F

After the United States declared war on Japan, Germany then declared war on the United States.

18) F

Roosevelt called December 7, 1941—the day Japan attacked Pearl Harbor—"a date which will live in infamy."

19) T

20) T

21) d

22) a

23) c

24) b

25) b

26) d

27) a

28) c

29) a

30) b

31) d

32) c

33) b

34) c

35) a

36) d

37) c

38) b

39) d

40) c

41) a

42) b

43) c

44) b

45) d

46) d

47) c

48) a

49) b

50) c

51) a

Call to Freedom

52) d

53) b

54) c

55) d

56) a

57) b

58) b

59) a

60) d

61) b
In early 1942, Japan seemed ready to strike at India or Australia, or even Hawaii and the West Coast of the United States. Using decoded Japanese messages, Admiral Nimitz learned that the Japanese planned to capture Port Moresby, in New Guinea. Nimitz sent an Allied fleet to cut off the Japanese invasion force in the Coral Sea northeast of Australia. In the Battle of the Coral Sea, U.S. planes sank one Japanese carrier and damaged another, and the Allied Powers stopped the Japanese from taking Port Moresby. Weeks later, Nimitz also stopped a Japanese fleet on the way to attack Midway Island. The U.S. victory put the Japanese on the defensive for the remainder of the war.

62) a
For two years, the Allies battled General Erwin Rommel, a master of warfare and surprise attacks, in a back-and-forth battle that raged over some 1,500 miles in North Africa. However, Rommel suffered a shortage of troops and supplies. Montgomery stopped Rommel's advance in the Battle of El Alamein as Eisenhower arrived with additional British-American forces. Eisenhower had a special talent for planning and organization. Soon Montgomery's and Eisenhower's troops had trapped Rommel's retreating soldiers, and Rommel surrendered.

63) c

In an act of appeasement, French and British leaders persuaded the Czechs to surrender the Sudentenland as Hitler demanded. Hitler promised no more territorial demands after the Sudentenland. Upon hearing of the appeasement, Churchill predicted that war would result. Churchill was right. Hitler did not stop his demands and later seized the rest of Czechoslovakia, then went on to invade France and bomb Britain. Germany's aggression led France and Britain—soon known as the Allied Powers—to declare war on Germany.

64) a

Hitler and other high-ranking Nazis thought it was impractical to imprison the millions of Jews of Europe in concentration camps. Therefore, they looked for other "solutions." In Poland, they forced Jews into ghettos. They also used special killing squads to round up and shoot Jews. At the Wannsee Conference in 1942, the Nazis agreed that the "final solution" was genocide. Therefore the Nazis built death camps across Europe, where they murdered millions and millions of people because they were Jews.

65) d

The Battle of the Atlantic broke out as U.S. aid to Britain increased. Cash-strapped Britain depended on supplies shipped by the United States. When German submarines attempted to sink Allied ships, the U.S. Navy escorted the ships and tracked German submarines. Cooperation between the U.S. and Britain was further spelled out in a statement of principles known as the Atlantic Charter, issued by Roosevelt and Churchill. They pledged not to acquire new territory as a result of war and to work for peace after the current conflict.

66) about 60 miles

67) north

68) Camp O'Donnell

69) Roosevelt called for increased aid to Britain, arguing that the United States would be in grave danger if all of Europe fell to Hitler. In March 1941 Congress passed the Lend-Lease Act, offering to loan $7 billion worth of weapons and other war supplies to cash-strapped Britain. After Hitler invaded the Soviet Union, Roosevelt extended Lend-Lease to the Soviets.

70) Roosevelt asked Congress to adjust U.S. neutrality laws which prevented the United States from providing war supplies to the Allies. Congress approved the cash-and-carry system which sold supplies to the Allies but required payment in cash and transportation of the goods out of the United States by Allied ships. When that was not enough Roosevelt also swapped 50 U.S. destroyers for 99-year leases on several of Britain's naval bases in the Caribbean. In 1940 the United States began its first peacetime draft to enlarge the armed forces. After France fell in 1940, Congress greatly increased the defense budget. Roosevelt ran for a third term in November 1940 so that the country wouldn't change leaders with a war coming on. In March 1941 Congress approved the Lend-Lease Act to loan Britain even more money and supplies.

71) The Allies planned to conquer one Pacific island after another, moving ever closer to Japan. Allied forces would land only on the most important islands, thus cutting off Japanese troops on bypassed islands. The Allies hoped this strategy of island-hopping would gain them bases near Japan—close enough for bombers to reach the country, and then for Allied forces to invade and conquer it. The island-hopping began in late 1943. In June 1944 the capture of the Marianas finally brought U.S. bombers within range of Japan's home islands.

72) Convoys—large groups of cargo chips—protected by navy escort ships were less vulnerable to attack than ships sailing alone. The Allies were able to ship more tons of supplies to Britain using this method. Until convoys were used, it was beginning to look like German submarines might win the war by cutting Britain off from supplies. When the atomic bomb was dropped on Japan, its destructive power was stunning. Its use against the Japanese in their homeland brought their resistance to an end and they surrendered.

73) After the United States entered World War II, officials asked civilians to limit canned foods, gasoline, tires, and other items needed to supply the troops. U.S. factories converted from producing domestic goods and turned out enormous quantities of tanks, jeeps, guns, and ammunition. Women kept industry operating at full capacity by working at jobs formerly held by men. Farmers produced enough crops to feed Americans as well as the European Allies. The War Production Board banned the production of cars so that automotive plants could focus on producing military equipment. Nearly 16 million Americans served in the military.

74) Due to Nazi violence and persecution, some 6 million European Jews perished in the Holocaust. The Nazis also sent thousands of European gypsies, Slavs, and other groups to be killed in death camps. The Nazis banished, imprisoned, enslaved, and tortured Jews, as well as stripping them of their civil rights, jobs, property, and their homelands. Jewish families were torn apart in the process. In the United States, African American civilians encountered frequent discrimination in the labor force. On average, they received less than half the pay of whites in similar jobs. African American troops also faced discrimination in the armed forces. Early in the war, the marines and the army air corps would not accept any black soldiers, while the navy gave them only simple, dirty jobs. The army refused to let African Americans serve in leadership roles. Later some of these rules began to change. The U.S. government acted against Japanese Americans by relocating or imprisoning them to remove what it saw as a threat of sabotage. Most Japanese people from the West Coast were removed from their homes and transported to remote camps throughout the western United States. Many had to abandon their houses, businesses, and farms. Mexican American civilians who took wartime jobs on the West Coast and in the Midwest faced discrimination as well. In June 1943, groups of sailors attacked Mexican Americans in Los Angeles, and over the course of 10 days, thousands of people roamed the city, assaulting Mexican Americans. Even so, some 300,000 Mexican Americans served in the military, as did 1 million African Americans. Despite internment, many Japanese Americans also volunteered for military service. Others played an important role in the Pacific as interpreters and translators with military intelligence units.

75) Germany's aggression was motivated by Hitler's dream of revenge for defeat in World War I. He was determined to expand Germany's control over a much wider territory. When Britain and France tried to prevent him from continuing his aggressive acts against Poland, Hitler pushed on and went to war with them. Hitler knew he had to take France out of the war because it posed a direct threat to Germany. In 1940 he invaded and quickly conquered France and nearly caught all the British forces at the Belgian port of Dunkirk. He planned to invade Britain, but he could never win control of the air in Britain and never dared invade. While Allied forces attempted to stop Hitler's advance across Europe, the United States gave aid to the Allies without officially declaring war on Germany. Meanwhile, Japan's aggression toward other nations had begun in the 1930s when Japan—after conquering much of China—set its sights on Southeast Asia and its valuable oil and other natural resources. Japan was determined to expand in the Pacific region to increase its economic and natural resources. In 1941 Japanese forces seized French Indochina. In response, President Roosevelt froze Japanese funds in the United States and blocked the sale of products critical to Japanese industry. U.S. officials demanded that Japan leave China and French Indochina. In response to these demands, Japan developed a plan to attack Hawaii, knock out the U.S. fleet, and buy time to complete the conquest of Southeast Asia. The day after the Japanese bombed Pearl Harbor, the United States declared war on Japan. Germany, which was allied with Japan, then declared war on the United States.

## Chapter 26 The Cold War Begins

**MATCHING**
**In the space provided, write the term or the name of the person that best fits the description. Choose your answers from the list below. Not all answers will be used.**

Cold War                McCarthyism              Potsdam Conference
blacklisting            Alger Hiss               McCarthyism
George C. Marshall      Internal Security Act    Taft-Hartley Act
Taft-Hartley Act        Thomas Dewey             Adlai Stevenson
containment             Yalta Conference         House Un-American Activities Committee

1) _____ outlawed closed shops and required union leaders to take an oath saying they were not Communists

2) _____ struggle between the United States and the Soviet Union for global power

3) _____ required organizations thought to be communist to register with the government

4) _____ policy that sought to prevent the Soviet Union from expanding into areas of strategic importance to the United States

5) _____ making vicious accusations without offering proof

6) _____ meeting at which Germany and Austria were divided into four zones of occupation

7) _____ Republican who ran against Harry S Truman in 1948

8) _____ refusing to hire

9) _____ former State Department official accused of being a communist spy

10) _____ World War II general who became Truman's secretary of state in 1947

**TRUE/FALSE**
**Write T is a statement is true or F if it is false. If a statement is false, explain why.**

11) _____ In 1948 David Ben-Gurion became the first prime minister of the independent state of Israel.

12) _____ Congress established the House Un-American Activities Committee to investigate the background of some 16,000 federal workers suspected of being Communists.

_____

13) _____ The Long March was a 6,000-mile, year-long retreat of Chinese Nationalists to northwestern China.

_____

14) _____ In 1945, representatives from Britain, Japan, the Soviet Union, and the United States met to write a charter for the United Nations—a new organization to promote world peace.

_____

15) _____ General Douglas MacArthur commanded the UN forces that supported South Korea.

_____

16) _____ After Julius and Ethel Rosenberg were convicted of passing secret atomic weapons information to the Soviet Union, they were sentenced to life in prison.

_____

17) _____ U.S. forces have remained stationed along the 38th parallel.

_____

18) _____ During the Nuremberg Trials, the UN Security Council convicted high-ranking Nazi leaders for committing "crimes against humanity."

_____

19) _____ United Mine Workers president John Lewis led some 400,000 union miners in two 1946 strikes.

_____

20) _____ Actor and athlete Paul Robeson moved to the Soviet Union after HUAC accusations damaged his career.

_____

Call to Freedom

## MULTIPLE CHOICE
**For each of the following, circle the letter of the best choice.**

21) "Let us not be deceived—we are today in the midst of a cold war," said

a. Mao Zedong of Nationalist Chinese-Communist Chinese relations.
b. George C. Marshall of U.S.-Chinese relations.
c. Adlai Stevenson of U.S.-Soviet relations.
d. Bernard Baruch of U.S.-Soviet relations.

22) The GI Bill of Rights offered veterans educational benefits

a. and insurance benefits for themselves and their families.
b. and termination pay based on the number of years they served in the military.
c. and loans for houses, farms, and businesses.
d. at colleges and technical schools.

23) The 38th parallel divided

a. North Korea and South Korea.
b. East Berlin and West Berlin.
c. Israel and Palestine.
d. Nationalist China and the People's Republic of China.

24) "An Iron Curtain has descended across the [European] Continent," said

a. President Truman.                     c. Winston Churchill.
b. President Eisenhower.                 d. Joseph Stalin.

25) In the Nuremberg Trials, 21 high-ranking Nazi leaders were found guilty and

a. sentenced to death.                   c. 12 were sentenced to death.
b. sentenced to life in prison.          d. 18 were sentenced to death.

26) When General MacArthur openly criticized Truman for not attacking China during the Korean War, Truman

a. relieved MacArthur of his command.
b. ordered air strikes on Chinese cities.
c. ordered a ground attack on the Chinese coast.
d. asked the UN to provide MacArthur with additional troops.

27) The UN General Assembly created Israel as a Jewish homeland, and

a. neighboring Arab states were very supportive.
b. some 400,000 Palestinian Arabs became refugees as a result.
c. both Palestine and Israel were admitted to the United Nations.
d. Israeli forces responded by attacking the armies of the Arab League.

28) When the United Mine Workers went on strike in April 1946, Truman

    a. agreed to end rationing of coal, oil, and gasoline.
    b. placed the mines under government control.
    c. asked Congress to give him the power to draft all striking workers.
    d. drafted all striking workers.

29) The Korean War took an unexpected turn when

    a. North Korea invited peace negotiations in July 1951.
    b. South Korean forces drove the North Koreans into a small area near the port city of Pusan.
    c. North Korean forces attacked UN forces from behind and captured the city of Inchon.
    d. Chinese troops advanced across the border to help the North Koreans.

30) During the civil war in China, the United States backed the corrupt Nationalist government because

    a. the Nationalists were fighting Chinese Communists.
    b. the People's Republic of China was a member of the UN.
    c. UN forces backing Mao Zedong asked for U.S. military aid.
    d. the Nationalists had allied with the U.S. during the Korean War.

31) George C. Marshall believed that economic instability in Europe

    a. threatened the world economy.        c. was not a problem.
    b. would keep new dictators from gaining power.    d. could benefit the United States.

32) Fighting in Korea settled into a standstill in 1951 when

    a. the UN Security Council called for a cease-fire.
    b. a UN offensive pushed enemy forces back across the 38th parallel.
    c. MacArthur's forces captured Pyongyang.
    d. Senator Joseph McCarthy told a West Virginia audience that Communists in the U.S. government were responsible for U.S. setbacks in the Korean War.

33) One of the few Americans who tried to expose Senator McCarthy as a liar was

    a. journalist Whittaker Chambers.    c. Senator Strom Thurmond.
    b. journalist Edward R. Morrow.    d. Illinois governor Adlai Stevenson.

34) The U.S. government ordered John Lewis to stand trial for contempt because he

    a. denied in court that he hid secret government papers on his farm.
    b. falsely accused Alger Hiss of passing secret atomic weapons information to the Soviet Union.
    c. ordered a railroad strike that brought the country to a standstill.
    d. called a second UMW strike while the mines were under government control.

35) After organizations such as the FBI, the Justice Department, state and local governments, and schools and universities instituted loyalty oaths and investigations,

a. thousands of people lost their jobs because of suspected communist sympathies.
b. about 100 people lost their jobs because of "reasonable grounds" to suspect their loyalty.
c. HUAC convicted 18 citizens on spy charges, imprisoned 16 of them, and executed two.
d. hundreds of workers were arrested even after they signed a loyalty oath.

36) Communist parties gained strength in Eastern Europe after World War II due to

a. the withdrawal of UN troops from Germany.
b. the withdrawal of U.S. troops from Germany and Poland.
c. postwar economic difficulties and the presence of Soviet troops.
d. the Soviets' refusal to accept U.S. economic aid for West Berlin.

37) North Korea and South Korea signed a cease-fire after

a. MacArthur launched a ground assault on the Chinese coast.
b. Truman ordered air strikes on Chinese cities.
c. a UN offensive pushed the Chinese and North Koreans back across the 38th parallel.
d. Eisenhower threatened to use atomic weapons if the conflict continued.

38) When members of Congress challenged McCarthy to reveal the names on his list of 57 communists who were involved with shaping U.S. foreign policy, McCarthy

a. accused Congress of being "soft on Communism."
b. offered one name.
c. offered documented proof that the 57 Americans were card-carrying members of the Communist Party.
d. produced an additional list to reveal that the U.S. Army had Communists in uniform.

39) President Truman created the Loyalty Review Board in 1947 to

a. investigate the background of some 16,000 federal workers.
b. control the hiring practices of closed shops.
c. gain government control of labor unions.
d. encourage women to give up their jobs to make room for veterans.

40) The U.S. policy that devoted economic aid to help foreign countries fight communism became known as the

a. Fair Deal.
b. Marshall Plan.
c. Truman Doctrine.
d. Berlin Airlift.

41) Mao Zedong was the leader of

a. North Korea.
b. the Chinese Communists.
c. communist guerillas in Greece.
d. Czechoslovakia.

42) The presidential campaign of 1948 was waged by

    a. two candidates.               c. four candidates.
    b. three candidates.           d. five candidates.

43) The Korean War ended when

    a. Eisenhower withdrew U.S. forces from South Korea.
    b. the UN Security Council voted to withdraw UN forces from the conflict.
    c. North Korean forces withdrew from all areas south of the 38th parallel.
    d. the two sides signed a cease-fire in 1953.

44) Between 1948 and 1952, the United States donated or loaned more than $13 billion to

    a. Western European countries.
    b. Eastern European countries.
    c. Nationalist China and the Republic of Korea.
    d. Japan as the U.S. Army began rebuilding Japan's devastated economy.

45) The right to arrest people suspected of subversive activities during times of national emergency was granted to the U.S. government by the

    a. HUAC.               c. Loyalty Review Board.
    b. Internal Security Act.      d. United Nations.

46) Truman vetoed the Taft-Hartley Act because he

    a. hoped to regain the support of organized labor.
    b. wanted presidential authority to force striking unions to call off their strikes for an 80-day "cooling off" period.
    c. thought that the Act placed too many restrictions on unions.
    d. disagreed with Republicans in Congress who wanted to grant more power to unions.

47) McCarthy blamed the spread of communism on

    a. labor unions whose striking members brought the nation to a standstill.
    b. executives in the film, radio, television, and theater industries.
    c. Eisenhower, whom he accused of letting Communists sneak into the government.
    d. the "traitorous actions" of individuals in the U.S. State Department.

48) The policy whereby the U.S. would offer "friendly aid" to help European countries rebuild was known as the

    a. Fair Deal.            c. Truman Doctrine.
    b. Marshall Plan.       d. Berlin Airlift.

49) In 1952 the Democratic presidential nominee was

a. Truman.
b. Eisenhower.

c. Stevenson.
d. Dewey.

50) The party that favored racial segregation and opposed African American voting rights nominated—as its 1948 presidential candidate—

a. Strom Thurmond.
b. Henry Wallace.

c. Joseph McCarthy.
d. General Walton "Bulldog" Walker.

51) Support for the establishment of a Jewish homeland grew as a result of the

a. Berlin Airlift.
b. Warsaw Pact.

c. International Military Tribunal for the Far East.
d. horrors of the Holocaust.

52) The People's Republic of China was founded

a. by Chinese Communists.
b. by North Korean refugees.

c. on the island of Taiwan by Chinese Nationalists.
d. by Hideki Tojo in 1949.

53) Alger Hiss was sentenced to five years in prison because he was found guilty of

a. treason.
b. perjury.

c. committing war crimes.
d. committing crimes against humanity.

54) The so-called Hollywood Ten were

a. writers who refused to cooperate with HUAC.
b. actors who were blacklisted by the HUAC.
c. film executives who refused to sign a loyalty oath.
d. producers who released more than 40 anticommunist films between 1948 and 1954.

55) In 1948 the newly formed States' Rights Party became known as the

a. People's Ticket.
b. Progressives.

c. Dixiecrats.
d. Fair Dealers.

56) After McCarthy was revealed as a liar and a bully, the Senate voted to

a. unseat him.
b. condemn him.

c. arrest him.
d. deport him.

57) John Lewis ordered striking UMW members back to work after

a. Truman vowed to "fight to the finish."
b. a railroad strike brought the country to a standstill.
c. Truman threatened to draft striking miners.
d. a federal court fined the UMW $3.5 million.

58) The Greek army was able to put down a communist revolt in 1946 after receiving

    a. U.S. economic aid.
    b. UN military aid.
    c. military advice from former General George C. Marshall.
    d. military advice from former General Dwight D. Eisenhower.

59) From 1910 to 1945, Korea was controlled by

    a. China.
    b. Japan.
    c. Britain.
    d. the Soviet Union.

60) War crimes trials in Germany and Japan established that there is no defense for committing

    a. violent acts of terrorism.
    b. calculated wrongs.
    c. devastating acts in areas of occupation.
    d. "crimes against humanity."

## ENHANCED QUESTIONS
**For each of the following, circle the letter of the best choice. Next, expand on the subject by answering the second question in the space provided.**

61) The North Atlantic Treaty Organization was formed by the United States,

    a. Britain, and Belgium.
    b. Britain, Belgium, and six Eastern European nations.
    c. and seven Western European nations.
    d. Canada, Iceland, and nine Western European nations.

What was the purpose of NATO, and how did the Soviet Union respond?

_____

_____

62) After meeting Stalin for the first time, Truman wrote,

    a. "I can deal with Stalin."
    b. "We must offer 'friendly aid.'"
    c. "That man is a walking crime against humanity."
    d. "We must fight to the end."

Why, according to one diplomat, was this idea mistaken?

_____

_____

Call to Freedom

63) The major issue in the presidential election of 1952 was

a. Communism.

b. the Korean War.

c. the Cold War.

d. McCarthyism.

How did this issue affect the outcome of the 1952 election?

_____

_____

64) During the Berlin Airlift, U.S. and British planes

a. brought more than 2 million tons of food into West Berlin.

b. flew more than 300,000 flights to being food and supplies to the people of Berlin.

c. brought food, fuel, and machinery for more than 2 million people in West Berlin.

d. airlifted more than 2 million people from the Soviet-controlled eastern zone of Berlin to new homes in Western Europe.

Why did the Berlin Airlift begin, and how did the Soviet Union respond?

_____

_____

65) McCarthy went too far in late 1953 when he claimed that

a. members of the State Department were selling military secrets to the Soviet Union.

b. the U.S. Army had Communists in uniform.

c. President Eisenhower was a Communist.

d. journalist Edward R. Murrow was a Soviet spy.

How were McCarthy's charges investigated, and what were the results?

_____

_____

# GRAPHIC IMAGE QUESTIONS
**Examine the image, and then answer the following questions.**

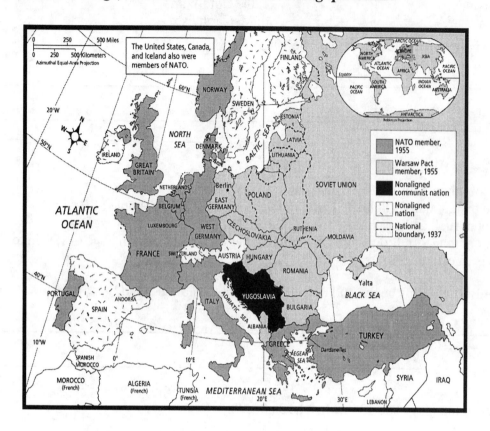

66) Which countries were members of NATO?

_____

67) Which country was a nonaligned communist nation?

_____

68) Which countries were nonaligned but were not communist?

_____

## SHORT ANSWER
**Write a brief answer for each of the following.**

69) What steps did Truman take to keep the country's finances strong after World War II?

_____

_____

_____

70) How did post-war popular culture reflect Cold War anxieties?

_____

_____

_____

71) Describe the significance of the Yalta Conference, and explain its impact on Poland.

_____

_____

_____

72) Why did the division of Korea lead to conflicts between the U.S. and the Soviet Union?

_____

_____

_____

73) What were the main goals of the Fair Deal, and how did Congress respond to these goals?

_____

_____

_____

# ESSAY
**On a seperate sheet of paper, write an essay on one of the following.**

74) Explain how two radically different political ideas led to the Cold War and how the Cold War affected some European nations between 1947 and 1949.

75) Explain why and how America became caught up in a hunt for Communists in the 1940s and 1950s, and why the hunt escalated into McCarthyism.

ANSWER KEY

1) Taft-Hartley Act

2) Cold War

3) Internal Security Act

4) containment

5) McCarthyism

6) Potsdam Conference

7) Thomas Dewey

8) blacklisting

9) Alger Hiss

10) George C. Marshall

11) T

12) F
Congress established HUAC to investigate disloyalty and harmful foreign influences in the United States.

13) F
During the Long March, Chinese Communists led by Mao Zedong fled from a Nationalist army attack to northwestern China.

14) F
The UN charter was the work of representatives from 50 nations.

15) T

Call to Freedom
463

16) F
   The Rosenbergs were executed for treason.

17) T

18) F

19) T

20) F
   Although HUAC accusations damaged his career, Robeson said, "My father was a slave, and my people died to build this country. No . . . people will drive me from it."

21) d

22) c

23) a

24) c

25) c

26) a

27) b

28) b

29) d

30) a

31) a

32) b

Call to Freedom

# ANSWER KEY

33)  b

34)  d

35)  a

36)  c

37)  d

38)  b

39)  a

40)  c

41)  b

42)  c

43)  d

44)  a

45)  b

46)  c

47)  d

48)  b

49)  c

50)  a

51)  d

52)  a

53)  b

54)  a

55)  c

56)  b

57)  d

58)  a

59)  b

60)  d

61)  d
NATO was a military alliance of members that pledged to defend the others if they were attacked. In 1955 the Soviet Union responded to NATO by creating its own military alliance, the Warsaw Pact, with its Eastern European satellite nations.

62)  a
Stalin was actually a brutal dictator who hid his cruel nature behind a quiet manner and expression.

63)  b
Knowing that many voters blamed him for the war, Truman chose not to seek re-election. General Eisenhower, the Republican nominee, was a well-liked war hero who probably clinched the election when he promised to end the Korean War. He easily defeated Democratic nominee Stevenson whom many voters viewed as out of touch with the "real world."

64)  c
In 1948 the Soviet Union blocked all rail and highway traffic between the western part of Germany and Berlin. This blockade deprived West Berlin of crucial supplies. To solve the crisis without direct military confrontation, the United States and Britain flew supplies into West Berlin. Unwilling to risk another war by using military force to stop the airlift, the Soviet Union lifted its blockade in 1949.

Call to Freedom

65) b
A group of senators decided to hold televised hearings. These Army-McCarthy hearings proved to be McCarthy's downfall. Over time, the army's attorney Joseph Welch won the other senators' favor with his charming, witty manner, and succeeded in exposing McCarthy. As a result, viewers across the nation finally saw McCarthy for what he was—a bully.

66) Portugal, Great Britain, Norway, Denmark, the Netherlands, Belgium, Luxembourg, France, West Germany, Italy, Greece, Turkey, the United States, Canada, and Iceland

67) Yugoslavia

68) Ireland, Spain, Andorra, Switzerland, Austria, Sweden, Finland

69) The Truman administration encouraged millions of women to give up their jobs to make way for veterans. New laws provided soldiers with termination pay, unemployment compensation for one year, job reinstatement and seniority rights and insurance benefits. The GI Bill of Rights played a major role in keeping unemployment low.

70) Magazines ran articles like "How Communists Get That Way" and "Communists Are After Your Child." Hollywood produced more than 40 anticommunist films. Science fiction movies, which became very popular, often combined anxiety over new forms of technology with the fear of communism.

71) During the Yalta Conference, Roosevelt, Churchill, and Stalin hammered out an agreement that would shape international affairs for years to come. The Yalta accord strongly supported the creation of a world peace-keeping organization. It also called for free elections and "governments responsive to the will of the people" in the nations being liberated from Axis control. Roosevelt and Churchill wanted to create a democratic government in Poland. Stalin, however, wanted a Soviet-controlled Poland. When Soviet troops liberated Poland after the war, they installed a procommunist government. Stalin later refused to hold free elections in Poland.

72) After World War II, the Allies divided Korea between U.S. and Soviet troops. The United States and the Soviet Union each established a friendly government in its area of occupation. However, when Soviet and U.S. troops pulled out in 1949, both the North and South Korean governments laid claim to the entire country. When the Soviet-equipped North Korean forces crossed the 38th parallel, Truman ordered U.S. forces into battle, and the UN called on its members to support South Korea.

73) The main goals of the Fair Deal were full employment, a higher minimum wage, a national health insurance plan, more affordable housing, and Social Security benefits and aid for farmers. The Fair Deal also had a substantial civil rights component, calling for anti-lynching and voter protection laws as well as anti-discrimination measures. Congress approved of some of the Fair Deal reforms, but rejected some civil rights legislation, federal aid to education, and the national health insurance program.

74) The conflicts between the United States and the Soviet Union stemmed from radically different political ideas—capitalism and democracy in the United States, and communism in the Soviet Union. The United States saw itself as a beacon of freedom for the world, while the Soviet Union hoped to spread communism across the globe. The conflict between the two nations initially focused on Central and Eastern Europe and particularly on the question of Germany's future. The Western allies wanted a united, demilitarized, and independent Germany. The Soviets feared a united Germany. In Eastern Europe, despite the Yalta agreement on free elections, the Soviet army of occupation remained and established communist "satellite states" with governments controlled by the Soviet Union. As communist parties gained strength in Eastern Europe, British and U.S. leaders feared that the Soviets would soon extend their control through the rest of Europe. When communist guerillas revolted in Greece in 1946, President Truman developed the Truman Doctrine and gave aid to Greece and neighboring Turkey. In 1948 another Soviet-backed communist revolt occurred in Czechoslovakia. In order to fight communism there, Congress passed the Marshall Plan, through which the United States donated $13 billion to Western European countries. However, the Soviet Union prevented their Eastern European satellites from accepting any U.S. aid. As the Cold War deepened, the United States adopted the policy of containment to prevent the Soviets from expanding into areas of strategic importance to the United States. Therefore, when in 1948 the Soviets blocked all traffic between the western part of Germany and Berlin, the United States initiated the Berlin Airlift which eventually led the Soviets to lift the blockade. The continuing cold war led the U.S. and nine Western European nations—along with Canada and Iceland—to form NATO. The Eastern European satellite nations were aligned with the Soviet Union under the terms of the Warsaw Pact. These two military alliances formally and firmly divided the participating democratic nations from the communist nations that lay behind the Iron Curtain.

75) When Attorney General McGrath of the Truman administration stated that Communists were "everywhere—in factories, offices, butcher shops, on street corners," he was addressing Americans' fears of growing domestic communism and the expansion of communism across Eastern Europe. This Red Scare had already led Congress to establish the House Un-American Activities Committee to investigate disloyalty and harmful foreign influences in the United States. In 1947 HUAC began trying to prove the presence of Communists both in Hollywood and in the State Department. That same year, Truman created the Loyalty Review Board to investigate the background of some 16,000 federal workers. Explosive spy cases in the late 1940s convinced Americans that communists had infiltrated the government and were guilty of treason. In 1950 the Internal Security Act required organizations thought to be communist to register with the government, and gave the government the right to arrest people suspected of subversive activities during times of national emergency. The outbreak of the Korean War in 1950 further increased Americans' anticommunist feelings. That same year, Senator Joseph McCarthy began a one-man campaign to expose Communists in the U.S. government. Claiming to have a list of U.S. foreign policy makers who were Communists, he stunned many people with his charges. Although an early investigation called his charges "a fraud and a hoax," he continued to make up more charges naming more people as procommunist. His method—making vicious accusations without offering proof—became known as McCarthyism. The Red Scare evolved into McCarthyism because Americans were not accustomed to questioning their public officials. Others were afraid of being labeled "soft on communism" if they challenged McCarthy. Also, many Americans wanted an explanation for the spread of communism in Eastern Europe and Asia, and McCarthy gave them an explanation. A few people attempted to stop McCarthy. However, when journalist Edward R. Murrow tried to expose McCarthy on the television show *See It Now*, Murrow received bundles of hate mail. Americans caught up in the Red Scare were unable to detect McCarthy's motives until the Army-McCarthy hearings proved publicly that the senator was a liar and a bully. By then, many citizens' lives and careers had been damaged by false accusations fueled by the Red Scare.

## Chapter 27 Peace and Prosperity

### MATCHING

**In the space provided, write the term or the name of the person that best fits the description. Choose your answers from the list below. Not all answers will be used.**

Jo Ann Robinson     Levittown     Rosa Parks
baby boom     Thurgood Marshall     covert operations
*Sputnik*     massive retaliation     A. Philip Randolph
automation     Orval Faubus     brinkmanship
silent generation     Sun Belt     James Baldwin

1) _____ the world's first artificial satellite

2) _____ African American labor leader who threatened to organize a massive protest unless Truman desegregated the military

3) _____ a typical suburb built by a developer on Long Island, New York

4) _____ the use of nuclear weapons to fight communism

5) _____ called out the National Guard to prevent black students from attending a segregated high school

6) _____ the use of machines in production

7) _____ professor who organized a campaign to get African Americans to boycott the Montgomery city bus system

8) _____ secret actions

9) _____ NAACP attorney who led courtroom battles to abolish segregated schools

10) _____ significant increase in the number of children born

### TRUE/FALSE

**Write T is a statement is true or F if it is false. If a statement is false, explain why.**

11) _____ People who moved to the Sun Belt made their homes in either Florida or Georgia.

_____

12) _____ During Eisenhower's presidency, Congress expanded Social Security and unemployment benefits and increased the minimum wage.

_____

13) _____ Between 1949 and 1953, the number of American households with television sets increased from less than a million to more than 20 million.

_____

14) _____ The hydrogen bomb was much stronger than the atomic bombs the United States dropped on Japan in World War II.

_____

15) _____ *To Secure These Rights*, the report of the Committee on Civil Rights, noted that racial discrimination existed only in the southern states.

_____

16) _____ When Rosa Parks refused to give up her seat to a white passenger, the mayor of Montgomery prohibited her from riding buses in the city transit system.

_____

17) _____ The Montgomery Improvement Association was formed to strengthen the bus boycott and to coordinate the efforts of local African American leaders.

_____

18) _____ The National Aeronautics and Space Administration conducted covert operations to advance America's position in the Cold War.

_____

19) _____ The Little Rock Nine were outstanding black students chosen by the school board to integrate Central High School in 1957.

_____

20) _____ By 1960, one fourth of the U.S. population lived in Sun Belt cities.

_____

## MULTIPLE CHOICE
**For each of the following, circle the letter of the best choice.**

21) Most residents of suburbs were

a. wealthy black and white immigrants.
b. poor black families.
c. white, middle-class Americans.
d. white and black families with three or more children.

22) The main goal of the NAACP was to

a. end the segregation of black and white Americans.
b. win court cases guaranteeing "separate-but-equal" educational facilities for black students.
c. segregate public educational facilities in the South.
d. segregate public transportation in southern cities.

23) Jack Kerouac's belief that people needed to reject traditional society and strike out to find themselves was expressed in his novel

a. *The Wild One.*
b. *Notes of a Native Son.*
c. *The Power of Positive Thinking.*
d. *On the Road.*

24) Racial discrimination in the hiring of federal employees was banned

a. in the same year that African Americans launched the Montgomery bus boycott.
b. three years after World War II ended.
c. as the result of Thurgood Marshall's 1954 argument before the Supreme Court.
d. during Eisenhower's presidency.

25) The nuclear arms race began when

a. Congress established the National Aeronautics and Space Administration.
b. the United States and the Soviet Union began testing hydrogen bombs.
c. the Soviet Union launched the world's first artificial satellite.
d. Soviets downed an American U-2 spy plane and captured its pilot.

26) In 1946, civil rights activists marched to the Lincoln Memorial to demand

a. equal pay.
b. the right to run for public office.
c. a crackdown on the Ku Klux Klan.
d. an end to literacy tests.

27) Presidential candidate Eisenhower was popular with

a. wealthy Republican voters.
b. the unemployed, and members of organized labor.
c. wealthy voters of both parties.
d. middle-class voters of both parties.

28) In *Notes of a Native Son*,

    a. James Baldwin criticizes America's obsession with race.
    b. Allen Ginsberg celebrates the rootless and carefree lifestyle of beat authors.
    c. James Dean portrays a troubled middle-class teen who felt like an outcast.
    d. Jack Kerouac questions the rules of American society.

29) When Elizabeth Eckford arrived at Central High School in 1957,

    a. NAACP president Daisy Bates escorted her to class.
    b. National Guard soldiers refused her entrance to the school.
    c. civil rights activists cheered as she walked into the building.
    d. she was arrested for attempting to integrate a segregated school.

30) The CIA's first important covert operation

    a. was Operation Aswan in Egypt.
    b. failed when Mosaddeq placed Iran's oil industry under government ownership.
    c. was Operation Ajax in Iran.
    d. succeeded when CIA pilots used Nicaraguan planes to invade Guatemala.

31) Linda Brown, Elizabeth Eckford, and Rosa Parks were

    a. three of the students known as the Little Rock Nine.
    b. arrested for keeping their seats on a Montgomery bus in 1954.
    c. civil rights activists who helped the NAACP lead the Montgomery Bus boycott.
    d. among the first black Americans who took a stand against segregation in the 1950s.

32) When Jacobo Arbenz Guzmán nationalized the American-owned United Fruit Company,

    a. the CIA intervened in Guatemala.
    b. the United States asked Britain to help overthrow Guzmán.
    c. Secretary of State Dulles argued that Iran had turned toward "international communism."
    d. the CIA hired an army to invade Iran.

33) In an attempt to break the Montgomery bus boycott,

    a. the Montgomery Improvement Association opened a rival transit system that served only white passengers.
    b. segregationists bombed the homes of civil rights leaders E. D. Nixon and Martin Luther King Jr.
    c. city officials shut down the city transit system.
    d. Governor Talmedge arrested Rosa Parks for breaking the city's segregation laws.

34) The case of *Sweatt* v. *Painter* proved that

a. black children had the right to attend neighborhood schools rather than be bused long distances to black schools.
b. black veterans deserved medical treatment in hospitals that treated white veterans.
c. black law students could attain a better education at the University of Texas than at the state's newly created black law school.
d. segregation led many black children to feel that they were less important than white children.

35) As a result of the Highway Act of 1956,

a. more Americans moved to suburbs and commuted to work.
b. each state developed its own highway system.
c. the population of the Sun Belt doubled by 1960.
d. many African Americans left the South and moved to northern cities.

36) The National Aeronautics and Space Administration was established to

a. test nuclear weapons and instruct citizens on how to build and equip bomb shelters.
b. conduct space research.
c. send spy planes into Soviet air space.
d. develop hydrogen bombs.

37) During the 1950s, the most popular program on television was

a. *Texaco Star Theatre.*            c. *Invisible Man.*
b. *Rebel Without a Cause.*          d. *I Love Lucy.*

38) The Montgomery Improvement Association chose as its leader

a. Rosa Parks.                       c. Martin Luther King Jr.
b. E. D. Nixon                       d. Jo Ann Robinson.

39) After A. Philip Randolph threatened to organize a massive protest,

a. Truman issued an executive order banning segregation in the military.
b. Truman appointed the Committee on Civil Rights to investigate racial discrimination.
c. South Carolina governor James F. Byrnes opened public schools to black students.
d. the Little Rock school board decided to integrate one high school in the city.

40) The advertising industry encouraged suburban residents to

a. purchase books and periodicals for entertainment.
b. compete with their neighbors in buying the latest clothes, gadgets, and cars.
c. prevent people who did not fit the mold from moving into their neighborhoods.
d. fill their homes with labor-saving devices so that both parents could work.

Call to Freedom

41) The Committee on Civil Rights was appointed by

a. President Eisenhower, to coordinate educational programs and to cut down on bureaucracy.
b. President Truman, to investigate racial discrimination and to suggest federal solutions to the problem.
c. the Little Rock school board, when it decided to integrate one high school, then slowly work down to the elementary level.
d. E. D. Nixon, in an effort to challenge the bus segregation law in Montgomery.

42) In November 1956 the Supreme Court ruled that

a. segregation in the military was illegal.
b. segregation in public schools was illegal.
c. the University of Texas must admit Heman Sweatt to its law school.
d. Montgomery's segregated bus system was illegal.

43) Businesses and individuals moved to the Sun Belt to

a. benefit from low taxes and a warm climate.
b. escape urban decay.
c. acquire personal happiness and material prosperity.
d. escape the fear of nuclear war that threatened northern cities.

44) In 1960 some 22 percent of all American families earned

a. between $3,000 and $10,000 a year.          c. less than $1,500 a year.
b. less than $3,000 a year.                              d. more than $10,000 a year.

45) The most important Soviet leader during the 1950s was

a. Joseph Stalin.                                              a. Abdel Nasser.
b. Nikita Khrushchev.                                     d. Mohammad Mosaddeq.

46) The isolation and alienation of African Americans in the postwar world was the theme of

a. David Riesman's *The Lonely Crowd.*
b. Norman Vincent Peale's *The Power of Positive Thinking.*
c. Ralph Ellison's *Invisible Man.*
d. James Baldwin's *Notes of a Native Son.*

47) South Carolina's governor responded to desegregation by

a. promising to follow the law.
b. closing all public schools in the state.
c. stating that desegregation "would mark the beginning of the end of civilization in the South as we have known it."
d. ordering the state's public schools to desegregate "with all deliberate speed."

48) Many young people in the 1950s identified with and tried to imitate young screen rebels such as

    a. Buddy Holly and Elvis Presley.
    b. James Baldwin and Milton Berle.
    c. Allen Ginsberg and Jack Kerouac.
    d. James Dean and Marlon Brando.

49) By the mid-1950s almost 60 percent of the population qualified as middle class, with annual incomes between

    a. $1,500 and $3,000.
    b. $3,000 and $10,000.
    c. $10,000 and $18,000.
    d. $18,000 and $25,000.

50) The thaw in the Cold War ended when the

    a. Soviets downed Francis Gary Powers' U-2 spy plane.
    b Soviets falsely accused Francis Gary Powers of executing a spying mission in Soviet air space.
    c. CIA launched covert operations in Hungary and Poland.
    d. Soviets tested a hydrogen bomb in the South Pacific.

51) When people spoke of "Mr. Television," they were referring to

    a. Desi Arnaz.
    b. James Dean.
    c. Marlon Brando.
    d. Milton Berle.

52) ". . . having to stand up because a particular driver wanted to keep a white person from having to stand was . . . most inhumane," said

    a. Martin Luther King Jr.
    b. Thurgood Marshall.
    c. Rosa Parks.
    d. Jo Ann Robinson.

53) A so-called New Look in U.S. foreign policy was created by President

    a. Eisenhower and the CIA.
    b. Eisenhower and Secretary of State John Foster Dulles.
    c. Truman and Secretary of State A. Philip Randolph.
    d. Truman and War Department secretary James Hicks.

54) During the Montgomery bus boycott, African American citizens

    a. deprived the city transit system of more than 75 percent of its regular passengers.
    b. stopped white citizens from using the city transit system.
    c. did not develop a carpool system.
    d. formed the Committee on Civil Rights to help other cities stage their own bus boycotts.

55) The most popular rock 'n' roll star of the 1950s was

    a. Chuck Berry.
    b. Fats Domino.
    c. Buddy Holly.
    d. Elvis Presley.

56) Desegregation was enforced at Central High School by

    a. the Arkansas National Guard.           c. the Little Rock school board.
    b. federal troops sent by President Eisenhower.    d. the Arkansas NAACP.


57) Nikita Khrushchev shocked the communist world when he

    a. threatened to "crush the aggressor" during the Suez Canal crisis.
    b. charged American spy planes with invading Soviet air space over Poland.
    c. said that capitalism and communism could peacefully co-exist.
    d. agreed to meet with Vice President Richard Nixon at a summit meeting in France.


58) Fictional character Holden Caulfield expressed his disgust with modern life and values in
 J. D. Salinger's popular book

    a. *The Catcher in the Rye.*           c. *The Power Elite.*
    b. *The Lonely Crowd.*            d. *Rebel Without a Cause.*


59) "Separate but equal" referred to separate

    a. court systems for African Americans and whites.
    b. educational facilities for black students in the North and the South.
    c. buses for black riders in southern cities.
    d. barracks for black soldiers in the U.S. armed forces.


60) The Fathers of Bebop were

    a. Little Richard and Fats Domino.        c. Chuck Berry and Elvis Presley.
    b. Jerry Lee Lewis and Buddy Holly.      d. Charlie Parker and Dizzy Gillespie.


## ENHANCED QUESTIONS
**For each of the following, circle the letter of the best choice. Next, expand on the subject by answering the second question in the space provided.**


61) Many factories increased automation due to new developments in

    a. management.              c. the workforce.
    b. nuclear power.           d. technology.

How did automation affect corporate structure and labor unions in the 1950s?

_____

_____

62) The Suez Canal crisis raised the possibility of a third world war because

a. Nasser closed the Suez Canal to non-communist countries.
b. Britain, France, and Israel invaded the areas around the Suez Canal.
c. the Soviet Union took control of the Suez Canal.
d. Iran charged a toll for entrance to the Suez Canal, which non-communist countries used to conduct trade.

How did the United States respond to this crisis, and how did observers react to America's stance?

_____

_____

63) ". . . In the field of public education the doctrine of 'separate but equal' has no place," ruled the Supreme Court in

a. *Plessy* v. *Ferguson*.　　　　　　　　c. *NAACP* v. *Board of Education of Little Rock*.
b. *Brown* v. *Board of Education of Topeka*.　　d. *Sweatt* v. *Painter*.

Why was this case brought before the U.S. Supreme Court?

_____

_____

64) "The ability to get to the verge without getting into war" was a foreign policy that John Foster Dulles described as

a. automation.　　　　　　　　c. brinkmanship.
b. massive retaliation.　　　　　　d. covert operations.

Why did some U.S. officials criticize this policy?

_____

_____

65) A number of important scholars, writers, and artists criticized 1950s society as

a. socialistic.　　　　　　　　c. selfish and shallow.
b. communistic.　　　　　　　　d. too complicated.

What were major complaints of these critics?

_____

_____

Call to Freedom

**Examine the image, and then answer the following questions.**

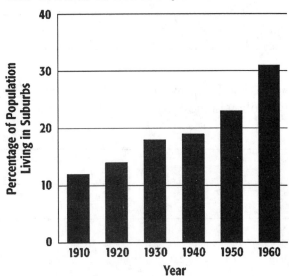

**The Growth of Suburbs, 1910–1960**

Source: John Kramer, *North American Suburbs*

66) Approximately what percentage of people lived in the suburbs in 1940?

_____

67) About how much did the percentage of people living in the suburbs increase between 1940 and 1960?

_____

68) During which period did the percentage of people living in suburbs increase most dramatically?

_____

**SHORT ANSWER**
**Write a brief answer for each of the following.**

69) Describe family life in the suburbs.

_____

_____

_____

70) Why did early civil rights leaders know from experience that there was a "difference between the law in books and the law in action"?

_____

_____

_____

71) Compare U.S. intervention in Iran, Guatemala, and Egypt with U.S. intervention in Hungary. What do you believe motivated U.S. foreign policy in these countries?

_____

_____

_____

72) Compare the beats with the silent generation.

_____

_____

_____

73) How did the Montgomery bus boycott affect the future of the civil rights movement?

_____

_____

_____

**ESSAY**
**On a seperate sheet of paper, write an essay on one of the following.**

74) Compare the federal government's role in the fight against communism with its role in the fight against racial discrimination. How involved were citizens in these fights?

75) How did bomb shelters and rock 'n' roll symbolize some of the fears that confronted suburban parents of baby boom youth?

# ANSWER KEY

1) *Sputnik*

2) A. Philip Randolph

3) Levittown

4) massive retaliation

5) Orval Faubus

6) automation

7) Jo Ann Robinson

8) covert operations

9) Thurgood Marshall

10) baby boom

11) F
The Sun Belt referred to the states of the South and the West.

12) T

13) T

14) T

15) F
The report noted the existence of racial discrimination throughout the country.

16) F
For refusing to give up her seat, Rosa Parks was arrested.

17) T

18) F

The CIA conducted covert operations.

19) T

20) F

By 1960 one fourth of the U.S. population lived in suburbs throughout the nation.

21) c

22) a

23) d

24) b

25) b

26) c

27) d

28) a

29) b

30) c

31) d

32) a

33) b

34) c

# ANSWER KEY

35) a

36) b

37) d

38) c

39) a

40) b

41) b

42) d

43) a

44) b

45) b

46) c

47) c

48) d

49) b

50) a

51) d

52) c

# ANSWER KEY

53) b

54) a

55) d

56) b

57) c

58) a

59) b

60) d

61) d
As machines replaced many low-level workers, the number of middle-management jobs increased dramatically. These new managers needed assistants, creating a rising need for clerical workers. Since few of the new management or clerical workers joined labor unions, membership in unions declined.

62) b
Many observers were shocked when the United States joined with the Soviet Union in condemning the aggression. Others wondered whether the alliance of Western nations would hold throughout the Cold War.

63) b
Linda Brown, a seven-year-old from Topeka, lived very close to a school for white children. However, Topeka law ruled that she had to travel across town to attend an all-black school. Her father sued to allow Linda to attend the white school nearby.

64) c
Some U.S. officials criticized brinkmanship on the grounds that it left the United States with few diplomatic options. They argued that not every Cold War conflict required nuclear weapons, and that just one use of the weapons could mean catastrophe for the world.

# ANSWER KEY

65)  d

Some critics complained that the consumer culture was wasteful. Professors argued that materialism and conformity were ruining traditional American values, such as defying the crowd to defend a moral principle. David Riesman argued that the attempt to fit in discouraged creativity and innovation in the workplace. C. Wright Mills argued that businesspeople gave up their true beliefs to fit into the corporate structure.

66)  about 19 percent

67)  by about 12 percent

68)  between 1950 and 1960

69)  By 1960 one fourth of the U.S. population lived in suburbs and commuted to work. Suburban houses were filled with labor-saving devices and offered spacious rooms and large lawns. Children participated in many organized activities, requiring mothers to drive them from one activity to another. Many mothers worked part-time to pay for these activities. Suburban life placed a particularly strong emphasis on consumer goods. Neighbors often quietly competed to see which family could buy the latest clothes, gadgets, and cars.

70)  In 1946 President Truman verbally supported civil rights such as better protection of black voters, desegregtion of the armed forces, and the establishment of a permanent Fair Employment Practices Commission. However, months dragged on with little real action by the president or Congress. In 1954 the Supreme Court ruled that segregation in public schools was illegal. In 1955 the Court ordered public schools to desegregate "with all deliberate speed." However, some white officials broke the law by fighting integration. In Little Rock, schools were closed until a 1959 court order forced the slow process of integration in that city.

71)  The U.S. helped Britain retain its monopoly on Iranian oil production, and invaded Guatemala when Guzmán nationalized property belonging to the American-owned United Fruit Company. When Hungarians fought for freedom from communism, the United States refused to intervene. Unlike in Iran and Guatemala, the U.S. and its allies had no financial investment in Hungary. When Nasser threatened to charge a toll for entrance to the Suez Canal, the nations whose trade this upset invaded the area. This time, the United States aligned with the Soviet Union in condemning the aggression. Having already backed out of the Aswan High Dam project, the U.S. had no financial interests in Egypt. Students may deduce that U.S. officials intervened only in situations that involved financial gain. Or they may deduce that America's primary motivator was the desire to stop the spread of communism without going to war with the Soviet Union.

72) A young generation of writers called beatniks or beats criticized American life through their unconventional writing and their defiant behavior. Beats led a rootless and carefree lifestyle. On the other hand, many critics argued that many young people were conformists, with a deep desire to avoid conflict and be one of the crowd. This belief led some people to call teenagers and college students of the time the silent generation. However, the silent generation did challenge American society—but in a quiet manner. They identified with young screen rebels such as James Dean and Marlon Brando, and with fictional characters such as Holden Caufield. Some liked comic books and *Mad* magazine that made fun of 1950s society.

73) In November 1956 the Supreme Court ruled that Montgomery's segregated bus system was illegal. This victory brought an important new leader—Martin Luther King Jr.—to the forefront of the civil rights movement, and also energized the black community. African Americans gained self-respect, and pride in the country that they would continue to work to improve.

74) During the Truman years, the United States had attempted to contain the spread of communism around the world. During the Eisenhower years, the United States wanted to "roll back communism." This policy relied on the idea of massive retaliation, or the use of nuclear weapons to fight communism. The United States was the first nation to test a hydrogen bomb. Very few officials wanted to use it. However, most officials realized that the United States might have to go to the very brink of nuclear war to fight communism. Eisenhower also relied on covert operations of the CIA to fight communism. In the fight against racial discrimination at home, the federal government did not take a stance until black veterans of World War II called attention to the fact that black citizens were treated like second class citizens in their own country. Black leaders appealed to Truman who responded by appointing the Committee on Civil Rights. However, the federal government took no steps to initiate change until African American labor leader A. Philip Randolph threatened to organize a massive protest if Truman did not at least desegregate the armed forces. In the fight to end segregation between black and white Americans, the Federal government became involved only when violence threatened to destroy the peace or when the NAACP brought issues before the Supreme Court. In landmark cases such as *Sweatt* v. *Painter*, and *Brown* v. *Board of Education*, the Supreme Court ruled that segregation was illegal. In 1956 the Supreme Court also ruled that Montgomery's segregated bus system was illegal. However, black citizens had already staged a months-long boycott to provoke this change. American citizens, black and white, were not directly involved in the fight against communism. In the fight against racial discrimination, however, black citizens and white citizens often fought each other. Some white officials in the south refused to obey the laws that granted equal rights to blacks. Segregationists bombed the homes of civil rights leaders, and shouted "Lynch her!" when a black girl arrived for her classes at Central High School in Little Rock. The Federal government became involved when the president sent troops to keep order. Overall, the American people were more involved in the fight against discrimination at home than in the fight against communism abroad, while the federal government took more initiative in the fight against communism than in the fight against racial discrimination in America.

Call to Freedom

75) While the U.S. government focused on fighting communism and stockpiling nuclear weapons, many American citizens were frightened by the threat of nuclear war. This fear was apparent when parents built underground bomb shelters to protect their families in case of attack. Bomb shelters that were built in the 1950s were symbolic of Americans' fear of war with the Soviet Union—a communist nation—at a time when the federal government was attempting to "roll back" communism. White middle-class Americans who lived in suburbs during the baby boom could afford to build bomb shelters. Since suburban life revolved around families and children, bomb shelters were a sign that affluent families were protecting themselves from outside attack. Suburban parents whose baby boom children liked rock 'n' roll also felt threatened by a musical style that drew heavily from African American rhythm and blues. In suburban neighborhoods where only white families lived, some parents were worried by the fact that their children's favorite music cut across racial lines. Many white teenagers were fans of black artists such as Chuck Berry, Fats Domino, and Little Richard. Parental concern over this musical integration mirrored the battles over civil rights already being fought in the South, and symbolized white suburban parents' fear of change: that a segregated nation was evolving during the 1950s into an integrated nation wherein black and white people would have equal rights, live in the same neighborhoods, and attend the same schools. Rock 'n' roll symbolized this black and white merger of tastes, ideas, and acceptance that appealed more to the baby boom generation than to their white parents.

# Chapter 28 A Time of Change

## MATCHING

In the space provided, write the term or the name of the person that best fits the description. Choose your answers from the list below. Not all answers will be used.

Great Society      March on Washington      Red Power movement
Black Power      American Indian Movement      Congress of Racial Equality
Warren Commission      Kerner Commission      New Frontier
Peace Corps      Medicare      Woodstock
pop art      Medicaid      Student Nonviolent Coordinating Committee

1) _____ nationwide demonstration in support of President Kennedy's proposed civil rights bill

2) _____ gathering that became a symbol of the counterculture's idealistic spirit

3) _____ investigated Kennedy's assassination

4) _____ sends American volunteers to developing countries to work on improvement projects

5) _____ social and political movement that called for African American power and independence

6) _____ formed by Native American activists to fight for the rights and properties guaranteed in earlier treaties with the federal government

7) _____ helps people over 65 meet medical expenses

8) _____ formed by African American student leaders to coordinate protest efforts and provide training

9) _____ Kennedy's proposals for his administration

10) _____ provides health insurance for people with low incomes

**TRUE/FALSE**

**Write T is a statement is true or F if it is false. If a statement is false, explain why.**

11) _____ Martin Luther King Jr. argued that the black community should work for social and economic independence rather than integration.

_____

12) _____ César Chávez formed a migrant farm workers' union that eventually became the United Farm Workers union.

_____

13) _____ Kennedy's New Frontier legislation marked the most active period of lawmaking since the New Deal.

_____

14) _____ Under President Kennedy, the United States attempted to fight communism in Africa, Asia, and Latin America with economic assistance rather than military force.

_____

15) _____ The National Organization for Women was organized to fight for equal pay from civil service jobs.

_____

16) _____ The most famous pop artist was Andy Warhol.

_____

17) _____ Members of the counterculture were called hippies.

_____

18) _____ HUD secretary Robert Weaver was the first African American appointed to a presidential cabinet.

_____

19) _____ Student protest groups emphasized individual freedom, nonviolence, and communal sharing.

_____

20) _____ By 1970, about 10.1 million people of Mexican descent lived in the United States.

_____

## MULTIPLE CHOICE
**For each of the following, circle the letter of the best choice.**

21) The Berlin Wall was

a. a political term for the disagreements between the leaders of democratic East Berlin and Soviet West Berlin.
b. erected in 1969 by Nikita Khrushchev.
c. designed to protect residents of East Berlin from attack by residents of West Berlin.
d. a barrier of cement and barbed wire between West and East Berlin.

22) The first American sent by NASA into space was

a. Edwin "Buzz" Aldrin.　　　　　c. Alan Shepard Jr.
b. Neil Armstrong.　　　　　　　　d. John Glenn.

23) The modern women's movement arose as more women

a. questioned their roles in society.　　c. worked in the home.
b. applied for civil service jobs.　　　　d. demanded equal voting rights.

24) The struggles of the poor and the oppressed were expressed in songs written by

a. Jimi Hendrix.　　　　　　　　c. the Moody Blues.
b. Bob Dylan.　　　　　　　　　d. Aretha Franklin.

25) *A Letter from Birmingham Jail* testified to

a. Martin Luther King Jr.'s faith in nonviolence.
b. James Meredith's struggle to enroll at the University of Alabama.
c. Malcolm X's belief that African Americans had the right to protect themselves from violence.
d. Diane Nash's determination to integrate Birmingham's bus terminals.

26) More than 300,000 people attended the Woodstock Music and Art Fair in

a. San Francisco, California.　　　　c. upstate New York.
b. Detroit, Michigan.　　　　　　　d. southern Mississippi.

27) The first African American student to register at the all-white University of Mississippi was

a. David Richmond.

c. Franklin McCain.

b. Joseph McNeil.

d. James Meredith.

28) NASA pushed far ahead of the Soviets in 1969 when

a. Neil Armstrong orbited the earth.

b. U.S. astronauts aboard *Apollo 11* reached the moon.

c. Alan Shepard Jr. orbited the moon.

d. John Glenn and Edwin "Buzz" Aldrin set foot on the moon.

29) The pop art movement criticized traditional art for its lack of

a. dignity.

c. form and substance.

b. intellect.

d. humor and humanity.

30) During the Cuban Missile Crisis

a. Cuba's threatened to attack the United States with missiles

b. the United States put a naval blockade around Cuba.

c. the United States threatened to attack Cuba with missiles.

d. Cuban exiles invaded Cuba.

31) Congress created the Department of Housing and Urban Development to

a. help improve housing for low-income families.

b. restore decaying urban neighborhoods.

c. provide grants for the construction of suburban subdivisions.

d. enforce integration in federally funded housing projects.

32) Barry Goldwater lost the 1964 presidential election because

a. he wanted to increase spending for federal social programs.

b. his proposal to reduce military spending frightened voters who feared an attack from Communist Cuba.

c. voters believed Democrats who accused him of being warlike because he wanted to expand the military.

d. voters feared he would eliminate Johnson's New Frontier programs.

33) The Voting Rights Act of 1975 required

a. the federal government to inspect local voter registration procedures to ensure that African Americans and Hispanic Americans had an equal opportunity to vote.

b. local voter registration officials to ensure that African Americans had an equal opportunity to vote.

c. the federal government to enforce the 1965 Supreme Court ruling on voter registration.

d. areas with large immigrant populations to provide ballots in voters' preferred language.

34) According to the Warren Commission, Kennedy's sole assassin was Soviet sympathizer

a. Fidel Castro.
b. James Earl Ray.

c. Lee Harvey Oswald.
d. Jack Ruby.

35) The strategy which calls for peaceful protest and the rejection of violence, even for self-defense, best describes

a. sit-ins.
b. nonviolent resistance.

c. Black Power.
d. Freedom Rides.

36) In forcing people to discuss the question, "What is Art?"

a. the Woodstock Music and Art Fair succeeded in bringing more than 300,000 people together in August 1969.
b. Claes Oldenburg's exhibits of art "as sweet and stupid as life itself" resulted in renewed public interest in attending art shows and other cultural events.
c. Andy Warhol was able to criticize as well as celebrate consumer culture.
d. the pop art movement challenged traditional views of both art and culture.

37) Johnson differed from Kennedy in his

a. personal background, political experience, and leadership style.
b. commitment to federal legislation for social programs.
c. desire to help poor Americans.
d. determination to pass civil rights and education bills.

38) The "Motown sound"

a. addressed political and social issues, and challenged people to fight injustice.
b. gained popularity after The Rolling Stones toured the United States.
c. was a form of soul music, the most popular form of African American music in the 1960s.
d. and its popularity opened new opportunities for British musicians in the United States.

39) When CIA-trained Cuban exiles invaded Cuba in 1961,

a. President Kennedy denied American involvement in launching the attack.
b. Castro's forces attacked them at the Bay of Pigs, and the invasion turned into a disaster.
c. Communist forces killed or captured all 300 after only three hours of fighting.
d. Castro agreed to withdraw long-range nuclear missiles from Cuba.

40) After Malcolm X left the Nation of Islam organization, he

a. helped train college students as civil rights workers.
b. traveled to Mississippi to help African Americans register to vote.
c. was shot and killed by three members of the Nation of Islam.
d. joined with Martin Luther King Jr. in organizing a voter registration march from Selma, Alabama, to Montgomery.

41) President Kennedy wanted to end the Freedom Rides, fearing

   a. more violence, and to avoid alienating white southern voters.
   b. mob violence of whites against black voting rights activists in the South.
   c. another racial riot in the Watts section of Los Angeles.
   d. that SNCC leaders had aligned with a violent wing of the Nation of Islam.

42) Many hippies who experimented with marijuana and LSD

   a. held sit-ins protesting the illegality of these drugs.
   b. became celebrated pop artists whose creative energies are still appreciated today.
   c. heightened their commitment to the student protest movement.
   d. developed disabling and deadly drug addictions.

43) Lee Harvey Oswald was never brought to trial for his crime because

   a. the Warren Commission determined that he was not a suspect.
   b. he was murdered by Jack Ruby.
   c. Cuban exiles abducted him and returned him to his native Cuba.
   d. U.S. marines opened fire on him as he was being transferred to another jail.

44) In 1969, U.S. astronaut Neil Armstrong

   a. orbited Earth.
   b. became the first American sent by NASA into space.
   c. took the first steps on the moon.
   d. joined Soviet cosmonaut Yuri Gagarin in orbiting the moon.

45) When Castro formed an alliance with the Soviet Union, Americans worried because

   a. Communist Cuba was located less than 90 miles from U.S. borders.
   b. Cuban exiles posed the threat of invading the United States from Cuba.
   c. Cuban exiles threatened to launch nuclear missiles at the United States.
   d. the CIA was said to be providing special training to Castro's army.

46) Martin Luther King Jr. delivered his "I Have a Dream" speech

   a. after four African American girls were killed by a bomb in Birmingham.
   b. during the March on Washington.
   c. while he was imprisoned in the Birmingham jail.
   d. to encourage Johnson to sign the Voting Rights Act of 1965.

47) Johnson's War on Poverty was designed to help

   a. around 10 million rural Americans living in poverty.
   b. more than 20 million Hispanic Americans and African Americans living in poverty.
   c. more than 30 million African American families living in poverty.
   d. around 50 million Americans living in poverty.

48) The "British Invasion" referred to the

a. experimental style and dress of British rock musician Jimi Hendrix.
b. success of Berry Gordy's Motown Record Corporation.
c. rise in popularity of the Beatles and other British performers in the United States.
d. wave of excitement among fans who welcomed Diana Ross and the Supremes to American concert halls.

49) When the first Freedom Riders reached Anniston, Alabama, in 1961,

a. the Anniston fire department turned high-pressure water hoses on the bus and the riders.
b. Police Commissioner Eugene "Bull" Connor ordered his police officers to let loose their attack dogs on riders who stepped off the bus.
c. CORE leaders called off the Freedom Ride due to threats of violence from state officials.
d. a white mob pounded the riders with clubs and bombed the bus.

50) The 1968 Elementary and Secondary Education Act required that

a. children whose first language was not English be instructed in both languages.
b. public schools provide a quality education to children with disabilities.
c. schools on federally controlled reservations provide a quality education to Native American children.
d. African American children in public schools be provided the same educational opportunities as white children in private schools.

51) A national debate on gender roles was launched by

a. Esther Peterson, director of the Women's Bureau in the Department of Labor.
b. Betty Friedan's book *The Feminine Mystique*.
c. the Civil Rights Act of 1964 that outlawed discrimination based on race but not on gender.
d. Michael Harrington's book *The Other America*.

52) One of the first major protests for student rights occurred on the campus of the

a. University of Mississippi.
b. Negro Agricultural and Technical College in Greensboro, North Carolina.
c. City College of Birmingham.
d. University of California at Berkeley.

53) After white mobs attacked the first Freedom Riders, CORE leaders

a. armed the riders with guns for their protection.
b. encouraged demonstrators to make out their wills.
c. called off the Freedom Rides, and SNCC leaders assumed the leadership.
d. recruited SNCC volunteers to complete the journey to New Orleans, Louisiana.

Call to Freedom

54) In 1968 the Indian Civil Rights Act

   a. guaranteed Native Americans the right to vote and own property.
   b. outlawed housing discrimination for Native Americans who chose not to live on reservations.
   c. guaranteed Native Americans the rights and properties guaranteed in earlier treaties.
   d. protected the constitutional rights of Native Americans and their right to self-government on reservations.

55) In 1961 the federal government issued a regulation banning segregation in

   a. interstate bus terminals.
   b. movie theaters.
   c. restaurants.
   d. hotels, motels, and rooming houses.

56) After biologist Rachel Carson published *Silent Spring*, the United States

   a. Supreme Court ruled in favor of migrant workers who boycotted grape growers.
   b. restricted the use of the pesticide DDT that caused bird deaths.
   c. Congress approved the Equal Pay Act which required many employers to pay men and women the same wages for the same job.
   d. Congress passed the Rehabilitation Act of 1973 outlawing discrimination by federal agencies against people with disabilities.

57) ". . . ask not what your country can do for you—ask what you can do for your country," said

   a. Martin Luther King Jr.
   b. President Kennedy.
   c. President Johnson.
   d. Edwin "Buzz" Aldrin.

58) A "generation gap" between older and younger people continued to grow as

   a. young people began dressing like the Beatles and styling their hair like Motown musicians.
   b. more and more hippies took part in sit-ins and participated in Freedom Rides.
   c. student protesters rejected traditional society and tried to create an alternative world.
   d. more young people protested against their parents' values and beliefs.

59) Many in the United States and other countries were horrified when Martin Luther King Jr. was assassinated by

   a. Lee Harvey Oswald.
   b. Jack Ruby.
   c. James Earl Ray.
   d. members of the Nation of Islam.

60) The first American to orbit the earth was

   a. John Glenn.
   b. Alan Shepard Jr.
   c. Neil Armstrong.
   d. Edwin "Buzz" Aldrin.

## ENHANCED QUESTIONS

**For each of the following, circle the letter of the best choice. Next, expand on the subject by answering the second question in the space provided.**

61) President Kennedy appointed the Commission on the Status of Women due to persuasion by

    a. Diane Nash.                    c. Esther Peterson.

    b. Betty Friedan.               d. Jacqueline Kennedy.

    What were the commission's findings, and how did the Kennedy administration respond?

_____

_____

62) Disabled in Action was formed to

    a. fight for equal pay and job opportunities for people with disabilities.

    b. gain jobs and benefits for disabled veterans.

    c. focus public attention on medical care for people with disabilities.

    d. coordinate reform efforts for people with disabilities.

    How successful was the DIA in achieving legislative change?

_____

_____

63) A crisis occurred in Cuba when

    a. Kennedy demanded that Khrushchev withdraw long-range nuclear missiles from Cuba.

    b. Castro launched an attack on U.S. navy ships in the Bay of Pigs.

    c. Khrushchev developed a plan to have the Soviet army train Cuban exiles.

    d. Cuban exiles attacked U.S. soldiers as they entered the Bay of Pigs.

    What was this crisis called, and how was it resolved?

_____

_____

64) Many Americans first grew aware of the life and death struggle of civil rights activists when

a. Malcolm X was murdered by a white mob in the Watts section of Los Angeles.
b. Martin Luther King Jr. published *A Letter from Birmingham Jail.*
c. television news programs showed men, women, and children being beaten, blasted with water, and attacked by police dogs during a protest march in Birmingham, Alabama.
d. the Kerner Commission reported that "the nation is rapidly moving toward two increasingly separate Americas"—one white and wealthy, the other black and poor.

How did Americans respond, and how did this response affect the civil rights movement?

_____

_____

65) During the summer of 1964, hundreds of college students traveled to Mississippi to

a. support James Meredith as he enrolled at the University of Mississippi.
b. help African Americans register to vote.
c. organize a voter registration march.
d. take part in sit-ins at every Woolworth's segregated lunch counter.

How successful were these students in achieving their goal? How did their actions help initiate change in Mississippi and the rest of the nation?

_____

_____

## GRAPHIC IMAGE QUESTIONS
**Examine the image, and then answer the following questions.**

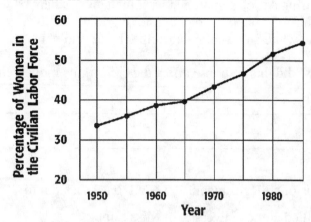

**Women in the Labor Force**

Source: *Statistical Abstract of the United States*

66)  Approximately what percentage of women were in the labor force in 1960?

_____

67)  About how much did the percentage of women in the labor force increase between 1960 and 1980?

_____

68)  Approximately what percentage of women were in the labor force in 1985?

_____

## SHORT ANSWER
**Write a brief answer for each of the following.**

69)  How did the Civil Rights Act of 1964 help African Americans and other minorities?

_____

_____

_____

70) Describe the agency and programs that Johnson created to fight the War on Poverty.

_____

_____

_____

71) Describe the first sit-in and its impact on the civil rights movement.

_____

_____

_____

72) How did Hispanic Americans work to achieve economic, political, and cultural change in the 1960s?

_____

_____

_____

73) Compare the ideals and goals of the Red Power and American Indian Movement with those of the Black Power movement.

_____

_____

_____

**ESSAY**
**On a seperate sheet of paper, write an essay on one of the following.**

74) Define the Great Society, and discuss how activists and President Johnson worked together to create a Great Society with "abundance and liberty for all."

75) Compare the goals of the SNCC, the youth revolution, and the counterculture. Discuss how each of these groups of young people influenced American society during the 1960s and 1970s.

# ANSWER KEY

1) March on Washington

2) Woodstock

3) Warren Commission

4) Peace Corps

5) Black Power

6) American Indian Movement

7) Medicare

8) Student Nonviolent Coordinating Committee

9) New Frontier

10) Medicaid

11) F
King supported racial integration. Malcolm X supported social and economic independence rather than integration.

12) T

13) F
Johnson's Great Society legislation was the most active period of lawmaking since the New Deal.

14) T

15) F
NOW was organized to fight for women's rights to pursue educational and career opportunities.

16) T

# ANSWER KEY

17) T

18) T

19) F
Students protested rigid college rules, racial discrimination, and the growing military presence in Vietnam among other causes. The youth counterculture emphasized individual freedom, nonviolence, and communal sharing.

20) F
By 1970 the Hispanic population of the United States had grown to 10.1 million. However, Hispanic Americans were a very diverse group of people from Mexico, Puerto Rico, Cuba, other Caribbean islands, and Latin America.

21) d

22) c

23) a

24) b

25) a

26) c

27) d

28) b

29) d

30) b

31) a

32) c

33)  d

34)  c

35)  b

36)  d

37)  a

38)  c

39)  b

40)  c

41)  a

42)  d

43)  b

44)  c

45)  a

46)  b

47)  d

48)  c

49)  d

50)  a

Call to Freedom

# ANSWER KEY

51) b

52) d

53) c

54) d

55) a

56) b

57) b

58) d

59) c

60) a

61) c
The commission reported that women commonly received unequal pay and job opportunities. In response, Kennedy issued an order outlawing gender discrimination in civil service jobs. Congress approved the Equal Pay Act, which required many employers to pay men and women the same wages for the same job.

62) d
The Rehabilitation Act of 1973 outlawed discrimination by federal agencies against people with disabilities. The Education of All Handicapped Children Act of 1975 requires public schools to provide a quality education for children with disabilities.

63) a
This crisis was known as the Cuban missile crisis, during which the U.S. navy surrounded Cuba to prevent Soviet ships from reaching the island. The ships approached the blockade, but turned around just before reaching it. Later, the Soviets agreed to remove their missiles in return for the United States's promise not to invade Cuba. Kennedy also agreed to remove some missiles from Italy and Turkey.

64) c

When Americans saw the televised events in Birmingham, they were shocked. With public pressure mounting for civil rights reform, in June 1963 Kennedy announced his support for a sweeping new civil rights bill to end racial discrimination completely. After Kennedy's death, President Johnson took up the challenge of passing the Civil Rights Act of 1964 which he signed into law on July 2.

65) b

The students soon confronted violence. Many suffered attacks. Two students and a black man from Mississippi were shot to death. As a result, the Johnson administration prepared a new bill to protect black voters. The Voting Rights Act of 1965 gave the federal government the power to inspect local voter registration procedures to ensure that African Americans had an equal opportunity to vote.

66) about 38 percent

67) by about 12 percent

68) about 55 percent

69) This law outlawed racial discrimination by employers and banned segregation in public places, such as restaurants and transportation facilities. The law also prohibited discrimination by employers, unions, or universities with federal government contracts on the basis of color, sex, religious, and national origin.

70) The Office of Economic Opportunity developed programs to help poor people earn money. The OEO started a new Job Corps to teach young adults basic job skills, as well as Head Start, an educational program to prepare poor children to begin school. The OEO also created a domestic version of the Peace Corps—the Volunteers in Service to America (VISTA).

71) Four black students went to the local Woolworth to stage a sit-in—a demonstration in which protesters sit down in a location and refuse to leave. The students sat down at the "whites only" section of the lunch counter and ordered coffee. When a waitress refused to serve them, one of the teens told her that he had just made a purchase in the store. He said, "Why is it that you serve me at one counter and deny me at another?" The young men remained at the counter all day without being served. They returned the next day with about 20 other students and the sit-in was reported in newspapers throughout the country. Soon other black students in the South staged similar sit-ins. Over time, Woolworth began to integrate its lunch counter, as did some other businesses and restaurants in the South.

72) Some Hispanic Rights activists worked to improve economic opportunities. César Chávez formed a union to improve pay and working conditions for migrant workers. His organization became the United Farm Workers union. The UFW helped inspire younger Hispanic reformers who led a fight against discrimination known as the Chicano movement. Some Chicano activists organized a political party such as *La Raza Unida*. Others, such as Rodolfo "Corky" Gonzales, emphasized pride in Hispanic culture.

73) The Red Power movement rejected the reform efforts of mainstream groups such as the NCAI as slow, and founded the more radical AIM. AIM activists rejected "civil rights in the white man's society" and fought for their own "sovereign rights" and the rights and properties guaranteed in earlier treaties. The Black Power movement attracted many younger reformers who criticized the civil rights movement. Some Black Power advocates wanted faster progress, while others rejected nonviolence. The Black Power movement encouraged African Americans to control their own communities and futures. Like AIM activists, some Black Power activists rejected integration as a final goal.

74) When Johnson became president in 1963, the civil rights movement was already in full swing with sit-ins, Freedom Rides, and the March on Washington. César Chávez had already formed a union in 1962 to improve pay and working conditions for migrant farm workers. The women's movement was also underway by 1963. Johnson was determined to pass civil rights and education bills that he had favored as a senator and that Kennedy had supported as president. To help poor Americans, Johnson launched the War on Poverty. After he was elected president in 1964, he set out to expand his domestic reforms with a new program he called the Great Society. He said, "The Great Society rests on abundance and liberty for all. It demands an end to poverty and racial injustice. . . . The Great Society is a place where every child can find knowledge to enrich his mind and to enlarge his talents." During Johnson's first 100 days in office as an elected president, he introduced and passed most of his Great Society legislation. Great Society reforms included Medicare, Medicaid, and HUD. In 1964 Johnson signed the Civil Rights Act of 1964. That same summer, as activists fought for voting rights for African Americans, Johnson prepared a new bill to protect black voters. He signed the Voting Rights Act of 1965, and within three years, more than half of all qualified black voters in the South had registered to vote. In the late 1960s Johnson appointed the Kerner Commission to investigate violence and racial riots in urban areas. In the same year that the report African American frustration with racism as a leading cause of the riots, Martin Luther King Jr. announced plans for a "Poor People's Campaign," but was killed in 1968 before it was launched. In 1968 the Johnson administration pushed ahead and passed the Elementary and Secondary Education Act that helped Hispanic Americans. Due to the work of Native American reformers and activists, the Johnson administration also passed the Indian Civil Rights Act in 1968. Thus President Johnson heard the voice of activists and included many of their requests in Great Society legislation.

75) African American student leaders formed the SNCC to coordinate efforts and provide training for students involved in the civil rights movement. The organization was formed after African American college students began staging sit-ins and practicing nonviolent resistance in order to protest segregation. Later, when Freedom Riders were attacked and CORE leaders called off the Freedom Rides, SNCC leaders decided to risk their lives and continue them, in spite of the enormous dangers they faced from white mobs. SNCC activists along with many others were among the college students who traveled to Mississippi in 1964 to lead the struggle for voting rights for African Americans in that state. The perseverance of SNCC members and other black and white student activists helped initiate federal legislation that outlawed segregation and granted civil rights and voting rights to African Americans. The Youth Revolution describes the college student movement against rigid college rules, racial discrimination, and the growing U.S. military presence in Vietnam, among other causes. Students launched a major protest at Berkeley and won the right to gather campus support for the African American civil rights movement in the South. After that, students throughout the country staged protests, challenging the rules by which college and universities governed students. Their actions opened what Columbia University president Grayson Kirk called a "generation gap" that continued to grow as more young people protested against their parents' values and beliefs. The counterculture consisted of young people called hippies who rejected traditional society entirely by building an alternative society emphasizing individual freedom, nonviolence, and communal sharing. Some young leaders tried to bring together members of the student movement and the counterculture. However, many student leaders believed that the aims of the counterculture were opposed to their own goals. Student activists challenged society in order to improve it, but hippies rejected society and tried to create an alternative world. The counterculture and the student movement both succeeded in changing mainstream society. They forced a greater tolerance for different preferences in dress, music, and interpersonal relationships. In addition, the counterculture and the student movement led many Americans to view traditional institutions of society—such as families, churches, schools, and the government—with less confidence and trust.

## Chapter 29 War in Vietnam

**MATCHING**
**In the space provided, write the term or the name of the person that best fits the description. Choose your answers from the list below. Not all answers will be used.**

| | | |
|---|---|---|
| Khmer Rouge | Ho Chi Minh | pacification |
| Henry Kissinger | hawks | Robert Kennedy |
| escalation | William Westmoreland | Tonkin Gulf Resolution |
| Vietcong | Ngo Dinh Diem | Vietnamization |
| doves | Vietminh | National Liberation Front |

1) _____ plan that gradually turned over all of the fighting to the South Vietnamese Army

2) _____ believed that the United States needed to send more troops and use more powerful weapons to win the war

3) _____ organization dedicated to fighting the South Vietnamese government

4) _____ increased American involvement in the war

5) _____ commanded the U.S. ground forces in Vietnam

6) _____ founded by Ho Chi Minh as the League for the Independence of Vietnam

7) _____ U.S. and South Vietnamese policy that created civilian areas guarded by government troops

8) _____ Cambodian communist army

9) _____ gave the president the authority "to take all necessary measures to repel any armed attack against the forces of the United States"

10) _____ nationalist leader who wanted a reunited Vietnam free of foreign troops

**TRUE/FALSE**
**Write T is a statement is true or F if it is false. If a statement is false, explain why.**

11) _____ Laos and Cambodia were officially neutral countries in the Vietnam War.

_____

12) \_\_\_\_\_ During Operation Rolling Thunder, U.S. planes dropped more than a million tons of explosives on North Vietnam and Cambodia.

_____

13) \_\_\_\_\_ During the 1967–68 school year, students held antiwar protests at nearly half of the college campuses across the country.

_____

14) \_\_\_\_\_ The Geneva Accords called for free elections to reunite North and South Vietnam under one government.

_____

15) \_\_\_\_\_ Of the thousands of U.S. soldiers listed as missing in action in Vietnam, more than 2,000 MIAs did not return home until after 1985.

_____

16) \_\_\_\_\_ More than 2 million U.S. soldiers served in the Vietnam War.

_____

17) \_\_\_\_\_ During the 1970s, U.S. political and public opinion turned against the war in Vietnam.

_____

18) \_\_\_\_\_ Members of the NLF were anticommunists dedicated to fighting communism in South Vietnam.

_____

19) \_\_\_\_\_ Most of the U.S. soldiers who served in Vietnam tended to be from minority groups and poor families.

_____

20) \_\_\_\_\_ The Tet Offensive strengthened U.S. public confidence in winning the Vietnam War.

_____

Call to Freedom

# MULTIPLE CHOICE
**For each of the following, circle the letter of the best choice.**

21) The Twenty-sixth Amendment

a. required that the president get congressional approval before committing U.S. troops to an armed struggle.
b. was proposed by Democratic senator George McGovern.
c. prevented adolescents aged 20 and younger from serving in the armed forces.
d. lowered the federal voting age from 21 to 18.

22) A riot broke out in Chicago when

a. George Wallace was nominated for president.
b. Hubert Humphrey won the Democratic nomination for president.
c. police officers moved in to stop a demonstration of antiwar protesters.
d. Robert Kennedy was assassinated.

23) When did France first conquer Vietnam?

a. the late 1700s
b. 1883

c. 1945
d. 1968

24) Student antiwar demonstrations resulted in tragedy when

a. students at Jackson State University set fire to a military training building.
b. police accidentally killed two students at Columbia University.
c. National Guardsmen killed 4 students and wounded 14 at Kent State University.
d. Nebraska State College students hurled rocks and tear gas at National Guard troops.

25) After officers aboard U.S. ships in the Gulf of Tonkin reported that their radar showed torpedo attacks, President Johnson

a. vowed to increase U.S. military support for South Vietnam.
b. named the reported attack an act of war, and order air strikes against North Vietnam.
c. called Vietnam a "test of American responsibility and determination in Asia."
d. began secret peace negotiations with North Vietnamese officials.

26) In 1945 Ho Chi Minh declared the independence of

a. French Indochina.
b. the Vietminh Republic.

c. North Vietnam.
d. the Democratic Republic of Vietnam.

27) A majority in Congress agreed with President Johnson that funding the war and

a. stopping communism in Vietnam took priority over funding America's antipoverty programs.
b. supporting the domino theory fulfilled America's pledge to support France and Japan during international conflicts.
c. supporting the Vietminh would help stop the spread of Japanese imperialism.
d. fighting the Khmer Rouge was more important than funding black Americans' fight for civil rights.

28) In a massive campaign to destroy supposed enemies of communism, the Khmer Rouge

a. increased air attacks on Laos and Cambodia in 1975.
b. planted land mines and traps along the Ho Chi Minh Trail.
c. killed some 2 million people in Cambodia.
d. captured the South Vietnamese capital of Saigon.

29) The most successful Vietnamese nationalist leader was

a. Ngo Dinh Diem.
b. Ho Chi Minh.
c. Quang Duc.
d. Dien Bien Phu.

30) Agent Orange was

a. the code word for U.S. combat units that President Nixon secretly deployed to Laos.
b. the first series of U.S. air strikes on North Vietnam.
c. a secret government source named in the Pentagon Papers.
d. a chemical poison released by American airplanes over the Ho Chi Minh Trail.

31) During the late 1880s, French Indochina was created to include

a. North and South Vietnam.
b. Vietnam and Cambodia.
c. Vietnam and Laos.
d. Vietnam, Laos, and Cambodia.

32) A policy to bring about "peace with honor" was created by

a. Eugene McCarthy.
b. Richard M. Nixon and Henry Kissinger.
c. John F. Kennedy and Hubert Humphrey.
d. J. William Fulbright.

33) Johnson increased U.S. military support for the South Vietnamese government after

a. a reported attack on U.S. ships.
b. the Vietminh suffered 7,000 casualties at Dien Bien Phu.
c. North Vietnamese officials killed thousands of farmers and imprisoned thousands more.
d. Ho Chi Minh refused to allow South Vietnam to participate in the 1956 elections.

34) More than 1.5 million Southeast Asians fled their homelands

    a. during the Tet Offensive.
    b. during the civil war that erupted in the late 1950s.
    c. after the Vietnam War ended.
    d. after Quang Duc accused Vietnamese Buddhists of being communist sympathizers.


35) Communist guerilla forces that fought for the NLF were called the

    a. Khmer Rouge.               c. Vietminh.
    b. Vietcong.                 d. North Vietnamese Army.


36) College students who did not want to serve in the armed forces during the Vietnam War

    a. were often drafted into service when U.S. officers requested more troops.
    b. were not required to register for the draft.
    c. could substitute community service for military service.
    d. could earn draft releases, called deferments, until they completed their education.


37) By the mid-1960s, support for the Vietnam War among soldiers continued to decline as

    a. more than 300 soldiers a week died in combat.
    b. civilian casualty rates increased in Vietnam and Cambodia.
    c. the Khmer Rouge began dropping napalm on U.S. ground forces in Laos.
    d. Congress withdrew military funding after Ho Chi Minh died.


38) In 1963 a group of South Vietnamese general took over the government and killed

    a. John F. Kennedy.          c. Diem and his brother.
    b. Dwight D. Eisenhower.     d. Ho Chi Minh.


39) In 1975, Laos and Cambodia

    a. drove out the Khmer Rouge and created democratic governments.
    b. fell to communist dictatorships.
    c. were brought unwillingly into the Democratic Republic of Vietnam.
    d. were conquered by the Vietcong when guerilla forces captured Saigon.


40) After conquering Vietnam, French officials

    a. banned Vietnamese farmers from owning more than a few acres of land.
    b. initiated widespread social reforms and land redistribution policies.
    c. used a secret police to protect the Vietnamese people from communist attacks.
    d. imposed harsh taxes and limited political freedoms.


41) The average age of U.S. soldiers who fought in Vietnam was

    a. 19.                c. 29.
    b. 21.                d. 31.

42) France surrendered its claim to Vietnam

    a. when Eisenhower funded and supplied Diem's army in 1952.
    b. during World War II when the Japanese drove the French out of Indochina.
    c. after the Vietminh defeated the French in 1954.
    d. when Ho Chi Minh formed the League for the Independence of Vietnam.

43) The "middle of the road" candidate elected president during the Vietnam War was

    a. Johnson.                  c. Nixon.
    b. Kennedy.              d. Eisenhower.

44) Who did Ho Chi Minh blame for North Vietnam's poverty?

    a. the United States        c. himself
    b. Japan                 d. landlords

45) Eugene McCarthy, Robert Kennedy, and Hubert Humphrey were

    a. Republican senators who voted against Johnson's request for more troops for service in Vietnam.
    b. Democrats who hoped to be elected president in 1968.
    c. hawks who withdrew support for the Vietnam War after the Tet Offensive.
    d. Republican candidates for president in 1972.

46) The Japanese drove the French out of Indochina

    a. and established Vietnam as a communist state.    c. after World War I.
    b. and established Buddhism as the state religion.    d. during World War II.

47) Effective guerilla tactics and better knowledge of the local geography aided

    a. U.S. ground forces in Vietnam.    c. the French.
    b. the Buddhists.               d. the Vietcong and the NVA.

48) Laos and Cambodia were drawn into the Vietnam War because

    a. they were bordered on the east by the Gulf of Tonkin.
    b. Johnson ordered bombing raids on both countries in 1969.
    c. Vietcong supply lines ran across their borders into North and South Vietnam.
    d. more than 400,000 North Vietnamese civilians fled to Laos and Cambodia in 1971.

49) The Tet Offensive and the war in general produced a massive shift in voter sympathies that led Johnson to

    a. withdraw from the 1968 presidential election.
    b. support Robert Kennedy in the 1968 presidential election.
    c. endorse antiwar critic Eugene McCarthy as Democratic nominee for president in 1968.
    d. secretly expand the war by sending 206,000 more troops for service in Vietnam.

Call to Freedom

512

50) People known as "doves"

    a. wanted more people to be drafted.
    b. called for American withdrawal from the conflict in Vietnam.
    c. believed that the United States needed to use more powerful weapons to win the war.
    d. supported Hubert Humphrey during the 1968 presidential campaign.

51) "I will not be the first President of the United States to lose a war," said

    a. Nixon.
    b. Johnson.
    c. Kennedy.
    d. Eisenhower.

52) The South Vietnamese government that U.S. officials supported during the 1950s was

    a. a Western-style government known as the Vietminh.
    b. the first government body to hold open elections since the 1700s.
    c. popular in America because of its widespread social reforms.
    d. dishonest and brutal.

53) After Robert Kennedy won the California primary in 1968, he

    a. selected Hubert Humphrey as his running mate.
    b. was assassinated by Sirhan Sirhan.
    c. lost the Democratic nomination to Senator Edmund Muskie.
    d. began to speak against American involvement in Vietnam.

54) When fighting broke out between North and South Vietnam in 1974, the United States

    a. established a demilitarized buffer zone to separate the two sides.
    b. honored the Paris Peace Accords by not sending troops back to support South Vietnam.
    c. sent troops to prevent the North Vietnamese from capturing Saigon.
    d. provided supplies and training to South Vietnam even as American troops left the country.

55) U.S. combat troops first arrived in South Vietnam in

    a. 1945.
    b. 1955.
    c. 1965.
    d. 1975.

56) America's involvement in Vietnam continued through the presidencies of

    a. Eisenhower, Kennedy and Nixon.
    b. Kennedy, Johnson, and Nixon.
    c. Johnson and Nixon.
    d. Eisenhower, Kennedy, Johnson, and Nixon.

57) When Diem refused to allow South Vietnam to participate in the 1956 reunification elections,

    a. American officials withdrew aid until the late 1950s.
    b. American officials backed Diem's decision.
    c. Eisenhower sent 400 special soldiers to Vietnam.
    d. Kennedy sent 800 U.S. military advisers to Vietnam.

58) Operation Rolling Thunder was a

a. series of U.S. air strikes to destroy North Vietnamese war industries and the Ho Chi Minh Trail.
b. massive ground assault on Cambodia.
c. surprise attack on North Vietnamese and Vietcong soldiers who had invaded the U.S. Embassy in Saigon.
d. battle between U.S. Navy vessels and North Vietnamese ships in the Gulf of Tonkin.


59) The Vietnam Veterans Memorial is a

a. 20-acre park surrounding the National Cathedral in Washington, D.C.
b. massive granite wall that displays the names of the dead and missing.
c. monument erected in 1982 outside the U.S. Embassy in Saigon.
d. marble statue sculpted by Maya Ying Lin, and dedicated in 1982 to the 58,000 Americans who died in Vietnam.


60) The North Vietnamese captured Saigon in

a. 1963.                                    c. 1972.
b. 1968.                                    d. 1975.


**ENHANCED QUESTIONS**
**For each of the following, circle the letter of the best choice. Next, expand on the subject by answering the second question in the space provided.**


61) The network of paths, small roads, and tunnels that led from North Vietnam through Laos and Cambodia and into South Vietnam was called

a. Tet.                                     c. the Gulf of Tonkin.
b. the Ho Chi Minh Trail.                   d. Khmer Rouge.

Explain its wartime importance, and its lasting effect on U.S. soldiers and Vietnamese civilians.

_____

_____


62) France gave up its claim to Vietnam by signing the

a. Geneva Accords.                          c. War Powers Act.
b. Paris Peace Accords.                     d. Tonkin Gulf Resolution.

How did this agreement affect Vietnam and its relationship with America?

_____

_____

63) The Paris Peace Accords

   a. resulted from months-long negotiations between the NLF and the United States.
   b. were signed by Nixon, Kissinger, Ho Chi Minh, and Ngo Dinh Diem.
   c. outlined the unification of Vietnam and prevented Communists in South Vietnam from taking part in politics.
   d. called for the removal of all U.S. troops from Vietnam and the return of American POWs.

   Describe U.S.-Vietnamese relations after 1973.

   _____

   _____

64) The Tet Offensive was a surprise attack by

   a. U.S. and South Vietnamese troops against the Vietcong in Cambodia.
   b. the Vietminh against U.S. ground forces guarding the U.S. Embassy in Saigon.
   c. North Vietnamese and Vietcong soldiers against U.S. forces in South Vietnam.
   d. U.S. bombers on the dense jungles of Laos and Cambodia.

   Why and how did the Tet Offensive shape U.S. public opinion about the war?

   _____

   _____

65) After President Nixon pledged to begin withdrawing U.S. ground troops from Vietnam, he

   a. expanded the war by secretly increasing air attacks in Laos and Cambodia.
   b. met with Ho Chi Minh to discuss Ho's vision of a reunited Vietnam free of foreign troops.
   c. sent 206,000 more troops to Vietnam.
   d. secretly—without the knowledge of Congress—ordered the destruction of enemy warships in the Gulf of Tonkin.

   Describe the 1973 congressional measure that was initiated by Nixon's actions. How did this measure affect the military power of future commanders-in chief?

   _____

   _____

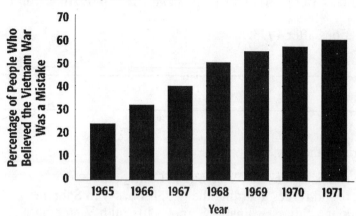

**American Opinions on the Vietnam War, 1965–1971**

Source: *Trends in Public Opinion: A Compendium of Survey Data*

66) In what year did the fewest people oppose the Vietnam War?

_____

67) Approximately what percentage of people opposed the Vietnam War in 1968?

_____

68) Approximately what percentage of people opposed the Vietnam War in 1970?

_____

## SHORT ANSWER
**Write a brief answer for each of the following.**

69) Compare U.S. search-and-destroy missions with Vietcong and NVA tactics.

_____

_____

_____

70) How did the war affect U.S. soldiers during and after their service in Vietnam?

_____

_____

_____

71) Describe the impact of the Pentagon Papers on public opinion and U.S. policy.

_____

_____

_____

72) Describe how college students attempted to change government policy toward Vietnam during the 1960s and 1970s, and how officials responded to their efforts.

_____

_____

_____

73) How did television and TV reporters influence public opinion, before and after the Tet Offensive?

_____

_____

_____

**ESSAY**
**On a seperate sheet of paper, write an essay on one of the following.**

74) Explain how Eisenhower's belief in the domino theory shaped U.S. policy toward Vietnam for nearly 20 years.

75) Describe the long-term effects of the Vietnam War on South Vietnam, Laos, and Cambodia.

# ANSWER KEY

1) Vietnamization

2) hawks

3) National Liberation Front

4) escalation

5) William Westmoreland

6) Vietminh

7) pacification

8) Khmer Rouge

9) Tonkin Gulf Resolution

10) Ho Chi Minh

11) T

12) F
Of more than a million tons of explosives, much of it was dropped on South Vietnam.

13) F
Antiwar protests took place on almost 75 percent of the country's college campuses.

14) T

15) F
More than 2,000 remain MIAs.

16) T

17) T

Call to Freedom

18) F
The NLF, an organization dedicated to fighting Diem's government, included a mixture of communist and anticommunist members.

19) T

20) F
The Tet Offensive weakened public confidence in the war effort.

21) d

22) c

23) a

24) c

25) b

26) d

27) a

28) c

29) b

30) d

31) d

32) b

33) a

34) c

35)  b

36)  d

37)  a

38)  c

39)  b

40)  d

41)  a

42)  c

43)  c

44)  d

45)  b

46)  d

47)  d

48)  c

49)  a

50)  b

51)  a

52)  d

Call to Freedom

ANSWER KEY

53) b

54) b

55) c

56) d

57) b

58) a

59) b

60) d

61) b
The Vietcong used the Ho Chi Minh Trail as their major supply route. In order to destroy it and possibly end the war, the United States dropped napalm and Agent Orange on the dense jungle that covered the trail. These chemicals were later blamed for environmental problems in the area and serious health problems among U.S. veterans and Vietnamese civilians. The location of the trail also drew Laos and Cambodia—officially neutral countries—into the war.

62) a
The Geneva Accords temporarily divided the country into two nations—North Vietnam and South Vietnam. North Vietnam was a communist state led by Ho Chi Minh and the Vietminh. South Vietnam was a Western-style government led by Ngo Dinh Diem, a committed anticommunist. Until 1954, the United States had supported France's claim to Indochina. After 1954, the U.S. stance against communism led U.S. officials to fully support Diem and South Vietnam. When civil war broke out in the late 1950s, the United States aided South Vietnam and considered North Vietnam the enemy. This relationship continued until the United States signed the Paris Peace Accords in 1973.

63) d
When North Vietnam invaded the south in 1975, the U.S. did not intervene. However, when South Vietnamese citizens who had aided U.S. troops in the war sought help at the U.S. Embassy during the fall of Saigon, U.S. helicopters carried many to safety. During the next 10 years, America also welcomed to its shores about half of the 1.5 million people who fled Southeast Asia in the wake of war and destruction. More than 2,000 U.S. soldiers remain MIAs in Vietnam.

64) c

The Tet Offensive deeply shocked Americans. General Westmoreland had said that the war would soon be over. The offensive showed the opposite—that the enemy forces still had the strength and the will to fight. The Tet Offensive convinced many Americans that officials could not be trusted to tell the truth about the war. The offensive also weakened public confidence in the war. After the offensive, only 33 percent of Americans believed that the United States was winning the war. About 49 percent said that the United States should never have gotten involved in the conflict.

65) a

In 1973 Congress passed the War Powers Act. It required that the president get congressional approval before committing U.S. troops in an armed struggle. The act did not apply to Vietnam, but was written to prevent any future undeclared wars. Passage of the War Powers Act gave Congress increased responsibility for setting U.S. war policy. Since then, presidents have had to exercise more caution in sending U.S. troops into war zones and inform Congress more fully when they did.

66) 1965

67) about 50 percent

68) about 57 percent

69) U.S. patrols searched for enemy camps and supplies hidden in the jungle, then destroyed them with massive firepower and air raids. The Vietcong and the NVA offset their inferior firepower with effective guerilla tactics and a better knowledge of the local geography. They moved secretly and set traps and mines to kill Americans and slow their advance. When the Vietcong and the NVA attacked, they usually did so in quick surprise assaults.

70) Many young soldiers supported the war in the beginning. However, as the war dragged on, many came to question their beliefs. Their support for the war declined even more as casualty rates increased to more than 300 a week. Almost 58,000 Americans died in Vietnam, and more than 2,000 remain MIAs. When they returned, some veterans faced taunts from antiwar protesters instead of a hero's welcome. Most readjusted well to civilian life, but some others suffered from depression and post-traumatic stress disorder. Some Vietnam veterans also suffered serious health problems as a result of their contact with the chemical poison, Agent Orange.

71) When the *New York Times* published secret U.S. government documents known as the Pentagon Papers—leaked to the newspaper by former Pentagon official Daniel Ellsberg— the public learned that U.S. government officials had been lying about the progress of the war for years. This discovery further divided public opinion, and led some members of Congress to threaten to cut off funds for the war altogether. Nixon ordered an end to the invasion of Cambodia, and became more open to compromise. Kissinger began secret peace negotiations with North Vietnamese officials.

Call to Freedom

72) College students often led the protests against the Vietnam War. The Students for a Democratic Society became one of the most powerful antiwar groups. SDS protested the draft system and the companies that manufactured weapons used in the war. In 1965 SDS led a 20,000-person protest march to Washington, D.C. As the war continued, the student movement grew more aggressive and sometimes even violent. In 1968, students took over several campus buildings at Columbia University to protest the school's ties to defense industries that supplied weapons for the war. After violent clashes between the protesters and police, school administrators eventually yielded to SDS demands. During the 1970s, violence escalated at Kent State when the governor called in the National Guard to restore order. Four students died and 14 were wounded when the Guardsmen opened fire during a demonstration. Police also killed two student demonstrators at Jackson State University in 1970.

73) Television enabled civilians to see real images of the war's brutality right in their own homes. TV reporters also played an important role in shaping public opinion about the war. As journalists covered stories about the war, they began to report their growing suspicions that the fighting was not going as well as some in the military claimed. Gradually, some people began to call for American withdrawal from the conflict. After the Tet Offensive, television news anchor Walter Cronkite expressed doubts about claims of success. Television also influenced public opinion when anti-war protesters at the 1968 Democratic convention began marching in the streets of Chicago. When a riot broke out, TV cameras broadcast live images. To the millions of Americans watching, the Chicago incident illustrated the loss of control and order in society and politics. Many voters blamed the situation on the Democrats who rejected a convention motion to support stronger peace efforts.

74) Beginning in 1954, President Eisenhower's policy toward Vietnam was based on his belief in the domino theory. He argued that if Vietnam fell to the Communists, all of Southeast Asia would fall as well, like dominos in a row. Therefore he funded and supplied the French in their move to retake Vietnam. When the Geneva Accords divided Vietnam into communist and Western-style governments, U.S. officials backed Diem and South Vietnam against the Communist state of North Vietnam. President Kennedy endorsed Eisenhower's stance against communism by sending more advisers and soldiers to Vietnam in 1961. When Johnson became president in 1963, he and his advisers refused to accept the possibility of a communist South Vietnam. The war intensified during his presidency, requiring more funding and more soldiers. Nonetheless, a majority in Congress agreed with Johnson that stopping communism in Vietnam took priority over domestic reform. After the Tet Offensive, Americans began to question their nation's involvement in Vietnam's internal conflict. President Nixon inherited the war, and planned to continue to provide supplies and training to South Vietnam even as American troops left the country. In his determination to end the war, he bombed Laos and Cambodia. After his reelection in 1972, he agreed to the Paris Peace Accords, withdrew U.S. troops from Southeast Asia, and officially ended U.S. intervention there. Eisenhower's belief in the domino theory—to stop communism lest it grow—had resulted in American involvement in Southeast Asia from 1954 to 1973, through four presidencies, and at a very high cost to the United States.

75) The Vietnam War left long-lasting problems in Southeast Asia. When the North Vietnamese captured Saigon in 1975 after 20 years of warfare, South Vietnamese citizens who had aided U.S. troops in the war hoped to escape before the communist takeover. They knew they faced imprisonment or death in the unified Vietnam. Although many did escape, many more were left behind to survive in their ruined homeland. More than 180,000 South Vietnamese soldiers and around 500,000 civilians had died during the war. Almost 1 million children were orphans. Cities and villages lay in ruins. Forests and farmlands lay bare. Laos and Cambodia were also in shambles after the war, and both fell to communist dictatorships in 1975. In Cambodia the Khmer Rouge killed some 2 million people in a massive campaign to destroy supposed enemies of communism. Cambodia has experienced constant conflict ever since. The people of Southeast Asia also suffered serious health problems and environmental problems as the result of napalm and Agent Orange that U.S. airplanes dropped on the jungles that hid the Ho Chi Minh Trail. Many of these problems have yet to be solved.

# Chapter 30 A Search for Order

## MATCHING

**In the space provided, write the term or the name of the person that best fits the description. Choose your answers from the list below. Not all answers will be used.**

affirmative action
Henry Kissinger
realpolitik
executive privilege
apartheid

Shirley Chisholm
pardon
Phyllis Schlafly
sanctions
détente

trade deficit
stagflation
Warren E. Burger
Camp David Accords
Strategic Arms Limitation Treaty

1) _____ era when relations between the United States and the Soviet Union were less hostile than in the past

2) _____ first African American woman elected to the U.S. Congress

3) _____ freedom from punishment

4) _____ system of laws requiring racial segregation in South Africa

5) _____ imbalance in which a nation imports more than it exports

6) _____ economic condition characterized by both high inflation and high unemployment

7) _____ economic penalties

8) _____ the president's right to keep information secret to protect national security

9) _____ foreign policy adviser who favored the practice of realpolitik

10) _____ 1978 peace agreements between Egypt and Israel

## TRUE/FALSE

**Write T is a statement is true or F if it is false.  If a statement is false, explain why.**

11) _____ The Strategic Arms Limitation Talks limited the numbers and types of nuclear missiles that the United States and the Soviet Union could have.

_____

12) _____ President Nixon condemned foreign governments that practiced torture or unlawful jailings or generally violated human rights—the basic rights and freedoms of all human beings.

_____

13) _____ The Panama Canal treaties transferred control of the canal to Panama in 1977.

_____

14) _____ Many people believed that the Camp David Accords were President Carter's greatest achievement.

_____

15) _____ Nixon was the first president to resign from office.

_____

16) _____ In March 1979, American activists sponsored the first Earth Day to protest a nuclear power accident on Three Mile Island, Pennsylvania.

_____

17) _____ Gerald Ford was the first president to obtain the office without being elected as either vice president or president.

_____

18) _____ Busing was the practice of transporting black students to predominantly white schools to achieve a racial balance.

_____

19) _____ Between 1966 and 1973, the number of African Americans enrolled in college more than doubled.

_____

20) _____ Watergate was a political scandal named after a burglarized building in Washington, D.C.

_____

## MULTIPLE CHOICE
**For each of the following, circle the letter of the best choice.**

21) Nixon's southern strategy was an attempt to win the support of southerners and other people who opposed

a. busing.

b. apartheid.

c. affirmative action.

d. further civil rights reforms.

22) Détente with the Soviet Union broke down completely as Carter

a. criticized the Soviet's many human rights abuses.

b. limited U.S. grain shipments to the country.

c. declared a boycott of the 1980 Summer Olympics in Moscow.

d. postponed talks on SALT II when the Soviets invaded Afghanistan.

23) Recorded conversations on tapes made in Nixon's office proved that Nixon had

a. failed to pay his taxes and had taken bribes while he was governor of California.

b. ordered the cover-up of the Watergate crime and had lied about it to Congress and the American people.

c. secretly fired H.R. Haldeman, John Ehrlichman, and Archibald Cox during the Saturday Night Massacre.

d. ordered the burglary of the Democratic National Committee headquarters, then lied to Bob Woodward and Carl Bernstein about his involvement in the ensuing scandal.

24) The Democrats nominated Jimmy Carter for president because they wanted a candidate

a. who based his political decisions on moral ideals such as equality and justice.

b. who was little-known in Washington political circles.

c. free from political scandals.

d. from the South.

25) The conservative activist who founded STOP ERA was

a. Shirley Chisholm.

b. Phyllis Schlafly

c. James McCord.

d. Andrew Young.

26) Nixon exercised his right to executive privilege when he

a. refused to turn over tapes to the Senate Judiciary Committee.

b. replaced Vice President Spiro Agnew with congressman Gerald Ford.

c. named Robert H. Bork as acting attorney general.

d. asked for the resignation of Attorney General Elliot Richardson.

27) By the 1970s the majority of immigrants to the United States came from

a. Europe.

b. Mexico and Vietnam.

c. Latin America.

d. Latin America and Asia.

28) Trade between the United States and the Soviet Union tripled in 1972 because

    a. SALT opened an era of détente between the two countries.
    b. the United States supported offshore oil exploration in Soviet waters.
    c. the Soviets bought millions of tons of grain from American farmers.
    d. Congress authorized increased exports to Soviet-held Afghanistan.

29) Nixon was re-elected in a landslide after

    a. denying that anyone in his administration was involved in the Watergate scandal.
    b. the Senate launched an investigation of Watergate.
    c. John Dean claimed that Nixon was directly involved in the Watergate cover-up.
    d. Spiro Agnew resigned from office.

30) Nixon appointed a conservative Chief Justice and three more conservative judges

    a. noted for their strong stance on civil rights.
    b. who favored placing limits on wage and price increases to fight stagflation.
    c. likely to support New Federalism and step back from earlier civil rights decisions.
    d. likely to support new civil rights legislation and limited grants to the states.

31) In what became known as the Saturday Night Massacre,

    a. Attorney General Elliot Richardson fired Archibald Cox.
    b. acting attorney general Robert H. Bork fired Archibald Cox.
    c. Nixon fired White House attorney John Dean.
    d. Nixon forced his chief of staff, H. R. Haldeman, to resign.

32) During the 1970s, the more people in the United States moved to the

    a. Northeast.             c. Sun Belt states.
    b. Midwest.            d. mid-Atlantic states.

33) Archibald Cox and Leon Jaworski were

    a. special prosecutors who investigated the Watergate cover-up.
    b. burglars who had ties to the Nixon administration.
    c. *Washington Post* reporters who investigated and wrote about the Watergate burglary.
    d. White House informants who provided valuable inside information about Watergate.

34) The approach that made American interests, rather than political or moral ideals, the first priority in foreign policy decisions was

    a. affirmative action.        c. détente
    b. stagflation.            d. realpolitik.

35) President Ford's approval rating dropped from 72 to 49 percent overnight when he

a. granted a pardon to former president Nixon.
b. pardoned CIA and FBI agents who had spied on radical groups without proper cause.
c. offered a conditional pardon to young men who had illegally avoided the draft during the Vietnam War.
d. pardoned Vice President Spiro Agnew for bribes he took as governor of Maryland.

36) U.S. problems in the Middle East increased when in 1979

a. the United States helped bring Anwar Sadat to power.
b. Ayatollah Khomeini overthrew the shah of Iran.
c. Egypt and Syria attacked Israel on Yom Kippur.
d. OPEC declared an embargo on the sale of oil to the United States.

37) In the 1970s segregation continued in many public schools in the North, largely due to

a. the use of quotas.
b. busing.
c. segregated housing patterns.
d. immigration patterns.

38) People's fears of the use of nuclear power as an alternative to oil increased because

a. of an accident at a nuclear power plant on Three Mile Island, Pennsylvania.
b. people distrusted Nixon's proposed "Project Independence."
c. the SALT treaty limited how much nuclear power the United States could produce.
d. revolutionaries in several OPEC nations protested U.S. production of nuclear power.

39) Under affirmative action, some businesses and government agencies gave special consideration to nonwhite or women applicants, when their qualifications were roughly

a. comply with the Supreme Court's decision in *Brown* v. *Board of Education.*
b. comply with a 1954 Supreme Court ruling.
c. encourage women and minorities to compete for college placements and better jobs.
d. make up for past discrimination.

40) ". . . even the highest executive officials are subject to the rule of the law," said

a. President Nixon.
b. special prosecutor Archibald Cox.
c. Senate Judiciary Committee chair Sam Ervin.
d. White House attorney John Dean.

41) President Carter supported sanctions to persuade

a. South Africa to reform its apartheid system.
b. the Soviet Union to remove troops from Afghanistan.
c. Argentina and Ethiopia not to violate citizens' human rights.
d. Iran to release U.S. hostages in Tehran.

42) The Supreme Court ruled that Allan Bakke had been unfairly denied admission to the University of California medical school because

a. he was Asian.
b. he was African American.
c. the university set admission quotas based on race.
d. the university had not complied with the Court's ruling on affirmative action.

43) The goal of "Project Independence" was to

a. construct an Alaskan oil pipeline.
b. support offshore oil exploration.
c. use nuclear energy as an alternative to oil.
d. end the use of foreign oil by 1980.

44) The first White House official to admit that Nixon was directly involved in a cover-up was

a. H. R. Haldeman.
b. John Erlichman.
c. John Dean.
d. James McCord.

45) Revolutionaries attacked the U.S. embassy in Tehran because the U.S. government

a. supported Ayatollah Khomeini in his overthrow of the shah of Iran.
b. allowed the shah into the United States for medical treatment.
c. omitted Ayatollah Khomeini from peace talks held at Camp David in 1978.
d. invited Khomeini to attend peace talks at Camp David.

46) Almost four times more African Americans

a. were enrolled in college in 1976 than in 1964.
b. held political office in 1976 than in 1964.
c. worked in high-tech industries in 1978 than in 1964.
d. served in state legislatures in 1978 than in 1964.

47) Carter believed that political decisions should be based on

a. the wellbeing of the majority.
b. U.S. economic gain.
c. American interests rather than moral ideals.
d. moral ideals such as equality and justice.

48) To protect animals threatened with extinction, Congress passed the

a. Endangered Species Act.
b. Environmental Protection Act.
c. Superfund Act.
d. Wildlife Protection Act.

49) Henry Kissinger advocated a balance of power between the world's strongest nations to

a. stop the spread of communism.
b. avoid war.
c. protect international human rights.
d. resist OPEC's control of the production and sale of oil.

50) Vice President Spiro Agnew resigned from office

    a. at the request of acting attorney general Bork.
    b. to avoid being questioned about the Watergate break-in.
    c. amid charges that he had failed to pay his taxes and had taken bribes as a public official.
    d. when the *Washington Post* revealed that he was the informant known as Deep Throat.

51) After Nixon took office, he stressed the need to scale back some actions of the federal government, particularly in the area of

    a. defense.                  c. civil rights.
    b. education.           d. Medicare and Medicaid.

52) The Republican candidate who defeated President Carter in a landslide in 1980 was

    a. Ronald Reagan.         c. Gerald Ford.
    b. Robert Dole.            d. Richard Nixon.

53) The purpose of the illegal activities that preceded Watergate was to

    a. acquire taped conversations that took place in the president's office.
    b. get President Nixon nominated again.
    c. force Vice President Agnew to resign.
    d. spread false stories about Democratic candidates.

54) Carter's greatest success and his worst failure were associated with the

    a. Camp David Accords.     c. Middle East.
    b. Soviet Union.            d. SALT II talks.

55) Many people's faith in the presidency and the government was shaken by the

    a. Saturday Night Massacre.    c. Iran hostage crisis.
    b. resignation of Agnew and Nixon.    d. Watergate scandal.

56) By 1970 the fastest-growing population group in the United States was the segment aged

    a. 4 to 18.               c. 30 to 45.
    b. 15 to 21.           d. 65 and older.

57) "... fairness, not force, should lie at the heart of our dealings with the nations of the world," said President

    a. Carter.               c. Nixon.
    b. Reagan.           d. Ford.

58) President Ford believed that the economy's "public enemy Number 1" was

    a. the energy crisis.                    c. stagflation.
    b. inflation.                           d. the trade deficit.

59) The Strategic Arms Limitation Talks were signed by Nixon and

    a. Anwar Sadat.                   c. Leonid Brezhnev.
    b. Mao Zedong.                   d. Menachem Begin.

60) In the late 1970s, Anwar Sadat and Menachem Begin were, respectively, the

    a. president of Egypt, and the prime minister of Israel.
    b. president of Syria, and the president of Egypt.
    c. senior foreign-policy adviser to Nixon, and the leader of the Soviet Union.
    d. leader of the Soviet Union, and the leader of China.

## ENHANCED QUESTIONS
**For each of the following, circle the letter of the best choice. Next, expand on the subject by answering the second question in the space provided.**

61) In the case of *University of California* v. *Bakke*, the Supreme Court ruled that

    a. the university must reserve a certain number of admissions spots, based on race.
    b. race could not be a factor in admissions.
    c. equal consideration must be given to minorities and women in admissions decisions.
    d. race could be a factor in admissions but using quotas was illegal.

Define affirmative action, and explain how this case tested affirmative action.

_____

_____

62) The Organization of Petroleum Exporting Countries was an alliance formed by

    a. five major oil-producing nations in 1961.    c. Egypt, Israel, and Iran in 1979.
    b. Arab countries opposed to Israel.           d. Egypt and Iran in 1973.

Why did OPEC declare an embargo on the sale of oil to the United States? What was the result of this embargo?

_____

_____

Call to Freedom

63) The Iran hostage crisis began when

a. Ayatollah Khomeini overthrew the shah of Iran, and imprisoned all Americans then living or working in Tehran.
b. the shah of Iran closed down the U.S. embassy in Tehran, and seized 22 American diplomats.
c. student revolutionaries attacked the embassy and seized 53 American hostages, whom they held captive for months.
d. people lost confidence in Carter's ability to free the hostages in Tehran.

How long were the hostages imprisoned, and when were they released?

_____

_____

64) The Silent Majority was the name given by President Nixon to the

a. Southerners and other people who opposed further civil rights reforms.
b. large number of conservative voters who disliked the protests and changes that took place in the 1960s.
c. voters who blamed the Johnson administration for setting high taxes.
d. large number of Republican voters who wanted to eliminate Johnson's Great Society programs.

How did the New Federalism address the concerns of the Silent Majority?

_____

_____

65) The Equal Rights Amendment was a Constitutional amendment proposed by

a. women's rights activists and ratified by Congress in 1972.
b. the National Woman's Party in 1972.
c. women's rights activists to outlaw discrimination based on sex.
d. Shirley Chisholm to outlaw discrimination based on race and sex.

How did Phyllis Schlafly respond to the ERA? How effective were her efforts?

_____

_____

**Examine the image, and then answer the following questions.**

## The Impeachment Process

**Grounds**  Officials establish grounds for impeachment, which could include treason, bribery, and other offenses.

**Phase 1**  The House of Representatives announces articles of impeachment, thus formally accusing an official.

**Phase 2**  The Senate holds a trial for the accused, with a two-thirds vote needed for a conviction.

**Penalty**  A convicted official is removed from his or her post and cannot hold any public office in the future.

66)   What is the first step in the impeachment process?

_____

67)   What is the penalty for a convicted official?

_____

68)   Which house of Congress convicts officials?

_____

## SHORT ANSWER
**Write a brief answer for each of the following.**

69)   Why and how did Nixon form closer relations with China? How did Americans respond to Nixon's decision?

_____

_____

_____

70) Why did Congress establish the Environmental Protection Agency?

_____

_____

_____

71) Why did détente become unpopular during Ford's presidency?

_____

_____

_____

72) How did the energy crisis affect Americans?

_____

_____

_____

73) Describe the media's role in Watergate.

_____

_____

_____

**ESSAY**
**On a seperate sheet of paper, write an essay on one of the following.**

74) Compare Nixon's policy of realpolitik with Carter's foreign policy views. How did Nixon's and Carter's policies affect U.S. relations with the Soviet Union?

75) Explain how Nixon and Carter lost popularity and political support. How did their policies influence the careers of their successors, Gerald Ford and Ronald Reagan?

# ANSWER KEY

1) détente

2) Shirley Chisholm

3) pardon

4) apartheid

5) trade deficit

6) stagflation

7) sanctions

8) executive privilege

9) Henry Kissinger

10) Camp David Accords

11) T

12) F
Nixon's foreign policy decisions centered on U.S. interests rather than moral ideas. Carter condemned foreign governments that violated citizens' human rights.

13) F
Signed in 1977, the treaties transferred control of the canal to Panama by the year 2000.

14) T

15) T

16) F
American activists sponsored the first Earth Day on April 22, 1970 to increase environmental awareness.

Call to Freedom

# ANSWER KEY

17) T

18) F
Busing was the practice of transporting white and black students to new schools outside their neighborhoods to achieve a racial balance.

19) F
Almost four times more African Americans were enrolled in college in 1976 than in 1964. Between 1966 and 1973, the number of African Americans serving in Congress and state legislatures more than doubled.

20) T

21) d

22) a

23) b

24) c

25) b

26) a

27) d

28) c

29) a

30) c

31) b

32) c

33) a

34) d

35)  a

36)  b

37)  c

38)  a

39)  d

40)  b

41)  a

42)  c

43)  d

44)  c

45)  b

46)  a

47)  d

48)  a

49)  b

50)  c

51)  c

52)  a

53)  b

54)  c

**Call to Freedom**

55) d

56) d

57) a

58) b

59) c

60) a

61) d

Affirmative action was the practice by some business or government agencies of giving special consideration to nonwhites or women applicants, when their qualifications were roughly equal, to make up for past discrimination. This policy was tested when Allan Bakke appealed to the Supreme Court, saying that he had been unfairly denied admission to medical school because the university set admission quotas.

62) a

Most OPEC members were Arab countries opposed to Israel. When Egypt and Syria attacked Israel on Yom Kippur in 1973, the United States sent military supplies to Israel. OPEC then declared an oil embargo that caused an energy crisis of fuel shortages and high fuel prices in the United States.

63) c

On January 21, 1981—the day of Reagan's inauguration—Iran released the hostages after 444 days of imprisonment.

64) b

Nixon understood that the Silent Majority blamed the federal government for setting high taxes and interfering in their lives. To reverse this trend, he proposed the New Federalism. Under the New Federalism, the central government gave broad, undefined grants to the states. Local leaders decided what local projects to fund.

65) c

Schlafly founded STOP ERA to block the amendment's ratification. She and her supporters argued that the ERA would break up families by encouraging women to focus on careers rather than on motherhood. Gradually, these kinds of arguments weakened support for the amendment. In June 1982 it fell three states short of ratification.

66) establishing grounds for impeachment

Call to Freedom

67) removed from post and unable to hold public office in the future

68) the Senate

69) President Nixon hoped to take advantage of a rivalry between China and the Soviet Union by forming closer relations with China. The advantages of the move were twofold: it would isolate the Soviet Union and give the United States a valuable ally as well. Two years after Nixon officials began secret talks with the Chinese, Nixon and his wife visited China. Though some people criticized Nixon for forging ties with Communists, many Americans applauded the move.

70) Congress helped protect the environment by passing laws to improve the quality of air and water and to limit the release of pollutants. In 1970 new legislation established the EPA to enforce these laws.

71) Some leaders felt that the Communists took détente as a sign of American weakness, and that the Western European powers saw it as a sign of American unreliability. As a result, conservatives in Congress increasingly took a firm position against Communism. They opposed future compromises with the Soviet Union in the arms race.

72) For the first time in many Americans' lives, gasoline was hard to get. Many gasoline stations remained open only part of the day, and many consumers waited in long lines to buy gas. The scarcity and high prices of oil caused other problems as well. Some schools and businesses shut down due to a lack of fuel for heat and transportation.

73) Bob Woodward, a reporter at the *Washington Post*, suspected more than a simple burglary at the Democratic National Committee headquarters at the Watergate. He believed that he had a big story on his hands, if he could get somebody to talk. After Nixon's reelection, Woodward and Carl Bernstein, another *Post* reporter, continued to investigate the break-in. After a secret White House informant—known only as Deep Throat—contacted Woodward, the two reporters began publishing stories in the *Post* of illegal activities during the election of 1972. They reported that CREEP had hidden illegal campaign contributions, spread false stories about Democratic candidates, and pulled other "dirty tricks" to help Nixon and fellow Republican candidates.

Call to Freedom

74) Nixon believed that U.S. interests, rather than political or moral ideas, should be the first priority in foreign policy decisions. He believed that the United States should cooperate with any nation, even communist countries, to advance its best interests. When Nixon opened relations with Communist China, the Soviets became more open to discussion and negotiation with U.S. leaders. Nixon and Brezhnev agreed to SALT in 1972, opening an era of détente between the two nations. As a result of détente, trade between the United States and the Soviet Union tripled in 1972 as the Soviets bought millions of tons of grain from American farmers. These new markets led many Americans to see realpolitik as a way to expand U.S. trade. However, some observers complained that realpolitik policies encouraged U.S. support for dictators who violated human rights. When Carter became president, he based his political decisions on moral ideals such as equality and justice. He believed that fairness not force should be the basis of U.S. foreign policy. He condemned foreign governments that violated citizens' human rights with torture or unlawful jailings. Détente with the Soviet Union broke down completely as Carter criticized the country's many human rights abuses. When the Soviets invaded Afghanistan in 1979, Carter reacted by postponing talks on SALT II. He also limited U.S. grain shipments to the Soviet Union and declared an American boycott of the 1980 Summer Olympics in Moscow. Although most Americans disapproved of the Soviet invasion, but the embargo and boycott hurt many U.S. Olympic athletes and farmers.

75) Nixon's political career was ruined by the Watergate scandal which proved that he had ordered the cover-up of the Watergate crime and lied about it to Congress and the American people. Even before the public heard the tapes that proved Nixon's guilt, the House Judiciary Committee was prepared to recommend that the entire House of Representatives vote to impeach the president. Many believed that Nixon had violated the Constitution with his Watergate crimes. There was little support for Nixon in the Senate, where he would be tried for impeachment. As Nixon continued to lose support in the Senate, he resigned from office. Nixon's successor, Gerald Ford, had a reputation for honesty and cooperation, and many people hoped that these qualities would help him restore confidence in the government after Nixon's resignation. However, he lost public support when he granted a pardon to Richard Nixon soon after taking office. Ford's approval rating dropped from 72 to 49 percent overnight. The public's dissatisfaction with President Ford led to his loss to Carter in the presidential election of 1976. Jimmy Carter's background and his open, straightforward approach impressed many people and won the most votes. He promised a "new era of honest, compassionate, responsive government." His words struck a deep chord with Americans still troubled by Watergate. However, as Carter began to work with Congress some accused him of inflexibility. Some claimed that he equated his opinions with morality and was unwilling to compromise to get legislation passed. He failed to pass a comprehensive energy legislation because he would not modify the bill or allow just parts of it to be passed. He never was able to get the energy crisis or inflation under control during his administration and people began to believe he was incapable of solving the nation's problems. His support of turning over the Panama Canal to Panama, as well as his decision to boycott the 1980 Moscow Olympics and limit grain sales to the Soviet Union in retaliation for the Soviet invasion of Afghanistan, made him unpopular with many. The issue that hurt him most, however, was the taking of American hostages in Iran. The crisis dragged on for months and many Americans began to look for a new direction in leadership. In 1980 Republican presidential candidate Ronald Reagan, asked voters, "Are you better off than you were four years ago?" and many answered "no." In November 1980 Reagan defeated Carter in a landslide.

# Chapter 31 America Looks to the Future

## MATCHING
**In the space provided, write the term or the name of the person that best fits the description. Choose your answers from the list below. Not all answers will be used.**

Boris Yeltsin                  Albert Gore                  Ross Perot
glasnost                        *Discovery*                  Colin Powell
Saddam Hussein          Contract with America    Norman Schwarzkopf
New Right                     Bob Dole                  perestroika
Mikhail Gorbachev       *Challenger*              supply-side economics

1) _____ highest-ranking African American ever to have served in the U.S. military

2) _____ political and economic reforms designed to restructure the economy of the Soviet Union

3) _____ Soviet leader who signed the Intermediate-Range Nuclear Forces Treaty

4) _____ Republican campaign pledge that promised smaller government and a balanced budget

5) _____ independent presidential candidate who received 19 percent of the popular vote in the 1992 election

6) _____ leader of Iraq during the Persian Gulf War

7) _____ NASA's first space shuttle

8) _____ diverse, growing number of conservative groups who supported President Reagan's approach to government

9) _____ Tennessee senator who was elected vice president in 1992

10) _____ freedom of expression

# TRUE/FALSE
**Write T is a statement is true or F if it is false.  If a statement is false, explain why.**

11) _____ The North American Free Trade Agreement (NAFTA) eliminated trade barriers between the United States, Canada, and Mexico.

_____

12) _____ In 1981 Sandra Day O'Connor became the first female Supreme Court justice.

_____

13) _____ Presidential candidate Bill Clinton created the Contract with America.

_____

14) _____ Through genetic engineering scientists in the 1980s determined the causes of cystic fibrosis and muscular dystrophy.

_____

15) _____ Iraq agreed to cease-fire conditions just four days after the UN coalition launched a massive ground invasion called Operation Desert Storm.

_____

16) _____ The Americans with Disabilities Act established hiring quotas for people with disabilities.

_____

17) _____ The World Health Organization estimated that in 1997, 30 million people worldwide—860,000 of them in North America—were living with HIV and AIDS.

_____

18) _____ The Clinton administration reformed the nation's health care system and provided universal coverage to all Americans.

_____

19) _____ On Super Tuesday 1988, African American leader Jesse Jackson won more votes than any other Democratic candidate.

_____

20) _____ In 1984 Geraldine Ferraro became the first woman to run for vice president on a major party ticket.

_____

## MULTIPLE CHOICE
**For each of the following, circle the letter of the best choice.**

21) The Intermediate-Range Nuclear Forces Treaty eliminated all medium-range nuclear weapons from

    a. Europe.
    b. Iraq.

    c. the United States.
    d. the Soviet Union.

22) The Democratic nominee in the 1988 presidential election was

    a. Bill Clinton.
    b. Michael Dukakis.

    c. Walter Mondale.
    d. Ross Perot.

23) The biggest issue of the 1992 presidential election was the

    a. Persian Gulf War.
    b. recession.

    c. national deficit.
    d. economy.

24) The disease that forces the body's immune system to shut down, making it easier for people to contract illnesses and die is

    a. HIV.
    b. AIDS.

    c. muscular dystrophy.
    d. cystic fibrosis.

25) To reduce the emissions of ozone-destroying chemicals, President Bush signed a bill to update the

    a. War on Drugs.
    b. Gramm-Rudman-Hollings Act.

    c. Clean Air Act.
    d. genetic engineering.

26) In 1981 John Hinckley Jr. attempted to assassinate

    a. President Reagan.
    b. President Bush.

    c. Ross Perot.
    d. Walter Mondale.

27) When Bill Clinton won the 1992 Democratic presidential nomination, he was governor of

    a. Massachusetts.
    b. Texas.

    c. California
    d. Arkansas.

28) Social studies teacher Christa McAuliffe

    a. was the first civilian to pilot a NASA space shuttle.
    b. was killed when the space shuttle *Challenger* exploded.
    c. was the first woman chosen for NASA's *Discovery* mission.
    d. orbited the earth in the space shuttle *Challenger*.

29) During the Persian Gulf War, the UN coalition was led by U.S. forces and U.S. general

    a. Bob Dole.                 c. Norman Schwarzkopf.
    b. Newt Gingrich.         d. Colin Powell.

30) President Reagan supported the Strategic Defense Initiative, a defense system that would

    a. shoot down Soviet missiles in space with laser weapons.
    b. track Soviet missiles in space with computer technology.
    c. eliminate the use of all nuclear weapons in space.
    d. end the Cold War between the United States and the Soviet Union.

31) The War on Drugs was an organized effort at home and abroad to

    a. stop the international trade in illegal drugs.
    b. end the illegal drug trade.
    c. impose stiff penalties on citizens who produce or use illegal drugs.
    d. impose sanctions on nations that produce or transport illegal drugs.

32) The 1996 presidential candidate who pledged to "build a bridge to the twenty-first century" was

    a. Bob Dole.                 c. Bill Clinton.
    b. George Bush.           d. Ross Perot.

33) Many people believed that the thinning ozone layer would increase cases of

    a. heart disease.            c. lung cancer.
    b. liver disease.            d. skin cancer.

34) Conflicts in the Middle East began in 1990 when

    a. Iraq invaded Kuwait.
    b. Kuwait invaded Saudi Arabia.
    c. the United Nations declared economic sanctions on Kuwait.
    d. the UN coalition launched Operation Desert Storm.

35) Pro-democracy activists tore down the Berlin Wall in

    a. 1981.                 c. 1995.
    b. 1989.                 d. 1996.

36) The national security aide who arranged a secret deal to illegally trade arms for hostages was

    a. Walter Mondale.                        c. Oliver North.
    b. James Brady.                            d. Colin Powell.

37) Some 1,200 were businesses burned and 53 people died during the

    a. Persian Gulf War.                  c. invasion of Panama.
    b. civil war in Bosnia.               d. Los Angeles Riots.

38) The president who oversaw the signing of a historic peace agreement between Israel and the Palestine Liberation Organization was

    a. Clinton in 1993.                   c. Reagan in 1981.
    b. Bush in 1989.                      d. Reagan in 1986.

39) In 1996 Republicans nominated World War II veteran and long-time congressional leader

    a. Newt Gingrich.                    c. Michael Dukakis.
    b. Bob Dole.                          d. Walter Mondale.

40) President Bush authorized the military invasion of Panama to arrest

    a. Aristide for overthrowing Panama's pro-American dictator.
    b. Saddam Hussein for supporting anti-Sandinista rebels.
    c. Manuel Noriega for drug smuggling.
    d. Boris Yeltsin for supplying missiles to Panama.

41) The worst crash in stock prices since the 1930s occurred in

    a. 1981 when defense spending increased to $279 billion.
    b. 1991 when the United States declared economic sanctions banning trade with Iraq.
    c. 1992 as a result of "junk bond" sales and S&L failures.
    d. 1987 when the stock market lost more than $1 trillion dollars in value.

42) During the late 1980s the overall economy grew weaker as a result of

    a. the growing federal deficit.
    b. increased spending for social programs such as low-income housing.
    c. the Boland Amendment that required the government to send aid to struggling nations.
    d. supply-side economics.

43) As traditional industries like steel and automobiles lost sales to foreign competitors,

    a. they changed their products.          c. they lowered the prices of their goods.
    b. they laid off thousands of workers.    d. they changed their advertising methods.

44) The Clinton administration suffered a setback in 1994 as a result of an investigation into the

a. *Challenger* disaster.
b. Los Angeles Riots.
c. Whitewater affair.
d. Iran-contra affair.

45) The United States sent troops to Grenada to

a. support the contras.
b. support the Sandinistas.
c. help restore Aristide to office.
d. overturn the communist government there.

46) The global system of computer networks in which people anywhere in the world can share information and communication is the

a. Information Revolution.
b. Internet.
c. World Wide Web.
d. Global Network.

47) Bush's War on Drugs focused on

a. drug treatment.
b. education efforts.
c. arresting major drug smugglers.
d. using law enforcement to end drug use.

48) When Clinton called himself a "New Democrat," he meant that he

a. favored some traditionally Republican positions.
b. favored policies to limit defense spending.
c. believed in running the government like a business.
d. favored reducing taxes.

49) The independent counsel investigating the Whitewater affair was

a. Janet Reno.
b. Donald Trump.
c. Dean Rader.
d. Kenneth Starr.

50) What did one writer call "the single worst financial scandal in U.S. history"?

a. supply-side economics
b. the Whitewater affair
c. the S&L failures
d. 1985's $279 billion budget deficit

51) International relations were transformed in 1991 by the

a. fall of the Berlin Wall.
b. breakup of the Soviet Union.
c. Persian Gulf War.
d. Strategic Defensive Initiative.

52) Reforms known as perestroika and glasnost were initiated by

a. Mikhail Gorbachev.
b. Boris Yeltsin.
c. the PLO.
d. NAFTA.

53) During the 1980s, the gap between rich and poor

a. decreased.
b. stayed about the same.

c. increased.
d. did none of the above.

54) The United States became the world's only superpower as a result of the

a. space shuttle program.
b. fall of the Soviet Union.

c. peace agreement between Israel and the PLO.
d. Persian Gulf War.

55) In 1990 the United States and 27 other nations sent troops to protect

a. Bosnia.
b. Grenada.

c. Kuwait.
d. Saudi Arabia.

56) In 1994 the United States sent 20,000 troops to help maintain peace in

a. Bosnia.
b. Grenada.

c. Kuwait.
d. Saudi Arabia.

57) When the Reagan administration cut taxes, Congress offset the reductions in tax revenue by

a. decreasing defense spending.
b. lifting regulations on the airline industry.

c. cutting social programs.
d. asking for aid from private citizens.

58) President Clinton's Republican opponent in the 1996 presidential election was

a. Oliver North.
b. Bob Dole.

c. Newt Gingrich.
d. Ross Perot.

59) Iraq's invasion of Kuwait threatened the world because

a. Kuwait lost an estimated 100,000 soldiers and civilians during Iraq's invasion.
b. Saddam Hussein claimed that Kuwait belonged to Iraq.
c. Iraq's assault on Kuwait upset the delicate balance of peace between Israel and the PLO.
d. many nations depended on oil from Kuwait and Saudi Arabia.

60) The U.S. leader who saw the Cold War as a fight of "good versus evil, right versus wrong" was

a. Reagan.
b. Bush.

c. Clinton.
d. Dole.

## ENHANCED QUESTIONS

**For each of the following, circle the letter of the best choice. Next, expand on the subject by answering the second question in the space provided.**

61) The use of violent attacks by individuals or small groups to advance political goals is

    a. hard-line communism.        c. glasnost.

    b. perestroika.                d. terrorism.

How were Americans affected by this idea in 1995?

_____

_____

62) The deficit is the government's total

    a. debt.                 c. defense budget.

    b. budget.            d. economic policy.

How did defense spending and the Gramm-Rudman-Hollings Act affect the deficit in the 1980s?

_____

_____

63) The Sandinistas were

    a. anti-revolutionary rebels who set up a communist dictatorship in El Salvador.

    b. a revolutionary Nicaraguan political party.

    c. communist leaders in Grenada.

    d. Iranian terrorists in Lebanon.

Who were the contras, and why did Reagan support them?

_____

_____

64) The Soviet Union disbanded when

    a. pro-democracy activists tore down the Berlin Wall.
    b. Estonia, Latvia, and Lithuania declared their independence.
    c. hard-line Communists gave in to demands for democracy.
    d. Gorbachev established glasnost.

    What alliance did many former Soviet republics form?

    _____

    _____


65) The Boland Amendment

    a. limited the release of certain chemicals that scientists believe may damage the ozone layer.
    b. lifted restrictions on investments by savings and loan associations.
    c. enforced the deregulation of S&Ls.
    d. banned the Pentagon and government intelligence agencies from sending aid to the contras.

    How did some members of the Reagan administration try to get around the Boland Amendment?

    _____

    _____

## GRAPHIC IMAGE QUESTIONS
**Examine the image, and then answer the following questions.**

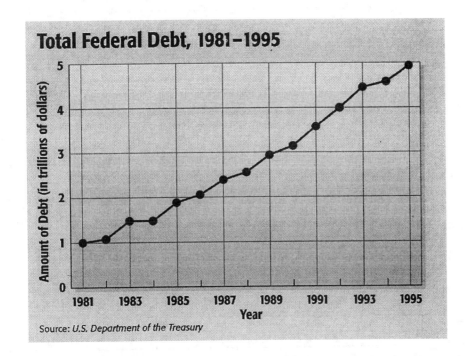

**Total Federal Debt, 1981–1995**

Source: *U.S. Department of the Treasury*

66) Approximately how much did the federal debt increase from 1981 to 1985?

_____

67) What was the amount of the federal debt in 1989?

_____

68) What was the amount of the federal debt in 1995?

_____

## SHORT ANSWER
**Write a brief answer for each of the following.**

69) How and why did the Cold War end?

_____

_____

_____

70) What was the Iran-contra affair?

_____

_____

_____

71) What is the Information Revolution?

_____

_____

_____

72) What are corporate takeovers and junk bonds?

_____

_____

_____

73) Explain the theory of supply-side economics.

_____

_____

_____

**ESSAY**
**On a seperate sheet of paper, write an essay on one of the following.**

74) In what nations and under what circumstances did the United States intervene to protect democracy and world peace during the 1980s and 1990s?

75) Discuss how American society changed during the 1980s and 1990s as a result of new technology, medical research, and scientific research.

Call to Freedom

# ANSWER KEY

1) Colin Powell

2) perestroika

3) Mikhail Gorbachev

4) Contract with America

5) Ross Perot

6) Saddam Hussein

7) *Challenger*

8) New Right

9) Albert Gore

10) glasnost

11) T

12) T

13) F
House minority leader Newt Gingrich and others created the Contract with America.

14) F
Scientists believed that through genetic engineering, the altering of genes, they could prevent many diseases from developing in individuals.

15) F
During Operation Desert Storm, airplanes pounded Iraq for six weeks with bombs and missiles. The Iraqis agreed to cease-fire conditions four days after the UN coalition launched a massive ground invasion.

16) F
The ADA guaranteed people with disabilities equal access to public accommodations, transportation, and employment opportunities.

17) T

18) F
These goals of the Clinton administration were not realized.

19) T

20) T

21) a

22) b

23) d

24) b

25) c

26) a

27) d

28) b

29) c

30) a

31) b

32) c

33) d

Call to Freedom

34)  a

35)  b

36)  c

37)  d

38)  a

39)  b

40)  c

41)  d

42)  a

43)  b

44)  c

45)  d

46)  b

47)  d

48)  a

49)  d

50)  c

51)  b

52)  a

53)  c

54) b

55) d

56) a

57) c

58) b

59) d

60) a

61) d
In 1995 terrorists bombed the federal office building in Oklahoma City, Oklahoma, killing 168 people.

62) a
From 1981 to 1985, defense spending increased from $180.5 billion to $279 billion, causing the deficit to increase dramatically. To prevent future deficits, Congress passed the Gramm-Rudman-Hollings Act in December 1985. The law required the government to cut spending when the deficit grew above a certain level. Yet previous years' deficits remained, and the total continued to grow.

63) b
Contras were anti-Sandinista rebels whom Reagan supported because the Sandinistas had overthrown Nicaragua's pro-American dictator. The United States became convinced that the Sandinistas wanted to set up a communist dictatorship.

64) c
After the Soviet Union disbanded, many of the former Soviet republics formed the Commonwealth of Independent States.

65) d
Some asked for contra aid donations from private citizens.

66) It approximately doubled, from $1 trillion to nearly $2 trillion.

67) about $3 trillion

# ANSWER KEY

68) about $5 trillion

69) Gorbachev pushed for reforms that weakened the Communist Party. After the Berlin Wall fell, demands for democracy intensified, with some of the republics declaring independence. Hard-line communist leaders attempted to stop the reforms, but citizens and leaders such as Boris Yeltsin stood firm. The hard-liners recalled their troops, and soon the Soviet Union disbanded, ending the Cold War.

70) Iranian terrorists in Lebanon took a group of Americans hostage. In secret dealings, they offered to free the hostages if Israel would give Iran U.S. weapons. The United States would then resupply Israel, in effect trading arms for hostages—an illegal practice. Oliver North arranged the secret deal, and passed the profits of the sales to the contras in violation of the Boland Amendment. The Iran-contra affair was the name given to the arms deal.

71) In the 1990s electronic computers increased the availability and easy transfer of information—a development called the Information Revolution. Computers have become essential to business, science, education and every activity that requires the organization of information. New technologies made these computers communicate and work together by linking them into networks, including a global system of networks known as the Internet.

72) In a takeover bid, a group of business leaders took loans to buy the stock of the targeted company. They then transferred the debt to the new company, which sold securities called "junk" bonds to repay the bank. These "junk" bonds paid higher returns than other investments but they were also high risk.

73) According to this theory, the government could balance the budget by cutting taxes. The theory held that tax cuts would increase personal and business profits. People would then invest or spend this extra income, thus expanding the economy and creating new jobs. This increase in business activity would produce greater tax revenues. As a result, at the same time that people were enjoying bigger incomes, increased tax revenues would balance the budget.

74) In 1983 Reagan sent U.S. troops to Grenada to overturn the communist government there. In 1984 he ended all aid to Nicaragua and supported the contras when the Sandinistas seemed to be trying to set up a communist dictatorship. When Hussein invaded Kuwait in 1990, Bush sent troops to protect Saudi Arabia. U.S. forces led a massive ground invasion that brought about a cease-fire in Iraq. The United States also attempted to help solve a civil war in Bosnia. To help settle the conflict, American diplomats hosted a peace conference in Dayton, Ohio. The warring sides signed a peace agreement, and the United States then sent 20,000 troops to the region to help maintain peace. In 1993 Clinton oversaw the signing of a historic peace agreement between Israel and the PLO.

75) During the 1980s and 1990s scientists and engineers made great strides in medicine and technology. Medical researchers determined the causes of some diseases, and believed that through genetic engineering they could prevent many diseases from developing in individuals. During the 1980s NASA launched its space shuttle program. In the 1990s the Information Revolution came about after engineers developed smaller, faster machines capable of performing multiple kinds of tasks. The Internet developed as a global system of computer networks in which people anywhere in the world can share information and communication.

Call to Freedom

# NOTES

# NOTES

# NOTES

# NOTES